Library of Congress
Catalog C and Number
65-26313

HYDRAULIC HANDBOOK

Fundamental Hydraulics
and Data useful in the
solution of pump applica-
tion problems.

Twelfth Edition

Price $9.00

 **Fairbanks Morse**
Pump Corporation

3601 FAIRBANKS AVENUE • KANSAS CITY, KANSAS 66110

Printed in U.S.A.

PREFACE

The Hydraulic Handbook is a Fairbanks Morse Pump Corporation publication compiled as an aid to the multitude of engineers who plan the installation of pumping machinery—and to plant managers and operators who are responsible for the efficient functioning of this machinery.

We have attempted to include enough of the fundamental principals of pumping to refresh the memories of those who work with pump applications at infrequent intervals. Also included are tables, data and general information which we hope will be of value to everyone who plans pumping equipment for public works, industry or agriculture.

Much of the material in the Hydraulic Handbook has been published previously and is reassembled in this single volume for your convenience. We sincerely appreciate permission to reprint—as generously granted by the Hydraulic Institute and others.

TABLE OF CONTENTS

ACKNOWLEDGEMENTS

In compiling the "Hydraulic Handbook," we used pertinent data from many sources. We sincerely appreciate the courtesies extended and are happy to give credit as follows:

For copyrighted material from the *Standards of the Hydraulic Institute, 10th Edition, 1964, and Pipe Friction Manual, Third Edition, 1961,* 122 East 42nd Street, New York, N.Y.

Various Tables from "Cameron Hydraulic Data"—*Ingersoll-Rand Company,* New York, N.Y.

American Standard Cast Iron Pipe Flanges and Flanged Fittings, (ASA B16b2-1931, B16.1-1948, B16b-1944 and B16b1-1931)—with the permission of the—*American Society of Mechanical Engineers,* 29 West 39th Street, New York, N.Y.

"Domestic and Industrial Requirements" from "Willing Water #25", December 1953—*American Water Works Association,* New York, N.Y.

Illustrations of gauges—*United States Gauge Division of American Machine & Metals, Inc.* Sellersville, Pa.

Approximate pH values from "Modern pH and Chlorine Control"—*W. A. Taylor & Company,* Baltimore, Md.

"Viscosity Temperature Chart"—*Byron Jackson Company,* Los Angeles, California.

Nozzle discharge tables from "Hydraulic Tables #31"—*Factory Mutual Engineering Division, Associated Factory Mutual Fire Insurance Companies,* Boston, Mass.

Chart "Vapor Pressure Versus Temperature For Motor and Natural Gasoline"—*Chicago Bridge & Iron Company,* Chicago, Ill.

Chart "Vapor Pressure Propane-Butane Mixture" — *Phillips Petroleum Company,* Bartlesville, Okla.

Table of the selection and horsepower rating of V-belt drives—*Dayton Rubber Manufacturing Co.,* Dayton, Ohio.

Text on Parallel and Series Operation—*De Laval Steam Turbine Company.* Trenton, New Jersey.

Tables of Cast Iron Pipe Dimensions—*Cast Iron Pipe Research Association,* Chicago, Illinois.

"Infiltration Rates of Soils"—*F. L. Duley and L. L. Kelly, S.C.S. Nebraska Experiment Station, Research Bulletin #12,* and "Peak Moisture Use for Common Irrigated Crops and Optimum Yields"—*A. W. McCullock, S.C.S. Reprinted from the Sprinkler Irrigation Handbook of the National Rain Bird Sales & Engineering Corp,* Azusa, Calif.

Food Pumping Installation from Hydro Pump Bulletin—*Chisholm Ryder Company, Inc.,* Niagara Falls, N.Y.

Text from "Pumps" by Kristal and Annett and "Piping Handbook" by Walker & Crocker—*by permission of McGraw-Hill Book Co., Inc.,* New York, N.Y.

Data from "Handbook of Water Control"—*Calco Division, Armco Drainage & Metal Products, Inc.,* Berkeley, Calif.

Illustration of Mechanical Seal—*Durametallic Corporation,* Kalamazoo, Michigan.

"Conversion Table for Approximate Hardness Numbers Obtained by Different Methods"—*from "Handbook of Engineering Fundamentals"—John Wiley & Sons,* New York, N.Y.

SECTION I—HYDRAULIC FUNDAMENTALS

CONTENTS

SECTION I — HYDRAULIC FUNDAMENTALS

HYDRAULICS

The science of hydraulics is the study of the behavior of liquids at rest and in motion. This handbook concerns itself only with information and data necessary to aid in the solution of problems involving the flow of liquids: viscous liquids, volatile liquids, slurries and in fact almost any of the rapidly growing number of liquids that can now be successfully handled by modern pumping machinery.

In a liquid at rest, the absolute pressure existing at any point consists of the weight of the liquid above the point, expressed in psi, plus the absolute pressure in psi exerted on the surface (atmospheric pressure in an open vessel). This pressure is equal in all directions and exerts itself perpendicularly to any surfaces in contact with the liquid. Pressures in a liquid can be thought of as being caused by a column of the liquid which, due to its weight, would exert a pressure equal to the pressure at the point in question. This column of the liquid, whether real or imaginary, is called the static head and is usually expressed in feet of the liquid.

Pressure and head are, therefore, different ways of expressing the same value. In the vernacular of the industry, when the term "pressure" is used it generally refers to units in psi, whereas "head" refers to feet of the liquid being pumped. These values are mutually convertible, one to the other, as follows:

$$\frac{\text{psi} \times 2.31}{\text{sg.}} = \text{Head in feet.}$$

Convenient tables for making this conversion for water will be found in Section III, Table 13 of this Handbook.

Pressure or heads are most commonly measured by means of a pressure gauge. The gauge measures the pressure above atmospheric pressure. Therefore, absolute pressure (psia) = gauge pressure (psig) plus barometric pressure (14.7 psi at sea level).

Since in most pumping problems differential pressures are used, gauge pressures as read and corrected are used without first converting to absolute pressure.

LIQUIDS IN MOTION

Pumps are used to move liquids.

A consideration of the heads required to cause flow in a system and the definition of the terms used can best be understood by referring to the following drawings and text.

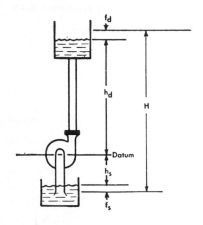
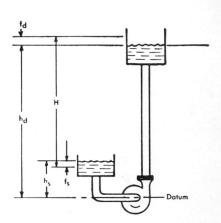

FIG. 1. Pump operating with suction lift. Suction bay level below center line of pump. Gauge reading at suction flange — vacuum.

FIG. 2. Pump operating with suction head. Suction bay level above center line of pump. Gauge reading at suction flange — pressure.

For Figure 1—Pump under suction lift—

$$H = h_d + h_s + f_d + f_s + \frac{V_d{}^2}{2g}$$

For Figure 2—Pump under suction head—

$$H = h_d - h_s + f_d + f_s + \frac{V_d{}^2}{2g}$$

Where—

H = Total head in feet (formerly known as total dynamic head) = the total head delivered by the pump when pumping the desired capacity. All heads are measured in feet of the liquid being pumped.

h_d = Static discharge head in feet = vertical distance between the pump datum and the surface of the liquid in the discharge bay. The datum shall be taken at the centerline of the pump for horizontal and double suction vertical pumps or at the entrance eye of the first stage impeller for single suction vertical pumps.

h_s = Static suction head or lift in feet = vertical distance from surface of water in suction bay to the pump datum. Notice in the equations above that this value is negative when operating under a suction head and positive when operating under a suction lift.

f_d = Friction head in discharge in feet = the head required to overcome friction in the pipe, valves, fittings, turns, etc. in the discharge system.

f_s = Friction head in suction in feet = the head required to overcome friction in the suction system.

$\dfrac{V_d^2}{2g}$ = The velocity head, in feet, at the discharge nozzle of the pump. Velocity head can be defined as the head required to cause the water to attain the velocity "V". It is velocity energy that is added to the liquid by the pump and since, in the illustrations Fig. 1 and 2, this velocity energy is lost at the sudden enlargement and never converted into pressure energy, it must be considered as part of the total head.

Since the velocity head in most installations will be less than two feet, on high head pumping installations it is a relatively small part of the total head. However, on low head pumping installations it is a significant part of the total head.

In pump testing, the total head is generally determined by gauge measurements. Since a gauge indicates the pressure energy only, the velocity head must always be calculated. The practice in testing horizontal centrifugal pumps differs from that used when testing vertical turbine or propeller pumps and is described in Chapter XI, Pump Testing.

For the various sizes of commercial pipe the velocity and velocity head are given for various capacities in the friction tables in Section II of this Handbook. When necessary to calculate the velocity head one of the following equations may be used:

$$\text{Velocity Head} = h_v = \frac{V^2}{2g} = 0.0155V^2 = \frac{0.00259 \text{ Gpm}^2}{D^4}$$

$$= \frac{0.00127 \text{ (Bbl. per Hour)}^2}{D^4}$$

The last two equations apply to circular piping having a diameter D inches and the last equation to barrels of 42 gal. each.

FLUID FLOW

Liquids are approximately incompressible—in fact, sufficiently so that no corrections need be made at low or medium pressures. However, at very high pressures there is a slight change in density that should be taken into consideration. Since liquids may be said to be incompressible there is always a definite relationship between the quantity of liquid flowing in a conduit and the velocity of flow. This relationship is expressed:

$$Q = AV \quad \text{or} \quad V = \frac{Q}{A}$$

OR $\quad V = \dfrac{0.4085 \text{ Gpm}}{D^2} = \dfrac{0.2859 \text{ Bbl.}\oplus \text{ per hour}}{D^2}$

Where
Q = Capacity in cubic feet per second
A = Area of conduit in square feet
V = Velocity of flow in feet per second
D = Diameter of circular conduit in inches
$\oplus$ = 42 gal. per barrel

WATER HAMMER

Water hammer is a series of pressure pulsations, of varying magnitude, above and below the normal pressure of water in the pipe. The amplitude and periodicity depends on the velocity of water extinguished, as well as the size, length and material of the pipe line. Shock results from these pulsations when any liquid, traveling with a certain velocity, is stopped in a short period of time. The pressure increase, when flow is stopped, is independent of the working pressure of the system. For example: if water is flowing in a pipe at five feet per second and a valve is instantaneously closed, the pressure increase will be exactly the same whether the normal pressure in the pipe line is 100 psig or 1000 psig.

Water hammer is often, though not always, accompanied by a sound comparable to that heard when a pipe is struck by a hammer, hence the name. Intensity of sound is no measure of pressure magnitude because tests show that if 15%, or even less, of the shock pressure is removed by absorbers or arresters installed in the line the noise is eliminated, yet adequate relief from the effect of the water hammer is not necessarily obtained.

Time of Valve Closure to Cause Maximum Water Hammer Pressure. Joukovski, who was the first great investigator of the water hammer theory to be verified by test, published his paper in Moscow, Russia. It was translated and printed in the Journal of the American Water Works Association in 1904. In brief, he postulated that the maximum pressure, in any pipe line, occurs when the total discharge is stopped in a period of time, equal or less than the time, required for the induced pressure wave to travel from the point of valve closure to the inlet end of the line and return. This time he stated as:

$$t = \frac{2L}{a}$$

Where:

    t = time, in seconds, for pressure wave to travel the length of the pipe and return.
    L = length, in feet, of the pipe line.
    a = velocity, in feet per second, of pressure wave.

One form of the formula, developed to determine the velocity of the pressure wave, is

$$a = \frac{12}{\sqrt{\dfrac{w}{g}\left(\dfrac{l}{k} + \dfrac{d}{Ee}\right)}}$$

Where:

    a = velocity of pressure wave, fps.
    g = acceleration caused by gravity = 32.2 feet per sec. per sec.
    w = weight of one cu. ft. of water, lbs.
    d = inside diameter of pipe, in.
    e = thickness of pipe wall, in.
    k = bulk modulus of compressibility of water; approximately 300,000 psi.
    E = modulus of elasticity of pipe material, psi; for steel—approximately 30,000,000. For cast iron—approximately 15,000,000.

Maximum Water Hammer Pressure. The formula that evaluates the maximum pressure caused by water hammer is:

$$p = \frac{0.433\, a\, V}{g}$$

Where:

    p = maximum pressure, psig.
    a = velocity of pressure wave, fps.
    V = velocity of water stopped, fps.
    g = acceleration caused by gravity = 32.2 ft. per sec. per sec.
0.433 = a constant used to convert feet of head to psi.

Computations of the preceding formulae permit the layout of the accompanying chart, Fig. 3, which discloses the maximum water hammer pressure for various pipe sizes, thickness, and the velocity of water stopped. This chart is for water only, but recent investigations by the petroleum industry, disclosed that the shock pressure caused by any relatively incompressible liquid can be obtained by the correct substitution of the formula of the physical constants of the liquid; namely, those of weight per cu. ft. and bulk modulus of elasticity.

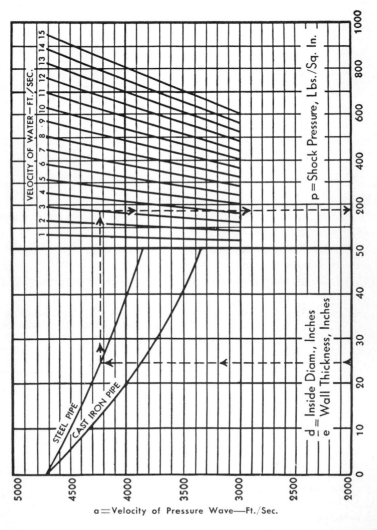

FIG. 3. Maximum shock pressure caused by water hammer (based on instantaneous closure of valves).

Example:

What is the maximum pressure caused by water hammer in an 8-inch steel pipe line (0.322-inches wall thickness) transporting water at a steady velocity of 3 fps?

Procedure in Using Chart:

Determine the ratio $\dfrac{d}{e} = \dfrac{\text{inside dia. of pipe, in.}}{\text{wall thickness of pipe, in.}} = \dfrac{7.981}{0.322} = 24.8$.

Enter the chart at $\dfrac{d}{e} = 24.8$ and project upward to the intersection with the line for steel pipe.

Note that the value of the velocity of the pressure wave, $a = 4225$ fps.

Project horizontally to the right, to an intersection with the 3 fps. velocity line and then down to the base line, where shock pressure of 170 psi is obtained.

SPECIFIC GRAVITY AND HEAD

The head developed by a centrifugal pump depends upon the peripheral velocity of the impeller. It is expressed thus:

$$H = \frac{u^2}{2g}$$

Where

H = Total Head at zero capacity developed by the pump in feet of liquid

u = Velocity at periphery of impeller in feet per second

Notice that the head developed by the pump is independent of the weight of the liquid pumped. Therefore in Fig. 4 the head H

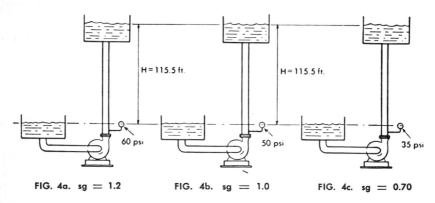

FIG. 4a. sg = 1.2   FIG. 4b. sg = 1.0   FIG. 4c. sg = 0.70

FIG. 4. Pressure—head relationship identical pumps handling liquids of differing specific gravities.

in feet would be the same whether the pump was handling water with a specific gravity of 1.0, gasoline with a sg. of 0.70, brine of a sg. of 1.2 or a fluid of any other specific gravity. The pressure reading on the gauge, however, would differ although the impeller diameter and speed is identical in each case.

$$\text{The gauge reading in psi} = \frac{H \times \text{sg.}}{2.31}$$

Refer to Fig. 5. All three of these pumps are delivering liquids at 50 psi. Because of the difference in specific gravity of the liquids each pump develops a different head in feet. Therefore, if the speed of all three pumps is the same, the pump in Fig. 5c must have the largest diameter impeller and that in Fig. 5a the smallest.

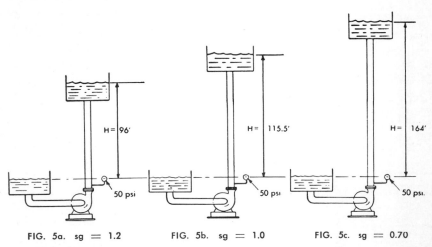

FIG. 5a. sg = 1.2   FIG. 5b. sg = 1.0   FIG. 5c. sg = 0.70

FIG. 5. Pressure—head relationship pumps delivering same pressure handling liquids of differing specific gravity.

Standard performance curves of pumps are generally plotted with total head in feet as ordinates against capacity in gpm as abscissae. Water is the liquid most often used in rating pumps. Since the head in feet developed by a centrifugal pump is independent of the specific gravity, if the head for a proposed application is figured in feet then the desired head and capacity can be read directly from the water curves without correction as long as the viscosity of the liquid is the same as that of water. The horsepower shown on the water curves will apply only to liquids with a specific gravity of 1.0. For other liquids multiply the water Hp by the specific gravity of the liquid being pumped.

POWER, EFFICIENCY AND ENERGY

The Horse Power (Hp) required to drive a pump may be figured from the following formulae:

Liquid Hp or useful work done by the pumps =

$$\text{Whp} = \frac{\text{lbs. of liquid raised per min.} \times H \text{ in feet}}{33,000}$$

$$= \frac{\text{gpm} \times H, \text{ft.} \times \text{sg.}}{3960}$$

The Brake Horsepower required to drive the pump =

$$\text{Bhp} = \frac{\text{gpm} \times H, \text{ft.} \times \text{sg.}}{3960 \times \text{Pump Eff.}}$$

$$\text{Pump Efficiency} = \frac{\text{Output}}{\text{Input}} = \frac{\text{Whp}}{\text{Bhp}}$$

$$\text{Electrical Hp input to Motor} = \frac{\text{Bhp}}{\text{Motor Eff.}}$$

$$= \frac{\text{Gpm} \times H, \text{ft.} \times \text{sg.}}{3960 \times \text{Pump Eff.} \times \text{Motor Eff.}}$$

$$\text{Kw input to Motor} = \frac{\text{Bhp} \times 0.746}{\text{Motor Eff.}}$$

$$= \frac{\text{Gpm} \times H, \text{ft.} \times \text{sg.} \times 0.746}{3960 \times \text{Pump Eff.} \times \text{Motor Eff.}}$$

Overall Eff. = Pump Eff. $\times$ Motor Eff.

$$\text{Kwh per 1000 gal. water pumped} = \frac{H, \text{ft.} \times 0.00315}{\text{Overall Eff.}}$$

Kwh per 1000 gal. water pumped $= K \times H$

Where $K =$ a constant depending upon the overall efficiency of the pumping unit obtained from Table 15 in Section III.

SPECIFIC SPEED

Specific speed may be defined as that speed in revolutions per minute at which a given impeller would operate if reduced proportionately in size so as to deliver a capacity of 1 GPM against a total dynamic head of 1 foot. The visualization of this definition, however, has no practical value for specific speed is used to classify impellers as to their type or proportions, as shown in Fig. 6 and as a means of predicting other important pump characteristics, such as, the suction limitation of the pump.

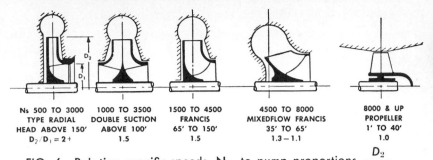

Ns 500 TO 3000	1000 TO 3500	1500 TO 4500	4500 TO 8000	8000 & UP
TYPE RADIAL	DOUBLE SUCTION	FRANCIS	MIXEDFLOW FRANCIS	PROPELLER
HEAD ABOVE 150'	ABOVE 100'	65' TO 150'	35' TO 65'	1' TO 40'
$D_2/D_1 = 2+$	1.5	1.5	1.3 − 1.1	1.0

FIG. 6. Relation specific speeds, N_s, to pump proportions, $\dfrac{D_2}{D_1}$

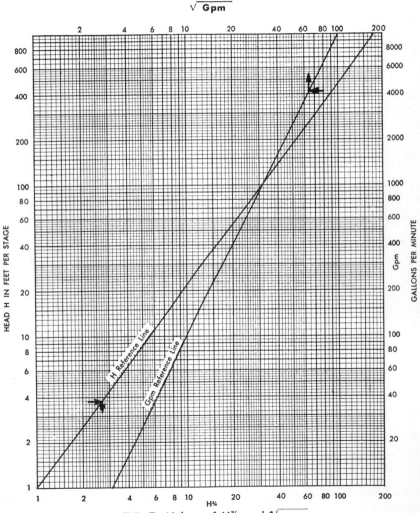

FIG. 7. Values of $H^{3/4}$ and $\sqrt{gpm}$

SPECIFIC SPEED—SUCTION LIMITATIONS†

Among the more important factors affecting the operation of a centrifugal pump are the suction conditions. Abnormally high suction lifts (low NPSH) beyond the suction rating of the pump, usually causes serious reductions in capacity and efficiency, and often leads to serious trouble from vibration and cavitation.

Specific Speed. The effect of suction lift on a centrifugal pump is related to its head, capacity and speed. The relation of these factors for design purposes is expressed by an index number known as the specific speed. The formula is as follows:

$$\text{Specific Speed, } N_s = \frac{\text{rpm}\sqrt{\text{gpm}}}{H^{3/4}}$$

where H = head per stage in feet (Fig. 7 shows the corresponding values of $H^{3/4}$ and $\sqrt{\text{gpm}}$).

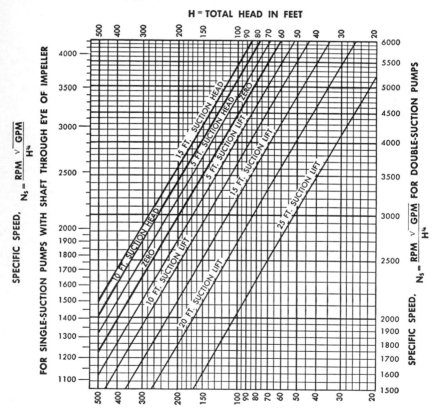

FIG. 8. Hydraulic Institute upper limits of specific speeds for single stage, single suction and double suction pumps with shaft through eye of impeller pumping clear water at sea level at 85°F.

†*Courtesy Hydraulic Institute. See page 6.*

The designed specific speed of an impeller is an index to its type when the factors in the above formula correspond to the performance at *Optimum Efficiency*. It is used when designing impellers to meet different conditions of head, capacity and speed. Impellers for high heads usually have low specific speeds and impellers for low heads usually have high specific speeds. The specific speed has been found to be a very valuable criterion in determining the permissible maximum suction lift, or minimum suction head, to avoid cavitation for various conditions of capacity, head and speed.

For a given head and capacity, a pump of low specific speed will operate safely with a greater suction lift than one of higher specific speed. If the suction lift is very high (over 15 feet) it is often necessary to use a slower speed and consequently larger pump, while if the suction lift is low, or there is a positive head on the suction, the speed may often be increased and a smaller pump may be used.

Specific Speed Limitations. Increased speeds without proper suction conditions often cause serious trouble from vibration, noise and pitting. Two specific speed curves (Figs. 8 and 9) represent upper limits of specific speed in respect to capacity, speed, head and suction lift. Centrifugal, mixed flow and axial flow pumps may be selected within the limits shown on these charts with reasonable assurance of freedom from cavitation.

The curves show recommended maximum specific speeds for normal rated operating conditions and are based upon the premise that the pump, at that rated condition, is operating at or near its point of *Optimum Efficiency*.

The suction lift or suction head is to be measured at the suction flange of the pump and referred to the centerline of the pump for horizontal and double suction vertical pumps, or to the entrance eye of the first stage impeller for single suction vertical pumps.

The curves apply to single stage pumps of double suction and single suction type which have the shaft through the eye of the impeller, and to single inlet mixed flow and axial flow pumps.

The first curve, Fig. 8, covers pumps of predominantly centrifugal types, for specific speeds from 1500 to 6000 for double suction pumps, and from 1100 to 4000 for single suction pumps. This type of pump finds application principally in the medium and high head range.

The second curve, Fig. 9, covers pumps of the single suction mixed flow and axial flow type for specific speeds from 4000 to 20000. Pumps of these types are applied advantageously for low head pumping.

Example I—Single suction pump with shaft through eye of impeller.

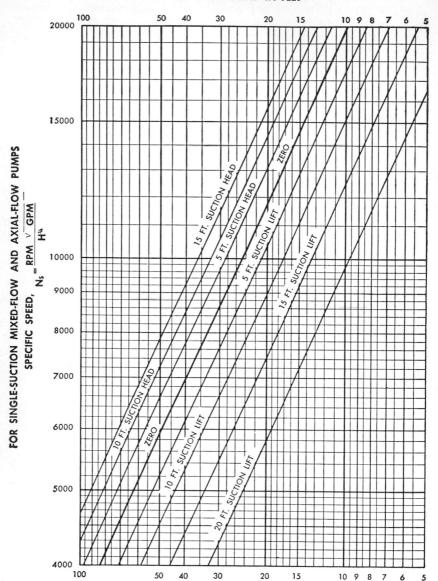

FIG. 9. Hydraulic Institute upper limits of specific speeds for single stage, single suction mixed flow and axial flow pumps pumping clear water at sea level at 85°F.

Given a total head of 100 feet and a total suction lift of 15 feet, what is the safe upper limit of specific speed to avoid danger of cavitation?

Referring to Fig. 8, the intersection, of the diagonal for 15 feet suction lift with the vertical line at total pump head of 100 feet, falls on the horizontal line corresponding to 2250 specific speed. The specific speed should not exceed this value.

Example II—Double suction pump.

Given a total head of 100 feet and a total suction lift of 15 feet, what is the safe upper limit of specific speed?

Referring to the first curve, Fig. 8, the intersection, of the diagonal for 15 feet suction lift with the vertical line for 100 feet total pump head, falls on the horizontal line corresponding to 3200 specific speed on the scale at the right side of the chart. This is the value of

$$\frac{\text{rpm}\sqrt{\text{gpm}}}{H^{3/4}} = N_s$$

in which the volume, or gpm, is the total gallons per minute capacity of the pumping unit including both suctions; and is the highest value which should be used for this head and suction lift.

Example III—Single suction mixed flow or axial flow pump.

Given a total head of 35 feet and a total suction head of 10 feet, corresponding to a submerged impeller, what is the safe upper limit of specific speed?

Referring to the second curve, Fig. 9, the intersection, of the vertical line for 35 feet total pump head and the diagonal for 10 feet suction head, falls on the horizontal line corresponding to 9400 specific speed on the scale at the left side of the chart. The specific speed should not exceed this value.

NET POSITIVE SUCTION HEAD (NPSH)

NPSH can be defined as the head that causes liquid to flow through the suction piping and finally enter the eye of the impeller.

This head that causes flow comes from either the pressure of the atmosphere or from static head plus atmospheric pressure. A pump operating under a suction lift has as a source of pressure to cause flow only the pressure of the atmosphere. The work that can be done, therefore, on the suction side of a pump is limited, so NPSH becomes very important to the successful operation of the pump. There are two values of NPSH to consider.

REQUIRED NPSH is a function of the pump design. It varies between different makes of pumps, between different pumps of the same make and varies with the capacity and speed of any one pump. This is a value that must be supplied by the maker of the pump.

AVAILABLE NPSH is a function of the system in which the pump operates. It can be calculated for any installation. Any pump installation, to operate successfully, must have an available NPSH equal to or greater than the required NPSH of the pump at the desired pump conditions.

When the source of liquid is above the pump:

> NPSH = Barometric Pressure, Ft. + Static Head on suction, ft. − friction losses in suction piping, ft. − Vapor Pressure of liquid, ft.

When the source of liquid is below the pump:

> NPSH = Barometric Pressure, ft. — Static Suction lift, ft. — friction losses in Suction piping, ft. — Vapor Pressure of liquid, ft.

To illustrate the use of these equations consider the following examples:

The required NPSH of a water pump at rated capacity is 17 ft. Water Temperature 85°F. Elevation 1000 ft. above sea level. Entrance and friction losses in suction piping calculated = 2 ft. What will be the maximum suction lift permissible?

To better visualize the problem the solution is presented graphically in Fig. 10. The two horizontal lines are spaced apart a distance equal to the barometric pressure in feet.

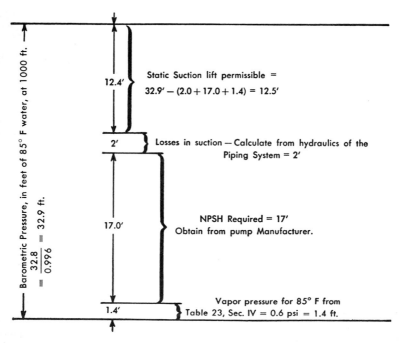

FIG. 10. Graphic solution NPSH problem for 85°F water.

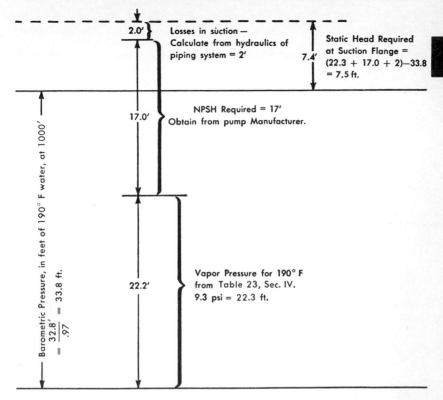

FIG. 11. Graphic solution NPSH problem for 190°F water.

As a further example consider the same data except that the water temperature is 190°F. What will be the suction lift or head required?

From Table 23 in Section IV water at 190° has a sg. of 0.97. The vapor pressure is 9.3 psi. In the graphic solution in Fig. 11 remember that all heads must be in feet of the liquid.

In this case because the sum of vapor pressure + NPSH required + losses in the suction system exceed the barometric pressure, a positive head or submergence must be provided to insure uninterrupted water flow to the pump.

This discussion of NPSH applies to any type of pump whether centrifugal, positive displacement, peripheral, angle or mixed flow or propeller. On centrifugal, angle or mixed-flow or propeller pumps the suction conditions must be correct or the pump will operate inefficiently or may fail to operate at all. However, the Westco peripheral type is more tolerant of improper suction conditions, for this type pump has the ability to pump both liquid and vapor without vapor binding. When pumping part vapor and part liquid the capacity is, of course, reduced. Advantage is taken of the suction tolerance of this pump and it is frequently installed under suction conditions quite impossible for a centrifugal pump. The manufacturer can supply ratings of their pumps under these adverse conditions.

CAVITATION

Cavitation is a term used to describe a rather complex phenomenon that may exist in a pumping installation. In a centrifugal pump this may be explained as follows. When a liquid flows through the suction line and enters the eye of the pump impeller an increase in velocity takes place. This increase in velocity is, of course, accompanied by a reduction in pressure. If the pressure falls below the vapor pressure corresponding to the temperature of the liquid, the liquid will vaporize and the flowing stream will consist of liquid plus pockets of vapor. Flowing further through the impeller, the liquid reaches a region of higher pressure and the cavities of vapor collapse. It is this collapse of vapor pockets that causes the noise incident to cavitation.

Cavitation need not be a problem in a pump installation if the pump is properly designed and installed, and operated in accordance with the designer's recommendations. Also, cavitation is not necessarily destructive. Cavitation varies from very mild to very severe. A pump can operate rather noiselessly yet be cavitating mildly. The only effect may be a slight drop in efficiency. On the other hand severe cavitation will be very noisy and will destroy the pump impeller and/or other parts of the pump.

Any pump can be made to cavitate, so care should be taken in selecting the pump and planning the installation. For centrifugal pumps avoid as much as possible the following conditions:

1. Heads much lower than head at peak efficiency of pump.

2. Capacity much higher than capacity at peak efficiency of pump.

3. Suction lift higher or positive head lower than recommended by manufacturer.

4. Liquid temperatures higher than that for which the system was originally designed.

5. Speeds higher than manufacturer's recommendation.

The above explanation of cavitation in centrifugal pumps cannot be used when dealing with propeller pumps. The water entering a propeller pump in a large bell-mouth inlet will be guided to the smallest section, called throat, immediately ahead of the propeller. The velocity there should not be excessive and should provide a sufficiently large capacity to fill properly the ports between the propeller blades. As the propeller blades are widely spaced, not much guidance can be given to the stream of water. When the head is increased beyond a safe limit, the capacity is reduced to a quantity insufficient to fill up the space between the propeller vanes. The stream of water will separate from the propeller vanes, creating a small space where pressure is close to a perfect vacuum. In a very small fraction of a second, this small vacuum space will be smashed by the liquid hitting the smooth surface of the propeller vane with an enormous force which starts the process of surface pitting of the vane. At the same time one will hear a sound like rocks thrown around in a barrel or a mountain stream tumbling boulders.

The five rules applying to centrifugal pumps will be changed to suit propeller pumps in the following way: Avoid as much as possible,

1. Heads much higher than at peak efficiency of pump.
2. Capacity much lower than capacity at peak efficiency of pump.
3. Suction lift higher or positive head lower than recommended by manufacturer.
4. Liquid temperatures higher than that for which the system was originally designed.
5. Speeds higher than manufacturer's recommendation.

Cavitation is not confined to pumping equipment alone. It also occurs in piping systems where the liquid velocity is high and the pressure low. Cavitation should be suspected when noise is heard in pipe lines at sudden enlargements of the pipe cross-section, sharp bends, throttled valves or like situations.

SIPHONS

It occasionally happens that a siphon can be placed in the discharge line so that the operating head of a pump is reduced. The reduction in head so obtained will lower the power costs for lifting a given amount of water and may make possible, in addition, the installation of a smaller pumping unit.

Successful operation of such a combination demands that the pump and siphon be designed as a unit under the following limitations.

1. In order to prime the siphon in starting, the pump must be able to deliver a full cross-section of water to the throat, or peak, of the siphon against the total head of that elevation and with a minimum velocity of five feet per second.

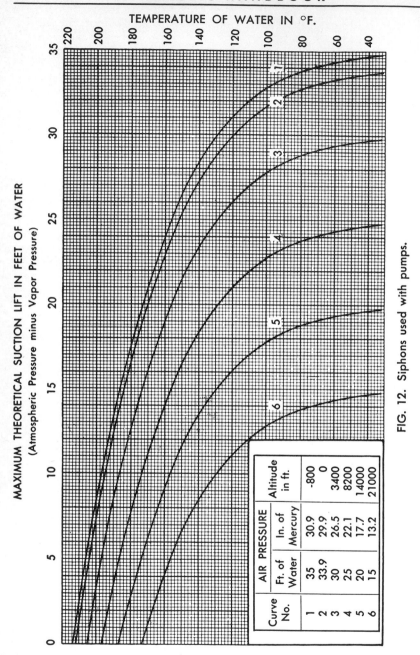

TEMPERATURE OF WATER IN °F.

MAXIMUM THEORETICAL SUCTION LIFT IN FEET OF WATER
(Atmospheric Pressure minus Vapor Pressure)

Curve No.	AIR PRESSURE		Altitude in ft.
	Ft. of Water	In. of Mercury	
1	35	30.9	-800
2	33.9	29.9	0
3	30	26.5	3400
4	25	22.1	8200
5	20	17.7	14000
6	15	13.2	21000

FIG. 12. Siphons used with pumps.

2.   After the siphon has been primed and steady flow has been established, the maximum velocity at the throat can not exceed the value for a throat pressure equal to the vapor pressure of the liquid under the operating conditions. Any attempt to exceed this limiting

velocity will result in "cavitation," or vaporization of the liquid, under the reduced pressure.

The theoretical pressure drop can be obtained from the curves in Fig. 12 which are based on the standard atmosphere as defined by the U. S. Bureau of Standards in its publication #82. A safe value for design purposes may be obtained directly from the curve for 75% of the actual atmospheric pressure. This value may be used as an estimate of the possible head reduction by the use of a siphon providing a reasonable allowance for friction losses is deducted from it.

3.   The pipe section at the throat must be designed to resist the external pressure caused by the reduction of pressure below that of the atmosphere.

4.   In practically all cases it is advisable that the discharge end of the siphon be sufficiently submerged to prevent the entrance of air. The exit losses at this point can be reduced by belling the end of the pipe and thus recovering a large part of the velocity head.

AFFINITY LAWS—CENTRIFUGAL PUMPS

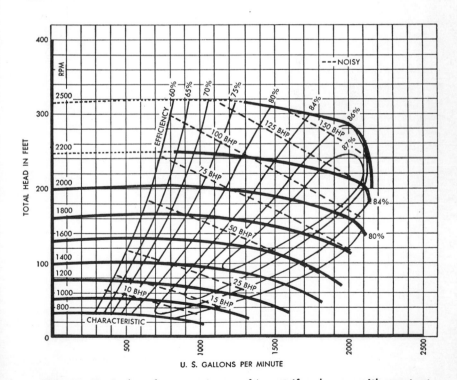

FIG. 13. Typical performance curve of a centrifugal pump with constant impeller diameter but varying speeds.

A typical characteristic curve of a centrifugal pump is shown in Fig. 13 and Fig. 14. It will be observed that both charts have plotted on them several head capacity curves with lines of constant efficiency and Hp superimposed on them. In Fig. 13 the impeller diameter is held constant and the speed varies whereas in Fig. 14 the speed is held constant and the impeller diameter varies. The mathematical relationships between these several variables are known as the affinity laws and can be expressed as follows:

With impeller diameter held constant | With speed held constant

$$\frac{Q_1}{Q_2} = \frac{N_1}{N_2} \qquad \text{Law 1a}$$

$$\frac{H_1}{H_2} = \left(\frac{N_1}{N_2}\right)^2 \qquad \text{Law 1b}$$

$$\frac{Bhp_1}{Bhp_2} = \left(\frac{N_1}{N_2}\right)^3 \qquad \text{Law 1c}$$

$$\frac{Q_1}{Q_2} = \frac{D_1}{D_2} \qquad \text{Law 2a}$$

$$\frac{H_1}{H_2} = \left(\frac{D_1}{D_2}\right)^2 \qquad \text{Law 2b}$$

$$\frac{Bhp_1}{Bhp_2} = \left(\frac{D_1}{D_2}\right)^3 \qquad \text{Law 2c}$$

Where

$Q_1 = $ Capacity and $H_1 = $ head at N_1 rpm or with impeller dia. D_1

$Q_2 = $ Capacity and $H_2 = $ head at N_2 rpm or with impeller dia. D_2

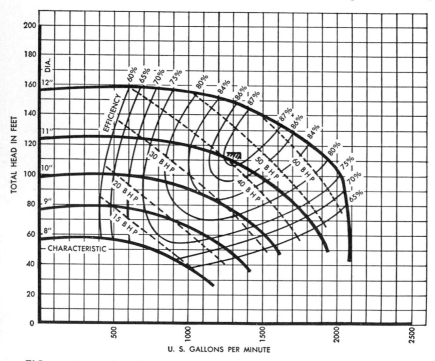

FIG. 14. Typical performance curve of a centrifugal pump at 1750 rpm but with varying impeller diameter.

These relations are graphically shown on Fig. 15.

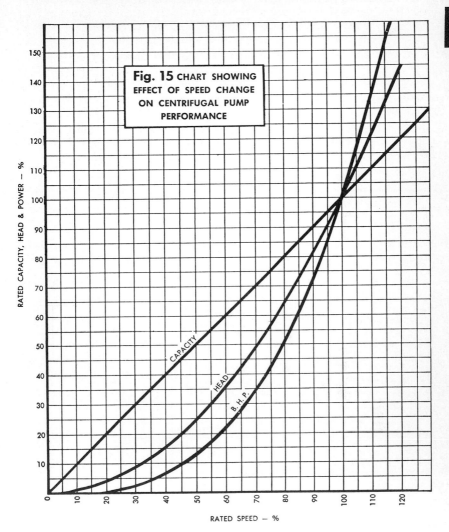

Fig. 15 CHART SHOWING EFFECT OF SPEED CHANGE ON CENTRIFUGAL PUMP PERFORMANCE

FIG. 15. Chart showing effect of speed change on centrifugal pump performance.

Where complete rating charts such as those shown in Figures 13 and 14, secured by actual test of the pump, are available, it is always best to use them to estimate intermediate points by interpolation. However, many field problems will arise where these data are not available and then approximations can be made by calculation, using the affinity laws.

Law 1a applies to Centrifugal, Angle Flow, Mixed Flow, Propeller, Peripheral, Rotary and Reciprocating pumps.

Law 1b and c apply to Centrifugal, Angle Flow, Mixed Flow, Propeller, and Peripheral pumps.

Law 2a, b, c apply to Centrifugal pumps only.

Examples illustrating the use of these laws follow. Note particularly from these examples that the calculated head-capacity characteristic using Law 1 agrees very closely to the test performance curves. However, this is true for Law 2 only under certain defined conditions. Law 2 must, therefore, be used with a great deal of caution.

Illustration Law 1

To illustrate Law 1, refer to Figure 17 which is a portion of the more complete curve shown in Figure 13. Consider that we have given the performance curve shown in Figure 17 at 2000 Rpm. We want to find, by calculation, the expected performance at 1600 Rpm. Proceed as follows:

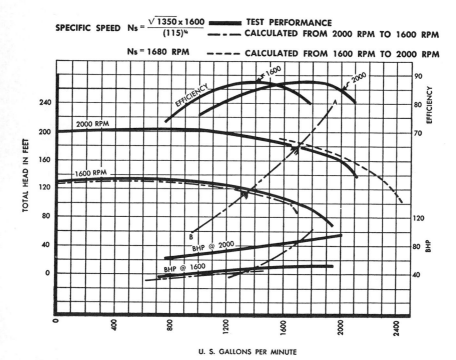

$$\text{SPECIFIC SPEED} \quad N_s = \frac{\sqrt{1350} \times 1600}{(115)^{\frac{3}{4}}}$$

$$N_s = 1680 \text{ RPM}$$

━━━ TEST PERFORMANCE
— ‑ — CALCULATED FROM 2000 RPM TO 1600 RPM
— — — CALCULATED FROM 1600 RPM TO 2000 RPM

U. S. GALLONS PER MINUTE

FIG. 17. Comparison of test performance with performance calculated using affinity laws for speed change.

Law 1a. $\dfrac{Q_1}{Q_2} = \dfrac{N_1}{N_2}$; $Q_1 = \dfrac{1600}{2000} \times 1700 = 1360$ gpm.

Law 1b. $\dfrac{H_1}{H_2} = \left(\dfrac{N_1}{N_2}\right)^{2}$; $H_1 = \left(\dfrac{1600}{2000}\right)^{2} \times 180 = 115.2$ ft.

Law 1c. $\dfrac{\mathrm{Bhp}_1}{\mathrm{Bhp}_2} = \left(\dfrac{N_1}{N_2}\right)^{3}$; $\mathrm{Bph}_1 = \left(\dfrac{1600}{2000}\right)^{3} \times 84 = 43$ Bhp

Note the close agreement between calculated values and actual test results. The agreement is good provided pump efficiency does not change too much. If you will plot 1700 gpm at 180 ft., the original capacity and head at 2000 rpm; and the final capacity and head, 1360 gpm at 115 feet at 1600 rpm, on the complete performance chart of this pump given in Figure 13, you will note that there has been no appreciable change in efficiency. This is generally the case when conditions are changed by speed adjustment, for the pump has not been altered physically. Note that the general shape of the iso-efficiency lines in Figure 13 are parabolic.

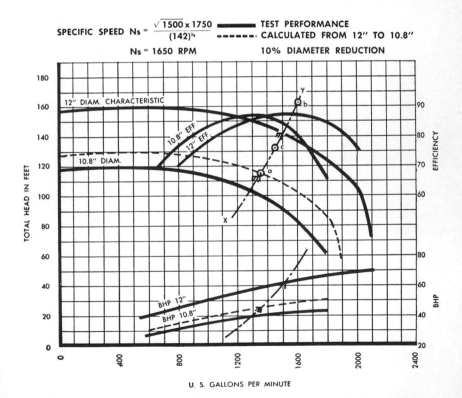

FIG. 18. Curves showing the disagreement between test and calculated performance when applying affinity laws for diameter change for a pump with specific speed Ns = 1650.

Therefore, the curve A-B in Fig. 17 passing through the two condition points on the 2000 rpm and 1600 Rpm curves, which is also parabolic, is approximately parallel to the iso-efficiency curves. The use of the Affinity Laws, therefore, to calculate performance when the speed is changed and the impeller diameter remains constant, is a quite accurate approximation. By calculating several points along a known performance curve, a new performance curve can be produced showing the approximate performance at the new speed.

Starting with the 1600 rpm characteristic and calculating the performance at 2000 rpm by the use of the affinity laws, the calculated performance exceeds the actual performance as shown in dotted curve on Figure 17. The discrepancy is slight but emphasizes the fact that the method is only a quite accurate approximation.

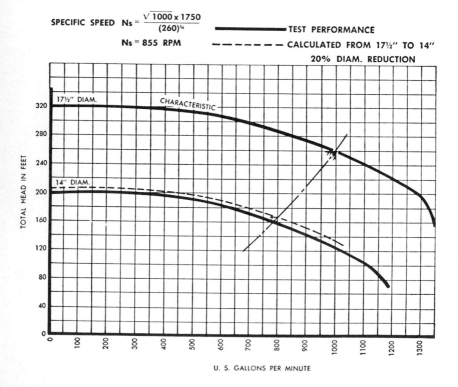

FIG. 20. Curves showing the relative agreement between test and calculated performance when applying affinity laws for diameter change for a pump with a very low specific speed Ns = 855.

Illustration Law 2

Probably this should not be considered as an affinity law, for when the impeller of a pump is reduced in diameter, the design relationships are changed, and in reality a new design results. Law 2, therefore, does not yield the accurate results of Law 1. It is always recommended that the pump manufacturer be consulted before changing the diameter of an impeller in the field.

Figure 20 illustrates the comparative accuracy of test performance to the calculated performance on a very low specific speed pump. Figure 18, however, shows rather wide discrepancy between test and calculated results on a pump of higher specific speed. On pumps of still higher specific speed the lack of agreement between test and calculated results is even more pronounced.

In general, agreement will be best on low specific speed pumps and the higher the specific speed the greater the disagreement. However specific speed is only one of the factors considered by the manufacturer when determining the proper impeller diameter.

When the affinity laws are used for calculating speed or diameter *increases,* it is important to consider the effect of suction lift on the characteristic for the increased velocity in the suction line and pump may result in cavitation that may substantially alter the characteristic curve of the pump.

PARALLEL AND SERIES OPERATION†

When the pumping requirements are variable, it may be more desirable to install several small pumps in parallel rather than use a single large one. When the demand drops, one or more smaller pumps may be shut down, thus allowing the remainder to operate at or near peak efficiency. If a single pump is used with lowered demand, the discharge must be throttled, and it will operate at reduced efficiency. Moreover, when smaller units are used opportunity is provided during slack demand periods for repairing and maintaining each pump in turn, thus avoiding plant shut-downs which would be necessary with single units. Similarly, multiple pumps in series may be used when liquid must be delivered at high heads.

In planning such installations a head-capacity curve for the system must first be drawn. The head required by the system is the sum of the static head (difference in elevation and/or its pressure equivalent) plus the variable head (friction and shock losses in the pipes, heaters, etc.). The former is usually constant for a given system whereas the latter increases approximately with the square of the flow. The resulting curve is represented as line AB in Figs. 21 and 22.

†*Courtesy De Laval Steam Turbine Co. See page 6.*

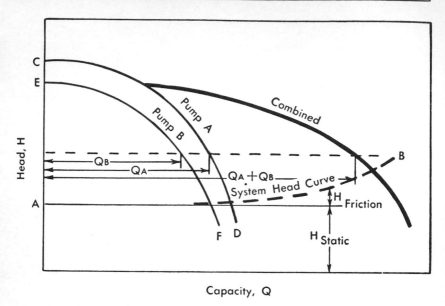

FIG. 21. Head capacity curves of pumps operating in parallel.†

Connecting two pumps in parallel to be driven by one motor is not a very common practice and, offhand, such an arrangement may appear more expensive than a single pump. However, it should be remembered that in most cases it is possible to operate such a unit at about 40 per cent higher speed, which may reduce the cost of the motor materially. Thus, the cost of two high-speed pumps may not be much greater than that of a single slow-speed pump.

For units to operate satisfactorily in parallel, they must be work-ing on the portion of the characteristic curve which drops off with increased capacity in order to secure an even flow distribution. Consider the action of two pumps operating in parallel. The system head-capacity curve AB shown in Fig. 21 starts at H static when the flow is zero and rises parabolically with increased flow. Curve CD represents the characteristic curve of pump A operating alone; the similar curve for pump B is represented by EF. Pump B will not start delivery until the discharge pressure of pump A falls below that of the shut-off head of B (point E). The combined delivery for a given head is equal to the sum of the individual capacities of the two pumps at that head. For a given combined delivery head, the capac-ity is divided between the pumps as noted on the figures Q_A and Q_B. The combined characteristic curve shown on the figure is found by plotting these summations. The combined brake horse-

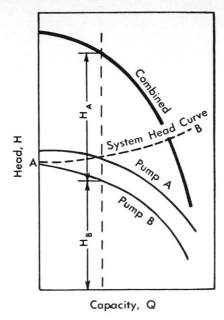

FIG. 22. Head capacity curves of pumps operating in series.†

power curve can be found by adding the brake horsepower of pump A corresponding to Q_A to that of pump B corresponding to Q_B, and plotting this at the combined flow. The efficiency curve of the combination may be determined by the following equation.

$$\text{Eff} = \frac{(Q_B,\ \text{Gpm} + Q_A,\ \text{Gpm})\ H}{3960\ (\text{Bhp at } Q_B + \text{Bhp at } Q_A)}$$

If two pumps are operated in series, the combined head for any flow is equal to the sum of the individual heads as shown in Fig. 22. The combined brake horsepower curve may be found by adding the horsepowers given by the curves for the individual pumps. Points on the combined efficiency curve are found by the following equation.

$$\text{Eff} = \frac{Q,\ \text{gpm}\ (H_A\ \text{ft.} + H_B,\ \text{ft.})}{3960\ (\text{Bhp at } H_A + \text{Bhp at } H_B)}$$

HYDRO-PNEUMATIC TANKS

In pumping installations the major use of hydro-pneumatic tanks is to make it possible to automatically supply water under pressure. They do provide relatively small quantities of water for storage, but this cannot be considered their primary function. However, this amount of water in storage is a very important factor when select-

†*Courtesy John Wiley & Sons, Inc. See page 6.*

ing the proper size tank to be used with the pump selected. The usable storage capacity should be such that the pump motor will not start frequently enough to cause overheating. Starting 10 to 15 times per hour will usually be satisfactory. The limit in the number of starts per hour depends upon the motor horsepower and speed. For the higher speeds and horse-powers use less starts per hour.

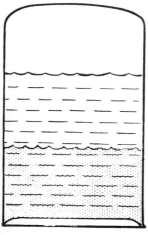

$-V_1 =$ Volume of water in tank at the High or Cut-Out pressure P_1 psia, in per cent of tank volume.

$-V_2 =$ Volume of water in tank at the Low or Cut-In pressure P_2 psia, in per cent of tank volume.

FIG. 23. Hydro-pneu-matic tank.

To determine the amount of water that can be withdrawn from a tank when the pressure drops from P_1 to P_2 psia use the following equation.

$V_1 - V_2 =$ Water withdrawn or storage capacity of tank, %

$$= \left(\frac{P_1}{P_2} - 1\right)\left(100 - V_1\right)$$

In this equation P_1 and P_2 must be expressed in psia—pounds per square inch absolute. V_1 and V_2 are expressed in per cent.

Example: In a 1000 gal. tank the gauge pressure at the cut-out point is 40 psi and the tank is 60% full of water. The cut-in pressure is 20 psi. What is the storage capacity of the tank?

$$\frac{P_1}{P_2} = \frac{40 + 14.7}{20 + 14.7} = \frac{54.7}{34.7} = 1.58$$

Storage Capacity $= (1.58 - 1)\ \ (100 - 60) = 23.2\%$

Therefore in the 1000 gal. tank the storage capacity $=1000 \times .232$
$= 232$ gal.

The storage capacity of tanks in percent can be read directly from the chart Fig. 24.

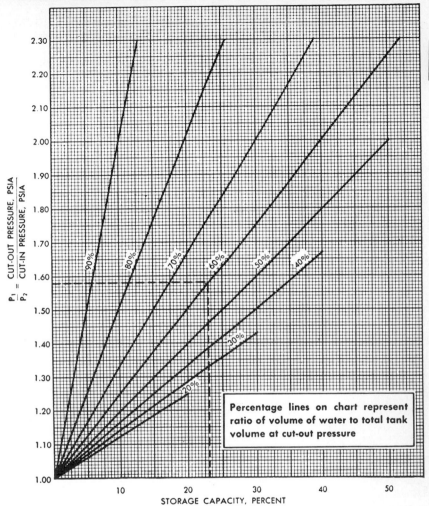

FIG. 24. Hydro-pneumatic tanks—relation between pressure range and storage capacity.

GALVANIC CORROSION †

(a) *Definition of Galvanic Corrosion* — Galvanic corrosion may be defined as the accelerated electro-chemical corrosion produced when one metal is in electrical contact with another more noble metal, both being immersed in the same corroding medium, which is called the electrolyte. Corrosion of this type results usually in an accelerated rate of solution for one member of the couple and protection for the other. The protected member, the one that does not corrode, is called the nobler metal. Note that as galvanic corrosion is generally understood, it consists of the total corrosion, which comprises the normal

†*Courtesy Hydraulic Institute. See page 6.*

corrosion that would occur on a metal exposed alone, plus the additional amount that is due to contact with the more noble material.

(b) *Galvanic Series* — With a knowledge of the galvanic corrosion behavior of metals and alloys, it is possible to arrange them in a series which will indicate their general tendencies to form galvanic cells, and to predict the probable direction of the galvanic effects. Such a series is provided in Fig. 25.

This series should not be confused with the familiar, "Electromotive Series," which is found in many textbooks and is of value in physical chemistry and thermodynamic studies.

It will be noticed that some of the metals in Fig. 25 are grouped together. These group members have no strong tendency to produce galvanic corrosion on each other, and from the practical standpoint they are relatively safe to use in contact with each other, but the coupling of two metals from *different* groups and *distant* from each other in the list will result in galvanic, or accelerated, corrosion of the one higher in the list. The farther apart the metals stand, the greater will be the galvanic tendency. This may be determined by measurement of the electrical potential difference between them, and this is often done, but it is not practical to tabulate these differences because the voltage values for combinations of the metals will vary with every different corrosive condition. What actually determines galvanic effect, is the quantity of current generated rather than the potential difference.

The relative position of a metal within a group sometimes changes with external conditions, but it is only rarely that changes occur from group to group. It will be seen that the chromium stainless steel and chromium-nickel stainless steel alloys are in two places in the table. They frequently change positions as indicated, depending upon the corrosive media. The most important reasons for this are the oxidizing power and acidity of the solutions, and the presence of activating ions, such as halides. Inconel and nickel also occasionally behave in a similar manner, though the variations of their position are less frequent and less extensive. In environments where these alloys ordinarily demonstrate good resistance to corrosion, they will be in their passive condition and behave accordingly in galvanic couples.

(c) *To Minimize Galvanic Corrosion*

1. Select combinations of metals as close together as possible in the Galvanic Series.

2. Avoid making combinations where the area of the less noble material is relatively small.

3. Insulate dissimiliar metals wherever practical, including use of plastic washers and sleeves at flanged joints. If complete insulation cannot be achieved, anything such as a paint or plastic coating at joints will help to increase the resistances of the circuit.

4. Apply coatings with caution. For example, do not paint the less noble material without also coating the more noble; otherwise, greatly accelerated attack may be concentrated at imperfections in coatings on the less noble metal. Keep such coatings in good repair.

5. In cases where the metals cannot be painted and are connected by a conductor external to the liquid, the electrical resistance of the liquid path may be increased by designing the equipment to keep the metals as far apart as possible.

6. If practical and dependent on velocity, add suitable chemical inhibitors to the corrosive solution.

7. If you must use dissimilar materials well apart in the series, avoid joining them by threaded connections, as the threads will probably deteriorate excessively. Welded or brazed joints are preferred. Use a brazing alloy more noble than at least one of the metals to be joined.

8. If possible, install relatively small replaceable sections of the less noble material at joints, and increase its thickness in such regions. For example, extra heavy wall nipples can often be used in piping, or replaceable pieces of the less noble material can be attached in the vicinity of the galvanic contact.

9. Install pieces of bare zinc, magnesium, or steel so as to provide a counteracting effect that will suppress galvanic corrosion.

FIG. 25. GALVANIC SERIES OF METALS AND ALLOYS

Corroded End (anodic, or least noble)

Magnesium
Magnesium alloys

Zinc

Aluminum 2S

Cadmium

Aluminum 17ST

Steel or Iron
Cast Iron

Chromium stainless steel, 400 Series (active)

Austenitic nickel or nickel-copper cast iron alloy

18-8 Chromium-nickel stainless steel, Type 304 (active)
18-8-3 Chromium-nickel-molybdenum stainless steel, Type 316 (active)

Lead-tin solders
Lead
Tin

Nickel (active)
Nickel-base alloy (active)
Nickel-molybdenum-chromium-iron alloy (active)

Brasses
Copper
Bronzes
Copper-nickel alloy
Nickel-copper alloy

Silver solder

Nickel (passive)
Nickel-base alloy (passive)

Chromium stainless steel, 400 Series (passive)
18-8 Chromium-nickel stainless steel, Type 304 (passive)
18-8-3 Chromium-nickel-molybdenum stainless steel, Type 316
(passive)

Nickel-molybdenum-chromium-iron alloy (passive)

Silver

Graphite
Gold
Platinum

Protected End (cathodic, or most noble)

Non-Metallic Construction Materials

Non-metallic materials, including various plastics, ceramics, and rubber, either in the solid state or as coatings on metals, are being used to a limited extent in pumps for particular services. These materials generally show excellent corrosion resistance. They should only be considered, however, for applications where the expected temperature range is suitable for the specific material to be used. Further, where coatings are involved, precautions must be taken to assure freedom from pin holes; otherwise, the corrosive liquid may attack the base metal and loosen the covering. In general, the plastics and ceramics are characterized by relatively poor strength which limits their use to pumps where the application is suitable.

GRAPHITIZATION

The surface of cast iron in contact with sea water or other electrolytes is gradually converted into a mechanical mixture of graphite and iron oxide by a galvanic reaction between the graphite flakes and the iron matrix. The phenomenon is known as graphitization. The graphitized layer, although cathodic to the base iron, becomes increasingly impervious to the penetration of the water as it increases in depth and, hence, the rate of attack on the underlying base iron is correspondingly decreased. Cast iron is thus a useful material in many applications as long as the graphitized surface remains intact. The layer, however, is comparatively soft and if constantly removed by high velocities or turbulence, the exposed anodic base iron is subject to continuous, rapid attack. The useful life of impellers and wearing rings made of cast iron, when handling corrosive waters, may be short unless the liquid velocities are quite low. The use of bronze and certain types of stainless steels for such parts is generally advisable. The cathodic nature of the graphitized iron explains the rather rapid failure of replacement parts when installed in contact with older, graphitized parts, and at the same time accounts for the usually false impression that the new iron is inferior to the old.

SECTION II—PIPE FRICTION—WATER

CONTENTS

SECTION II—FRICTION OF WATER

INTRODUCTION:

The flow of water is basic to all hydraulics. Friction losses incident to water flow may seriously affect the selection or performance of hydraulic machinery. The major portion of the head against which many pumps operate is due largely to the friction losses caused by the created flow. A basic understanding of the nature of the loss and an accurate means of estimating its magnitude is therefore essential.

GENERAL:

It is well established that either laminar or turbulent flow of incompressible fluids in pipe lines can be treated by the basic formula:

$$h_f = f\frac{L}{D}\ \frac{V^2}{2g}$$

where: h_f = friction loss in feet of liquid.
  f = friction factor
  L = length of pipe in feet
  D = average internal diameter of pipe in feet
  V = average velocity in pipe in feet per second
  g = acceleration due to gravity in feet per second per second

The theoretical and empirical studies of engineers who have worked on this problem comprise a roster of names that includes practically every important hydraulic authority for the past century. This work has provided a simple method for determining friction factor "f" as a function of relative pipe roughness and/or the Reynolds Number of flow.

A comprehensive anaylsis of this mass of experimentation has recently been conducted under the sponsorship of the Hydraulic Institute. A very complete treatise, "Pipe Friction" has been published as a Technical Pamphlet by the Hydraulic Institute; it is an important contribution to the authoritative literature on the subject.

The following tables are a condensation of these data in a form convenient for use. The tables show frictional resistance for water flowing in new schedule #40 steel pipe (ASA specification B36.10) or in new asphalt-dipped cast-iron pipe.

The tables show discharge in U. S. gallons per minute, the average velocity in feet per second for circular pipe, the corresponding velocity head, and the friction loss (h_f) in feet of fluid per 100 feet of pipe for 60°F water or any liquid having a Kinematic viscosity $v = 0.00001216$ square feet per second (1.130 centistokes).

Table 1. for new schedule #40 steel pipe is based upon an absolute roughness $\epsilon = 0.00015$ feet. Table 2. for new asphalt-dipped cast-iron pipe is based upon an absolute roughness of 0.0004 feet.

TABLE 1.
FRICTION LOSS PER 100 FEET FOR WATER IN NEW WROUGHT IRON OR SCHEDULE 40 STEEL PIPE†

¼″
0.364″ inside dia.

U.S. Gals. Per Min.	vel. V f.p.s.	vel. head V²/2g feet	frict. loss h_f feet
0.8	2.47	0.09	12.7
1.0	3.08	0.15	19.1
1.2	3.70	0.21	26.7
1.4	4.32	0.29	35.3
1.6	4.93	0.38	45.2
1.8	5.55	0.48	56.4
2.0	6.17	0.59	69.0
2.5	7.71	0.92	105.0
3.0	9.25	1.33	148.0
3.5	10.79	1.81	200.0
4.0	12.33	2.36	259.0
5.0	15.42	3.69	398.0

⅜″
0.493″ inside dia.

U.S. Gals. Per Min.	vel. V f.p.s.	vel. head V²/2g feet	frict. loss h_f feet
1.4	2.35	0.09	7.85
1.6	2.68	0.11	10.1
1.8	3.02	0.14	12.4
2.0	3.36	0.18	15.0
2.5	4.20	0.27	22.6
3.0	5.04	0.39	31.8
3.5	5.88	0.54	42.6
4.0	6.72	0.70	54.9
5.0	8.40	1.10	83.5
6.0	10.08	1.58	118.0
7.0	11.80	2.15	158.0
8.0	13.40	2.81	205.0
9.0	15.10	3.56	258.0
10.0	16.80	4.39	316.0

½″
0.622″ inside dia.

U.S. Gals. Per Min.	vel. V f.p.s.	vel. head V²/2g feet	frict. loss h_f feet
2.0	2.11	0.07	4.78
2.5	2.64	0.11	7.16
3.0	3.17	0.16	10.0
3.5	3.70	0.21	13.3
4.0	4.22	0.28	17.1
5.0	5.28	0.43	25.8
6.0	6.34	0.62	36.5
7.0	7.39	0.85	48.7
8.0	8.45	1.11	62.7
9.0	9.50	1.40	78.3
10.0	10.56	1.73	95.9
12.0	12.70	2.49	136.0
14.0	14.80	3.40	183.0
16.0	16.90	4.43	235.0

¾″
0.824″ inside dia.

U.S. Gals. Per Min.	vel. V f.p.s.	vel. head V²/2g feet	frict. loss h_f feet
3.0	1.81	0.05	2.50
3.5	2.11	0.07	3.30
4.0	2.41	0.09	4.21
5.0	3.01	0.14	6.32
6.0	3.61	0.20	8.87
7.0	4.21	0.28	11.8
8.0	4.81	0.36	15.0
9.0	5.42	0.46	18.8
10.0	6.02	0.56	23.0
12.0	7.22	0.81	32.6
14.0	8.42	1.10	43.5
16.0	9.63	1.44	56.3
18.0	10.80	1.82	70.3
20.0	12.00	2.25	86.1
22.0	13.20	2.72	104.0
24.0	14.40	3.24	122.0
26.0	15.60	3.80	143.0
28.0	16.80	4.41	164.0

CAUTION: No allowance has been made for age, differences in diameter resulting from manufacturing tolerances or any abnormal conditions of interior pipe surface. It is recommended that for commercial application a reserve or margin of safety to cover these effects be added to the values shown in the tables. Where no careful analysis of these effects are made a reserve of 15% is recommended.

†*Courtesy Hydraulic Institute. See Page 6.*

TABLE 1. (Cont.)
FRICTION LOSS PER 100 FEET FOR WATER IN NEW WROUGHT IRON OR SCHEDULE 40 STEEL PIPE

1"
1.049" inside dia.

1¼"
1.380" inside dia.

U.S. Gals. Per Min.	vel. V f.p.s.	vel. head $V^2/2g$ feet	frict. loss h_f feet	U.S. Gals. Per Min.	vel. V f.p.s.	vel. head $V^2/2g$ feet	frict. loss h_f feet
6	2.23	0.08	2.68	10	2.15	0.72	1.77
8	2.97	0.14	4.54	12	2.57	0.10	2.48
10	3.71	0.21	6.86	14	3.00	0.14	3.28
12	4.45	0.31	9.62	16	3.43	0.18	4.20
14	5.20	0.42	12.8	18	3.86	0.23	5.22
16	5.94	0.55	16.5	20	4.29	0.29	6.34
18	6.68	0.69	20.6	22	4.72	0.35	7.58
20	7.42	0.86	25.1	24	5.15	0.41	8.92
22	8.17	1.04	30.2	25	5.36	0.45	9.6
24	8.91	1.23	35.6	30	6.44	0.64	13.6
25	9.27	1.34	38.7	35	7.51	0.87	18.2
30	11.1	1.93	54.6	40	8.58	1.14	23.5
35	13.0	2.63	73.3	45	9.65	1.44	29.4
40	14.8	3.43	95.0	50	10.7	1.79	36.0
45	16.7	4.34	119.0	55	11.8	2.16	43.2
50	18.6	5.35	146.0	60	12.9	2.57	51.0
55	20.4	6.46	176.0	65	13.9	3.02	59.6
60	22.3	7.71	209.0	70	15.0	3.50	68.8
65	24.2	9.10	245.0	75	16.1	4.03	78.7
70	26.0	10.49	283.0	80	17.2	4.58	89.2
75	27.9	12.10	324.0	85	18.2	5.15	100.0
80	29.7	13.7	367.0	90	19.3	5.79	112.0
				95	20.4	6.45	125.0
				100	21.5	7.15	138.0
				120	25.7	10.3	197.0
				140	30.0	14.0	267.0

1½"
1.610" inside dia.

U.S. Gals. Per Min.	vel. V f.p.s.	vel. head $V^2/2g$ feet	frict. loss h_f feet	U.S. Gals. Per Min.	vel. V f.p.s.	vel. head $V^2/2g$ feet	frict. loss h_f feet
14	2.21	0.08	1.53	65	10.24	1.63	27.1
16	2.52	0.10	1.96	70	11.03	1.89	31.3
18	2.84	0.12	2.42	75	11.8	2.16	35.8
20	3.15	0.15	2.94	80	12.6	2.47	40.5
22	3.47	0.19	3.52	85	13.4	2.79	45.6
24	3.78	0.22	4.14	90	14.2	3.13	51.0
25	3.94	0.24	4.48	95	15.0	3.49	56.5
30	4.73	0.38	6.26	100	15.8	3.86	62.2
35	5.51	0.47	8.37	120	18.9	5.56	88.3
40	6.30	0.62	10.79	140	22.1	7.56	119.0
45	7.04	0.78	13.45	160	25.2	9.88	156.0
50	7.88	0.97	16.4	180	28.4	12.50	196.0
55	8.67	1.17	19.7	200	31.5	15.40	241.0
60	9.46	1.39	23.2				

CAUTION: No allowance has been made for age, differences in diameter resulting from manufacturing tolerances or any abnormal conditions of interior pipe surface. It is recommended that for commercial application a reserve or margin of safety to cover these effects be added to the values shown in the tables. Where no careful analysis of these effects are made a reserve of 15% is recommended.

TABLE 1. (Cont.)
FRICTION LOSS PER 100 FEET FOR WATER IN NEW WROUGHT IRON OR SCHEDULE 40 STEEL PIPE

2″ 2.067″ inside dia.				**2½″** 2.469″ inside dia.			
U.S. Gals. Per Min.	vel. V f.p.s.	vel. head $V^2/2g$ feet	frict. loss h_f feet	U S. Gals. Per Min.	vel. V f.p.s.	vel. head $V^2/2g$ feet	frict. loss h_f feet
24	2.29	0.08	1.20	25	1.68	0.04	0.54
25	2.39	0.09	1.29	30	2.01	0.06	0.75
30	2.87	0.13	1.82	35	2.35	0.09	1.00
35	3.35	0.17	2.42	40	2.68	0.11	1.28
40	3.82	0.23	3.10	45	3.02	0.14	1.60
45	4.30	0.29	3.85	50	3.35	0.17	1.94
50	4.78	0.36	4.67	60	4.02	0.25	2.72
55	5.25	0.43	5.51	70	4.69	0.34	3.63
60	5.74	0.51	6.59	80	5.36	0.45	4.66
65	6.21	0.60	7.70	90	6.03	0.57	5.82
70	6.69	0.70	8.86	100	6.70	0.70	7.11
75	7.16	0.80	10.15	120	8.04	1.00	10.0
80	7.65	0.91	11.40	140	9.38	1.37	13.5
85	8.11	1.03	12.6	160	10.7	1.79	17.4
90	8.60	1.15	14.2	180	12.1	2.26	21.9
95	9.09	1.29	15.8	200	13.4	2.79	26.7
100	9.56	1.42	17.4	220	14.7	3.38	32.2
120	11.5	2.05	24.7	240	16.1	4.02	38.1
140	13.4	2.78	33.2	260	17.4	4.72	44.5
160	15.3	3.64	43.0	280	18.8	5.47	51.3
180	17.2	4.60	54.1	300	20.1	6.28	58.5
200	19.1	5.68	66.3	350	23.5	8.55	79.2
220	21.0	6.88	80.0	400	26.8	11.2	103.0
240	22.9	8.18	95.0				
260	24.9	9.60	111.0				
280	26.8	11.14	128.0				
300	28.7	12.8	146.0				

3″
3.068″ inside dia.

U.S. Gals. Per Min.	vel. V f.p.s.	vel. head $V^2/2g$ feet	frict. loss h_f feet	U.S. Gals. Per Min.	vel. V f.p.s.	vel. head $V^2/2g$ feet	frict. loss h_f feet
50	2.17	0.07	0.66	220	9.55	1.42	10.7
60	2.60	0.11	0.92	240	10.4	1.69	12.6
70	3.04	0.14	1.22	260	11.3	1.98	14.7
80	3.47	0.19	1.57	280	12.2	2.29	16 9
90	3.91	0.24	1.96	300	13.0	2.63	19.2
100	4.34	0.29	2.39	350	15.2	3.58	26.1
120	5.21	0.42	3.37	400	17.4	4.68	33.9
140	6.08	0.57	4.51	500	21.7	7.32	52.5
160	6.94	0.75	5.81	550	23.8	8.85	63.2
180	7.81	0.95	7.28	600	26.0	10.5	74.8
200	8.68	1.17	8.90	700	30.4	14.3	101.0

CAUTION: No allowance has been made for age, differences in diameter resulting from manufacturing tolerances or any abnormal conditions of interior pipe surface. It is recommended that for commercial application a reserve or margin of safety to cover these effects be added to the values shown in the tables. Where no careful analysis of these effects are made a reserve of 15% is recommended.

TABLE 1. (Cont.)
FRICTION LOSS PER 100 FEET FOR WATER IN NEW WROUGHT IRON OR SCHEDULE 40 STEEL PIPE

4" 4.026" inside dia.				5" 5.047" inside dia.			
U.S. Gals. Per Min.	vel. V f.p.s.	vel. head V²/2g feet	frict. loss h_f feet	U.S. Gals. Per Min.	vel. V f.p.s.	vel. head V²/2g feet	frict. loss h_f feet
90	2.27	0.08	0.52	140	2.25	0.08	0.380
100	2.52	0.10	0.62	160	2.57	0.10	0.487
120	3.02	0.14	0.88	180	2.89	0.13	0.606
140	3.53	0.19	1.17	200	3.21	0.16	0.736
160	4.03	0.25	1.49	220	3.53	0.19	0.879
180	4.54	0.32	1.86	240	3.85	0.23	1.035
200	5.04	0.40	2.27	260	4.17	0.27	1.200
220	5.54	0.48	2.72	280	4.49	0.31	1.38
240	6.05	0.57	3.21	300	4.81	0.36	1.58
260	6.55	0.67	3.74	350	5.61	0.49	2.11
280	7.06	0.77	4.30	400	6.41	0.64	2.72
300	7.56	0.89	4.89	450	7.22	0.81	3.41
350	8.82	1.21	6.55	500	8.02	1.00	4.16
400	10.10	1.58	8.47	550	8.81	1.21	4.94
450	11.4	2.00	10.65	600	9.62	1.44	5.88
500	12.6	2.47	13.0	700	11.20	1.96	7.93
550	13.9	3.00	15.7	800	12.80	2.56	10.22
600	15.1	3.55	18.6	900	14.40	3.24	12.90
700	17.6	4.84	25.0	1000	16.00	4.00	15.80
800	20.2	6.32	32.4	1200	19.20	5.76	22.50
900	22.7	8.00	40.8	1400	22.50	7.83	30.40
1000	25.2	9.87	50.2	1600	25.7	10.2	39.5
				1800	28.80	12.90	49.70

6"
6.065" inside dia.

U.S. Gals. Per Min.	vel. V f.p.s.	vel. head V²/2g feet	frict. loss h_f feet	U.S. Gals. Per Min.	vel. V f.p.s.	vel. head V²/2g feet	frict. loss h_f feet
200	2.22	0.08	0.30	800	8.88	1.23	4.03
220	2.44	0.09	0.357	850	9.43	1.39	4.50
240	2.66	0.11	0.419	900	9.99	1.55	5.05
260	2.89	0.13	0.487	950	10.55	1.73	5.61
280	3.11	0.15	0.56	1000	11.10	1.92	6.17
300	3.33	0.17	0.637	1100	12.20	2.32	7.41
350	3.89	0.24	0.851	1200	13.30	2.76	8.76
400	4.44	0.31	1.09	1300	14.40	3.24	10.2
450	5.00	0.39	1.36	1400	15.50	3.76	11.8
500	5.55	0.48	1.66	1500	16.70	4.31	13.5
600	6.66	0.69	2.34	1600	17.80	4.91	15.4
650	7.21	0.81	2.72	1700	18.90	5.54	17.3
700	7.77	0.94	3.13	1800	20.00	6.21	19.4
750	8.32	1.08	3.59	1900	21.10	6.92	21.6
				2000	22.20	7.67	23.8

CAUTION: No allowance has been made for age, differences in diameter resulting from manufacturing tolerances or any abnormal conditions of interior pipe surface. It is recommended that for commercial application a reserve or margin of safety to cover these effects be added to the values shown in the tables. Where no careful analysis of these effects are made a reserve of 15% is recommended.

TABLE 1. (Cont.)
FRICTION LOSS PER 100 FEET FOR WATER IN NEW WROUGHT IRON OR SCHEDULE 40 STEEL PIPE

8" 7.981" inside dia.				10" 10.020" inside dia.			
U.S. Gals. Per Min.	vel. V f.p.s.	vel. head $V^2/2g$ feet	frict. loss h_f feet	U.S. Gals. Per Min.	vel. V f.p.s.	vel. head $V^2/2g$ feet	frict. loss h_f feet
400	2.57	0.10	0.279	600	2.44	0.093	0.190
450	2.89	0.13	0.348	650	2.64	0.108	0.224
500	3.21	0.16	0.424	700	2.85	0.126	0.256
600	3.85	0.23	0.597	750	3.05	0.145	0.291
650	4.16	0.27	0.694	800	3.25	0.164	0.328
700	4.49	0.31	0.797	850	3.46	0.187	0.366
750	4.80	0.36	0.911	900	3.66	0.209	0.410
800	5.13	0.41	1.02	950	3.87	0.233	0.455
850	5.45	0.46	1.13	1000	4.07	0.257	0.500
900	5.77	0.52	1.27	1100	4.48	0.311	0.600
950	6.10	0.58	1.42	1200	4.88	0.370	0.703
1000	6.41	0.64	1.56	1300	5.29	0.435	0.818
1100	7.05	0.77	1.87	1400	5.70	0.505	0.94
1200	7.70	0.92	2.20	1500	6.10	0.579	1.07
1300	8.34	1.08	2.56	1600	6.51	0.659	1.21
1400	8.98	1.25	2.95	1700	6.92	0.743	1.36
1500	9.62	1.44	3.37	1800	7.32	0.835	1.52
1600	10.3	1.64	3.82	1900	7.73	0.930	1.68
1700	10.9	1.85	4.29	2000	8.14	1.030	1.86
1800	11.5	2.07	4.79	2100	8.55	1.135	2.05
1900	12.2	2.31	5.31	2200	8.94	1.240	2.25
2000	12.8	2.56	5.86	2500	10.2	1.62	2.86
2100	13.5	2.83	6.43	3000	12.2	2.31	4.06
2200	14.1	3.08	7.02	3500	14.2	3.14	5.46
2500	16.0	4.00	8.90	4000	16.3	4.12	7.07
3000	19.2	5.75	12.8	4500	18.3	5.20	8.91
3500	22.4	7.84	17.5	5000	20.3	6.42	11.00
4000	25.7	10.2	22.6	6000	24.4	9.29	15.90

12"
11.938" inside dia.

U.S. Gals. Per Min.	vel. V f.p.s.	vel. head $V^2/2g$ feet	frict. loss h_f feet	U.S. Gals. Per Min.	vel. V f.p.s.	vel. head $V^2/2g$ feet	frict. loss h_f feet
800	2.29	0.08	0.140	2000	5.73	0.51	0.776
850	2.44	0.09	0.154	2100	6.01	0.56	0.853
900	2.58	0.10	0.173	2200	6.29	0.61	0.936
950	2.72	0.12	0.191	2500	7.17	0.80	1.187
1000	2.87	0.13	0.210	3000	8.60	1.15	1.68
1100	3.15	0.15	0.251	3500	10.0	1.56	2.25
1200	3.44	0.18	0.296	4000	11.5	2.04	2.92
1300	3.73	0.22	0.344	4500	12.9	2.59	3.65
1400	4.01	0.25	0.395	5000	14.3	3.19	4.47
1500	4.30	0.29	0.450	6000	17.2	4.60	6.39
1600	4.59	0.33	0.509	7000	20.1	6.26	8.63
1700	4.87	0.37	0.572	8000	22.9	8.17	11.20
1800	5.16	0.41	0.636	9000	25.8	10.3	14.10
1900	5.45	0.46	0.704				

CAUTION: No allowance has been made for age, differences in diameter resulting from manufacturing tolerances or any abnormal conditions of interior pipe surface. It is recommended that for commercial application a reserve or margin of safety to cover these effects be added to the values shown in the tables. Where no careful analysis of these effects are made a reserve of 15% is recommended.

TABLE 1. (Cont.)
FRICTION LOSS PER 100 FEET FOR WATER IN NEW WROUGHT IRON OR SCHEDULE 40 STEEL PIPE

14″
13.126″ inside dia.

16″
15.000″ inside dia.

U.S. Gals. Per Min.	vel. V f.p.s.	vel. head $V^2/2g$ feet	frict. loss h_f feet	U.S. Gals. Per Min.	vel. V f.p.s.	vel. head $V^2/2g$ feet	frict. loss h_f feet
1000	2.37	0.09	0.131	1400	2.54	0.10	0.127
1100	2.61	0.11	0.157	1500	2.72	0.12	0.14
1200	2.85	0.13	0.185	1600	2.90	0.13	0.163
1300	3.08	0.15	0.215	1700	3.09	0.15	0.183
1400	3.32	0.17	0.247	1800	3.27	0.17	0.203
1500	3.56	0.20	0.281	1900	3.45	0.19	0.225
1600	3.79	0.22	0.317	2000	3.63	0.21	0.248
1700	4.03	0.25	0.355	2500	4.54	0.32	0.377
1800	4.27	0.28	0.395	3000	5.45	0.46	0.535
1900	4.50	0.32	0.438	3500	6.35	0.63	0.718
2000	4.74	0.35	0.483	4000	7.26	0.82	0.921
2500	5.93	0.55	0.738	4500	8.17	1.04	1.15
3000	7.11	0.79	1.04	5000	9.08	1.28	1.41
3500	8.30	1.07	1.40	6000	10.9	1.84	2.01
4000	9.48	1.40	1.81	7000	12.7	2.51	2.69
4500	10.7	1.78	2.27	8000	14.5	3.28	3.49
5000	11.9	2.18	2.78	9000	16.3	4.15	4.38
6000	14.2	3.14	3.95	10000	18.2	5.12	5.38
7000	16.6	4.28	5.32	11000	20.0	6.22	6.50
8000	19.0	5.59	6.90	12000	21.8	7.38	7.69
9000	21.3	7.08	8.70	13000	23.6	8.66	8.95
10000	23.7	8.74	10.7	14000	25.4	10.04	10.40
11000	26.0	10.55	12.9	15000	27.2	11.50	11.90
12000	28.5	12.60	15.2	16000	29.0	13.10	13.50

18″
16.876″ inside dia.

U.S. Gals. Per Min.	vel. V f.p.s.	vel. head $V^2/2g$ feet	frict. loss h_f feet	U.S. Gals. Per Min.	vel. V f.p.s.	vel. head $V^2/2g$ feet	frict. loss h_f feet
1800	2.58	0.10	0.114	7000	10.0	1.57	1.49
1900	2.73	0.12	0.126	8000	11.5	2.05	1.93
2000	2.87	0.13	0.139	9000	12.9	2.59	2.42
2500	3.59	0.20	0.211	10000	14.3	3.20	2.97
3000	4.30	0.29	0.297	11000	15.8	3.89	3.57
3500	5.02	0.39	0.397	12000	17.2	4.60	4.21
4000	5.74	0.51	0.511	13000	18.6	5.37	4.89
4500	6.45	0.65	0.639	14000	20.1	6.27	5.69
5000	7.17	0.80	0.781	15000	21.5	7.18	6.50
6000	8.61	1.15	1.11	16000	22.9	8.19	7.41
				18000	25.8	10.36	9.33
				20000	28.7	12.8	11.5

CAUTION: No allowance has been made for age, differences in diameter resulting from manufacturing tolerances or any abnormal conditions of interior pipe surface. It is recommended that for commercial application a reserve or margin of safety to cover these effects be added to the values shown in the tables. Where no careful analysis of these effects are made a reserve of 15% is recommended.

TABLE 1. (Cont.)
FRICTION LOSS PER 100 FEET FOR WATER IN NEW WROUGHT IRON OR SCHEDULE 40 STEEL PIPE

20" 18.814" inside dia.				24" 22.626" inside dia.			
U.S. Gals. Per Min.	vel. V f.p.s.	vel. head $V^2/2g$ feet	frict. loss h_f feet	U.S. Per Gals. Min.	V vel. f.p.s.	vel. $V^2/2g$ head feet	frict. loss h_f feet
2000	2.31	0.08	0.0812	3000	2.39	0.09	0.070
2500	2.89	0.13	0.123	3500	2.79	0.12	0.093
3000	3.46	0.19	0.174	4000	3.19	0.16	0.120
3500	4.04	0.25	0.232	4500	3.59	0.20	0.149
4000	4.62	0.33	0.298	5000	3.99	0.25	0.181
4500	5.19	0.42	0.372	6000	4.79	0.36	0.257
5000	5.77	0.52	0.455	7000	5.59	0.49	0.343
6000	6.92	0.75	0.645	8000	6.38	0.63	0.441
7000	8.08	1.01	0.862	9000	7.18	0.80	0.551
8000	9.23	1.32	1.11	10000	7.98	0.99	0.671
9000	10.39	1.68	1.39	11000	8.78	1.20	0.810
10000	11.5	2.07	1.70	12000	9.58	1.42	0.959
11000	12.7	2.51	2.05	13000	10.4	1.68	1.12
12000	13.8	2.98	2.44	14000	11.2	1.94	1.29
13000	15.0	3.50	2.86	15000	12.0	2.24	1.48
14000	16.2	4.08	3.29	16000	12.8	2.53	1.67
15000	17.3	4.65	3.75	17000	13.6	2.88	1.88
16000	18.5	5.30	4.26	18000	14.4	3.21	2.10
18000	20.8	6.71	5.35	19000	15.2	3.59	2.33
20000	32.1	8.28	6.56	20000	16.0	3.96	2.58
22000	25.4	10.02	7.91	25000	20.0	6.20	4.04
24000	27.7	11.9	9.39	30000	23.9	8.91	5.68
				35000	27.9	12.20	7.73

30"
29.000" inside dia.

U.S. Gals. Per Min.	vel. V f.p.s.	vel. head $V^2/2g$ feet	frict. loss h_f feet	U.S. Gals. Per Min.	vel. V f.p.s.	vel. head $V^2/2g$ feet	frict. loss h_f feet
5000	2.43	0.09	0.053	15000	7.28	0.83	0.426
6000	2.91	0.13	0.075	16000	7.77	0.94	0.478
7000	3.40	0.18	0.100	17000	8.25	1.06	0.538
8000	3.89	0.24	0.129	18000	8.74	1.19	0.598
9000	4.37	0.30	0.161	19000	9.21	1.32	0.661
10000	4.86	0.37	0.196	20000	9.71	1.47	0.732
11000	5.35	0.44	0.237	25000	12.1	2.29	1.13
12000	5.83	0.53	0.277	30000	14.6	3.30	1.61
13000	6.31	0.62	0.320	35000	17.0	4.49	2.17
14000	6.80	0.72	0.371	40000	19.4	5.87	2.83
				45000	21.9	7.42	3.56
				50000	24.3	9.17	4.38
				60000	29.1	13.2	6.23

CAUTION: No allowance has been made for age, differences in diameter resulting from manufacturing tolerances or any abnormal conditions of interior pipe surface. It is recommended that for commercial application a reserve or margin of safety to cover these effects be added to the values shown in the tables. Where no careful analysis of these effects are made a reserve of 15% is recommended.

TABLE 1. (Cont.)
FRICTION LOSS PER 100 FEET FOR WATER IN NEW WROUGHT IRON OR SCHEDULE 40 STEEL PIPE

36" 36.000" inside dia.				42" 42.000" inside dia.			
U.S. Gals. Per Min.	vel. V f.p.s.	vel. head $V^2/2g$ feet	frict. loss h_f feet	U.S. Gals. Per Min.	vel. V f.p.s.	vel. head $V^2/2g$ feet	frict. loss h_f feet
8000	2.52	0.10	0.044	10000	2.32	0.08	0.0314
9000	2.84	0.13	0.055	11000	2.55	0.10	0.0380
10000	3.15	0.15	0.067	12000	2.78	0.12	0.0441
11000	3.46	0.19	0.081	13000	3.01	0.14	0.0511
12000	3.78	0.22	0.094	14000	3.24	0.16	0.0591
13000	4.10	0.26	0.109	15000	3.47	0.19	0.0680
14000	4.41	0.30	0.126	16000	3.71	0.21	0.0758
15000	4.73	0.35	0.144	17000	3.94	0.24	0.0852
16000	5.04	0.40	0.162	18000	4.17	0.27	0.0944
17000	5.35	0.45	0.182	19000	4.40	0.30	0.104
18000	5.67	0.50	0.203	20000	4.63	0.33	0.115
19000	5.98	0.57	0.224	25000	5.79	0.52	0.176
20000	6.30	0.62	0.248	30000	6.95	0.75	0.250
25000	7.88	0.97	0.378	35000	8.11	1.02	0.334
30000	9.46	1.39	0.540	40000	9.26	1.33	0.433
35000	11.0	1.89	0.724	45000	10.4	1.69	0.545
40000	12.6	2.47	0.941	50000	11.6	2.08	0.668
45000	14.1	3.13	1.18	60000	13.9	3.00	0.946
50000	15.8	3.86	1.45	70000	16.2	4.08	1.27
60000	18.9	5.56	2.07	80000	18.5	5.33	1.66
70000	22.1	7.56	2.81	90000	20.8	6.75	2.08
80000	25.2	9.88	3.66	100000	23.2	8.33	2.57
90000	28.4	12.5	4.59	120000	27.8	12.0	3.67

48"
48" inside dia.

U.S. Gals. Per Min.	vel. V f.p.s.	vel. head $V^2/2g$ feet	frict. loss h_f feet	U.S. Gals. Per Min.	vel. V f.p.s.	vel. head $V^2/2g$ feet	frict. loss h_f feet
14000	2.48	0.10	0.031	60000	10.64	1.76	0.484
16000	2.84	0.13	0.039	70000	12.4	2.39	0.652
18000	3.19	0.16	0.049	80000	14.2	3.13	0.849
20000	3.55	0.20	0.060	90000	16.0	3.96	1.06
25000	4.43	0.31	0.091	100000	17.7	4.89	1.30
30000	5.32	0.44	0.128	120000	21.3	7.03	1.87
35000	6.21	0.60	0.172	140000	24.8	9.57	2.51
40000	7.09	0.78	0.222	160000	28.4	12.5	3.26
45000	7.98	0.99	0.278				
50000	8.87	1.22	0.341				

CAUTION: No allowance has been made for age, differences in diameter resulting from manufacturing tolerances or any abnormal conditions of interior pipe surface. It is recommended that for commercial application a reserve or margin of safety to cover these effects be added to the values shown in the tables. Where no careful analysis of these effects are made a reserve of 15% is recommended.

TABLE 1. (Cont.)
FRICTION LOSS PER 100 FEET FOR WATER IN NEW WROUGHT IRON OR SCHEDULE 40 STEEL PIPE

54" 54" inside dia.				**60"** 60" inside dia.			
U.S. Gals. Per Min.	vel. V f.p.s.	vel. head $V^2/2g$ feet	frict. loss h_f feet	U.S. Gals. Per Min.	vel. V f.p.s.	vel. head $V^2/2g$ feet	frict. loss h_f feet
18000	2.52	0.10	0.027	20000	2.27	0.08	0.020
20000	2.80	0.12	0.033	25000	2.84	0.13	0.030
25000	3.50	0.19	0.050	30000	3.40	0.18	0.042
30000	4.20	0.27	0.071	35000	3.97	0.25	0.057
35000	4.90	0.37	0.096	40000	4.54	0.32	0.073
40000	5.60	0.49	0.124	45000	5.11	0.41	0.092
45000	6.30	0.62	0.155	50000	5.67	0.50	0.112
50000	7.00	0.76	0.189	60000	6.81	0.72	0.158
60000	8.40	1.10	0.267	70000	7.94	0.98	0.213
70000	9.81	1.49	0.358	80000	9.08	1.28	0.275
80000	11.21	1.95	0.465	90000	10.21	1.62	0.344
90000	12.6	2.47	0.586	100000	11.3	2.00	0.420
100000	14.0	3.05	0.715	120000	13.6	2.88	0.600
120000	16.8	4.39	1.02	140000	15.9	3.92	0.806
140000	19.6	5.98	1.38	160000	18.2	5.12	1.040
160000	22.4	7.81	1.80	180000	20.4	6.48	1.32
180000	25.2	9.88	2.26	200000	22.7	8.00	1.62
200000	28.0	12.2	2.77	250000	28.4	12.5	2.52

72" 72" inside dia.			
U.S. Gals. Per Min.	vel. V f.p.s.	vel. head $V^2/2g$ feet	frict. loss h_f feet
30000	2.37	0.09	0.017
35000	2.76	0.12	0.023
40000	3.16	0.16	0.030
45000	3.55	0.20	0.037
50000	3.94	0.24	0.045
60000	4.73	0.35	0.064
70000	5.52	0.47	0.085
80000	6.31	0.62	0.110
90000	7.10	0.78	0.138
100000	7.89	0.97	0.168
120000	9.47	1.39	0.237
140000	11.0	1.89	0.321
160000	12.6	2.47	0.414
180000	14.2	3.13	0.522
200000	15.8	3.87	0.642
250000	19.7	6.04	1.00
300000	23.7	8.70	1.42
350000	27.6	11.8	1.92

CAUTION: No allowance has been made for age, differences in diameter resulting from manufacturing tolerances or any abnormal conditions of interior pipe surface. It is recommended that for commercial application a reserve or margin of safety to cover these effects be added to the values shown in the tables. Where no careful analysis of these effects are made a reserve of 15% is recommended.

TABLE 2. FRICTION LOSS PER 100 FEET FOR WATER IN NEW ASPHALT DIPPED CAST IRON PIPE†

3"
3" inside dia.

4"
4" inside dia

U.S. Gals. Per Min.	vel. V f.p.s.	vel. head V²/2g feet	frict. loss h_f feet	U.S. Gals. Per Min.	vel. V f.p.s.	vel. head V²/2g feet	frict. loss h_f feet
50	2.27	0.08	0.83	90	2.30	0.08	0.59
60	2.72	0.12	1.17	100	2.55	0.10	0.72
70	3.18	0.16	1.56	120	3.06	0.15	1.03
80	3.63	0.21	2.02	140	3.57	0.20	1.38
90	4.08	0.26	2.55	160	4.08	0.26	1.78
100	4.54	0.32	3.10	180	4.60	0.33	2.24
120	5.45	0.46	4.40	200	5.11	0.41	2.74
140	6.35	0.63	5.93	220	5.62	0.49	3.28
160	7.26	0.82	7.71	240	6.13	0.58	3.88
180	8.17	1.04	9.73	260	6.64	0.69	4.54
200	9.08	1.28	11.90	280	7.15	0.79	5.25
220	9.98	1.55	14.30	300	7.66	0.91	6.03
240	10.90	1.85	17.00	350	8.94	1.25	8.22
260	11.80	2.17	19.80	400	10.20	1.62	10.70
280	12.70	2.51	22.80	450	11.50	2.05	13.40
300	13.60	2.88	26.10	500	12.80	2.53	16.60
350	15.90	3.93	35.70	550	14.00	3.05	19.90
400	18.20	5.12	46.80	600	15.30	3.65	23.60
450	20.50	6.50	59.70	700	17.90	4.96	32.10
500	22.70	8.00	72.30	800	20.40	6.48	41.60
550	25.00	9.73	87.70	900	23.00	8.20	52.30
600	27.20	11.50	102.00	1000	25.50	10.10	64.20
				1200	30.60	14.60	92.80

6"
6" inside dia.

U.S. Gals. Per Min.	vel. V f.p.s.	vel. head V²/2g feet	frict. loss h_f feet	U.S. Gals. Per Min.	vel. V f.p.s.	vel. head V²/2g feet	frict. loss h_f feet
200	2.27	0.08	0.35	550	6.24	0.61	2.42
220	2.50	0.10	0.42	600	6.81	0.72	2.84
240	2.72	0.12	0.49	700	7.94	0.98	3.87
260	2.95	0.14	0.57	800	9.08	1.28	5.06
280	3.18	0.16	0.66	900	10.20	1.62	6.34
300	3.40	0.18	0.75	1000	11.30	2.00	7.73
350	3.97	0.25	1.01	1200	13.60	2.88	11.20
400	4.55	0.32	1.30	1400	15.90	3.92	15.10
450	5.11	0.41	1.64	1600	18.20	5.12	19.80
500	5.67	0.50	2.02	1800	20.40	6.48	24.80
				2000	22.70	8.00	30.50
				2200	25.00	9.73	37.00
				2500	28.40	12.50	47.10

CAUTION: No allowance has been made for age, differences in diameter resulting from manufacturing tolerances or any abnormal conditions of interior pipe surface. It is recommended that for commercial application a reserve or margin of safety to cover these effects be added to the values shown in the tables. Where no careful analysis of these effects are made a reserve of 15% is recommended.

†*Courtesy Hydraulic Institute. See Page 6.*

TABLE 2. (Cont.) FRICTION LOSS PER 100 FEET FOR WATER IN NEW ASPHALT DIPPED CAST IRON PIPE

8"
8" inside dia.

U.S. Gals. Per Min.	vel. V f.p.s.	vel. head $V^2/2g$ feet	frict. loss h_f feet
400	2.55	0.10	0.30
450	2.87	0.13	0.38
500	3.19	0.16	0.46
550	3.51	0.19	0.56
600	3.83	0.23	0.66
700	4.47	0.31	0.88
800	5.11	0.41	1.14
900	5.74	0.51	1.44
1000	6.38	0.63	1.76
1200	7.66	0.91	2.53
1400	8.93	1.24	3.40
1600	10.20	1.62	4.45
1800	11.50	2.05	5.58
2000	12.80	2.53	6.84
2200	14.00	3.05	8.26
2500	15.90	3.96	10.60
3000	19.10	5.70	16.20
3500	22.30	7.77	20.70
4000	25.50	10.10	27.00
4500	28.70	12.80	34.20

10"
10" inside dia.

U.S. Gals. Per Min.	vel. V f.p.s.	vel. head $V^2/2g$ feet	frict. loss h_f feet
600	2.45	0.09	0.21
700	2.86	0.13	0.29
800	3.27	0.17	0.37
900	3.68	0.21	0.46
1000	4.09	0.26	0.57
1200	4.90	0.37	0.81
1400	5.72	0.51	1.09
1600	6.54	0.66	1.42
1800	7.35	0.84	1.78
2000	8.17	1.04	2.17
2200	8.99	1.26	2.64
2400	9.80	1.49	3.12
2600	10.60	1.75	3.63
2800	11.40	2.03	4.18
3000	12.30	2.33	4.79
3200	13.10	2.66	5.47
3400	13.90	3.00	6.18
3600	14.70	3.36	6.91
3800	15.50	3.74	7.68
4000	16.30	4.15	8.50
4500	18.40	5.25	10.70
5000	20.40	6.48	13.20
5500	22.50	7.85	15.90
6000	24.50	9.43	18.90
6500	26.60	11.00	22.20
7000	28.60	12.70	25.80
8000	32.70	16.60	33.60

12"
12" inside dia.

U.S. Gals. Per Min.	vel. V f.p.s.	vel. head $V^2/2g$ feet	frict. loss h_f feet	U.S. Gals. Per Min.	vel. V f.p.s.	vel. head $V^2/2g$ feet	frict. loss h_f feet
800	2.27	0.08	0.15	3600	10.20	1.62	2.70
900	2.55	0.10	0.18	3800	10.80	1.81	3.00
1000	2.84	0.13	0.22	4000	11.30	2.00	3.31
1200	3.40	0.18	0.32	4500	12.80	2.53	4.18
1400	3.97	0.25	0.43	5000	14.20	3.12	5.13
1600	4.54	0.32	0.55	5500	15.60	3.78	6.17
1800	5.11	0.41	0.70	6000	17.00	4.50	7.30
2000	5.67	0.50	0.86	6500	18.40	5.28	8.55
2200	6.24	0.61	1.03	7000	19.90	6.13	9.92
2400	6.81	0.72	1.22	8000	22.70	8.00	13.00
2600	7.38	0.85	1.43	9000	25.50	10.10	16.40
2800	7.94	0.98	1.65	10000	28.40	12.50	20.20
3000	8.51	1.13	1.88				
3200	9.08	1.28	2.13				
3400	9.65	1.45	2.41				

CAUTION: No allowance has been made for age, differences in diameter resulting from manufacturing tolerances or any abnormal conditions of interior pipe surface. It is recommended that for commercial application a reserve or margin of safety to cover these effects be added to the values shown in the tables. Where no careful analysis of these effects are made a reserve of 15% is recommended.

TABLE 2. (Cont.) FRICTION LOSS PER 100 FEET FOR WATER IN NEW ASPHALT DIPPED CAST IRON PIPE

14″ inside dia.				16″ inside dia.			
U.S. Gals. Per Min.	vel. V f.p.s.	vel. head $V^2/2g$ feet	frict. loss h_f feet	U.S. Gals. Per Min.	vel. V f.p.s.	vel. head $V^2/2g$ feet	frict. loss h_f feet
1200	2.50	0.10	0.15	1400	2.23	0.08	0.11
1400	2.92	0.13	0.20	1600	2.55	0.10	0.13
1600	3.33	0.17	0.25	1800	2.87	0.13	0.16
1800	3.75	0.22	0.32	2000	3.19	0.16	0.20
2000	4.17	0.27	0.39	2200	3.51	0.19	0.24
2200	4.59	0.33	0.47	2400	3.83	0.23	0.29
2400	5.00	0.39	0.56	2600	4.15	0.27	0.33
2600	5.42	0.46	0.65	2800	4.47	0.31	0.38
2800	5.83	0.53	0.75	3000	4.79	0.36	0.44
3000	6.25	0.61	0.86	3200	5.11	0.41	0.49
3200	6.67	0.69	0.97	3400	5.42	0.46	0.55
3400	7.08	0.78	1.10	3600	5.74	0.51	0.62
3600	7.50	0.87	1.22	3800	6.06	0.57	0.68
3800	7.92	0.97	1.35	5000	6.38	0.63	0.75
4000	8.34	1.08	1.50	4500	7.18	0.80	0.95
4500	9.38	1.37	1.88	5000	7.98	0.99	1.17
5000	10.40	1.69	2.30	5500	8.78	1.20	1.41
5500	11.50	2.04	2.79	6000	9.57	1.42	1.66
6000	12.50	2.43	3.31	6500	10.40	1.67	1.95
6500	13.60	2.86	3.89	7000	11.20	1.94	2.26
7000	14.60	3.30	4.50	8000	12.80	2.53	2.96
8000	16.70	4.32	5.87	9000	14.40	3.20	3.73
9000	18.80	5.47	7.42	10000	16.00	3.96	4.57
10000	20.80	6.75	9.15	12000	19.00	5.70	6.52
12000	25.00	9.72	13.00	14000	22.30	7.75	8.81
14000	29.20	13.20	17.60	16000	25.50	10.10	11.50
				18000	28.70	12.80	14.60

18″
18″ inside dia

U.S. Gals. Per Min.	vel. V f.p.s.	vel. head $V^2/2g$ feet	frict. loss h_f feet	U.S. Gals. Per Min.	vel. V f.p.s.	vel. head $V^2/2g$ feet	frict. loss h_f feet
2500	3.15	0.15	0.166	10000	12.60	2.47	2.480
3000	3.78	0.22	0.240	12000	15.10	3.55	3.560
3500	4.41	0.30	0.326	14000	17.70	4.84	4.850
4000	5.04	0.40	0.415	16000	20.20	6.32	6.340
4500	5.67	0.50	0.525	18000	22.70	8.00	8.020
5000	6.30	0.62	0.645	20000	25.20	9.88	9.880
6000	7.56	0.89	0.920	22000	27.70	12.00	11.900
7000	8.83	1.21	1.240				
8000	10.09	1.84	1.610				
9000	11.30	1.99	2.020				

CAUTION: No allowance has been made for age, differences in diameter resulting from manufacturing tolerances or any abnormal conditions of interior pipe surface. It is recommended that for commercial application a reserve or margin of safety to cover these effects be added to the values shown in the tables. Where no careful analysis of these effects are made a reserve of 15% is recommended.

TABLE 2. (Cont.) FRICTION LOSS PER 100 FEET FOR WATER IN NEW ASPHALT DIPPED CAST IRON PIPE

20″ 20″ inside dia.				24″ 24″ inside dia.			
U.S. Gals. Per Min.	vel. V f.p.s.	vel. head $V^2/2g$ feet	frict. loss h_f feet	U.S. Gals. Per Min.	vel. V f.p.s.	vel. head $V^2/2g$ feet	frict. loss h_f feet
2500	2.55	0.10	0.0998	3500	2.48	0.10	0.0759
3000	3.06	0.15	0.140	4000	2.84	0.13	0.098
3500	3.57	0.20	0.188	4500	3.19	0.16	0.122
4000	4.08	0.26	0.243	5000	3.55	0.20	0.149
4500	4.59	0.33	0.306	6000	4.26	0.28	0.211
5000	5.11	0.41	0.376	7000	4.96	0.38	0.284
6000	6.13	0.58	0.533	8000	5.67	0.50	0.368
7000	7.15	0.79	0.721	9000	6.38	0.63	0.464
8000	8.17	1.04	0.935	10000	7.09	0.78	0.571
9000	9.19	1.31	1.18	12000	8.51	1.13	0.816
10000	10.20	1.62	1.45	14000	9.93	1.53	1.11
12000	12.30	2.33	2.07	16000	11.35	2.00	1.43
14000	14.30	3.18	2.80	18000	12.76	2.53	1.80
16000	16.30	4.15	3.66	20000	14.20	3.13	2.21
18000	18.40	5.25	4.62	22000	15.60	3.78	2.67
20000	20.40	6.48	5.67	24000	17.00	4.50	3.16
22000	22.50	7.84	6.85	26000	18.40	5.28	3.71
24000	24.50	9.33	8.13	28000	19.80	6.10	4.30
26000	26.50	10.95	9.54	30000	21.30	7.03	4.97
28000	28.50	12.64	11.05	35000	24.90	9.58	6.78
30000	30.60	14.60	12.70	40000	28.40	12.50	8.75

30″ 30″ inside dia.

U.S. Gals. Per Min.	vel. V f.p.s.	vel. head $V^2/2g$ feet	frict. loss h_f feet	U.S. Gals. Per Min.	vel. V f.p.s.	vel. head $V^2/2g$ feet	frict. loss h_f feet
5000	2.27	0.08	0.0488	20000	9.08	1.28	0.703
6000	2.72	0.12	0.069	22000	10.00	1.55	0.856
7000	3.18	0.16	0.092	24000	10.90	1.84	1.01
8000	3.63	0.21	0.119	26000	11.80	2.16	1.17
9000	4.08	0.26	0.149	28000	12.70	2.50	1.34
10000	4.54	0.32	0.183	30000	13.60	2.88	1.57
12000	5.45	0.46	0.260	35000	15.90	3.92	2.13
14000	6.35	0.63	0.351	40000	18.20	5.12	2.77
16000	7.26	0.82	0.455	45000	20.40	6.48	3.50
18000	8.17	1.04	0.572	50000	22.70	8.00	4.30
				60000	27.20	11.50	6.19

CAUTION: No allowance has been made for age, differences in diameter resulting from manufacturing tolerances or any abnormal conditions of interior pipe surface. It is recommended that for commercial application a reserve or margin of safety to cover these effects be added to the values shown in the tables. Where no careful analysis of these effects are made a reserve of 15% is recommended.

TABLE 2. (Cont.) FRICTION LOSS PER 100 FEET FOR WATER IN NEW ASPHALT DIPPED CAST IRON PIPE

36″
36″ inside dia.

U.S. Gals. Per Min.	vel. V f.p.s.	vel. head $V^2/2g$ feet	frict. loss h_f feet
8000	2.52	0.10	0.0475
9000	2.84	0.13	0.0593
10000	3.15	0.15	0.0724
12000	3.78	0.22	0.103
14000	4.41	0.30	0.139
16000	5.04	0.40	0.180
18000	5.67	0.50	0.227
20000	6.30	0.62	0.279
22000	6.93	0.75	0.338
24000	7.56	0.89	0.400
25000	7.88	0.97	0.430
26000	8.20	1.05	0.464
28000	8.83	1.21	0.538
30000	9.46	1.39	0.617
35000	11.03	1.89	0.832
40000	12.60	2.47	1.08
45000	14.10	3.13	1.36
50000	15.80	3.86	1.68
55000	17.40	4.73	2.03
60000	18.90	5.56	2.40
70000	22.10	7.56	3.25
80000	25.20	9.88	4.23
90000	28.40	12.50	5.35

42″
42″ inside dia.

U.S. Gals. Per Min.	vel. V f.p.s.	vel. head $V^2/2g$ feet	frict. loss h_f feet
10000	2.32	0.08	0.0337
12000	2.78	0.12	0.0477
14000	3.24	0.16	0.0641
16000	3.71	0.21	0.0829
18000	4.17	0.27	0.104
20000	4.63	0.33	0.127
22000	5.09	0.40	0.154
24000	5.55	0.48	0.181
25000	5.79	0.52	0.196
26000	6.01	0.56	0.212
28000	6.49	0.65	0.243
30000	6.95	0.74	0.279
35000	8.11	1.02	0.377
40000	9.26	1.33	0.490
45000	10.42	1.69	0.619
50000	11.60	2.08	0.760
55000	12.75	2.53	0.915
60000	13.90	3.00	1.09
70000	16.20	4.08	1.48
80000	18.50	5.33	1.92
90000	20.80	6.75	2.42
100000	23.20	8.33	2.98
120000	27.80	12.00	4.30

48″
48″ inside dia.

U.S. Gals. Per Min.	vel. V f.p.s.	vel. head $V^2/2g$ feet	frict. loss h_f feet	U.S. Gals. Per Min.	vel. V f.p.s.	vel. head $V^2/2g$ feet	frict. loss h_f feet
14000	2.48	0.10	0.0327	35000	6.21	0.60	0.192
16000	2.84	0.13	0.0422	40000	7.09	0.78	0.248
18000	3.19	0.16	0.0529	45000	7.98	0.99	0.314
20000	3.55	0.20	0.0648	50000	8.87	1.22	0.384
22000	3.90	0.24	0.0776	55000	9.75	1.48	0.459
24000	4.25	0.28	0.0917	60000	10.64	1.76	0.548
25000	4.43	0.31	0.0996	70000	12.40	2.39	0.742
26000	4.60	0.33	0.107	80000	14.20	3.13	0.968
28000	4.97	0.38	0.124	90000	16.00	3.96	1.22
30000	5.32	0.44	0.142	100000	17.70	4.89	1.50
				120000	21.30	7.03	2.15
				140000	24.80	9.57	2.92
				160000	28.40	12.50	3.81

CAUTION: No allowance has been made for age, differences in diameter resulting from manufacturing tolerances or any abnormal conditions of interior pipe surface. It is recommended that for commercial application a reserve or margin of safety to cover these effects be added to the values shown in the tables. Where no careful analysis of these effects are made a reserve of 15% is recommended.

TABLE 2. (Cont.) FRICTION LOSS PER 100 FEET FOR WATER IN NEW ASPHALT DIPPED CAST IRON PIPE

54" 54" inside dia.				60" 60" inside dia.			
U.S. Gals. Per Min.	vel. V f.p.s.	vel. head V²/2g feet	frict. loss h_f feet	U.S. Gals. Per Min.	vel. V f.p.s.	vel. head V²/2g feet	frict. loss h_f feet
18000	2.52	0.10	0.0294	20000	2.27	0.08	0.0212
20000	2.80	0.12	0.0360	25000	2.84	0.13	0.0325
25000	3.50	0.19	0.0550	30000	3.40	0.18	0.0460
30000	4.20	0.27	0.0782	35000	3.97	0.25	0.0618
35000	4.90	0.37	0.106	40000	4.54	0.32	0.0800
40000	5.60	0.49	0.137	45000	5.11	0.41	0.100
45000	6.30	0.62	0.172	50000	5.67	0.50	0.124
50000	7.00	0.76	0.211	60000	6.81	0.72	0.176
60000	8.40	1.10	0.301	70000	7.94	0.98	0.237
70000	9.81	1.49	0.408	80000	9.08	1.28	0.307
80000	11.21	1.95	0.530	90000	10.21	1.62	0.387
90000	12.60	2.47	0.668	100000	11.30	2.00	0.478
100000	14.00	3.05	0.820	120000	13.60	2.88	0.688
120000	16.80	4.39	1.180	140000	15.90	3.92	0.930
140000	19.60	5.98	1.590	160000	18.20	5.12	1.20
160000	22.40	7.81	2.070	180000	20.40	6.48	1.52
180000	25.20	9.88	2.620	200000	22.70	8.00	1.87
200000	28.00	12.20	3.220	250000	28.40	12.50	2.92

72"
72" inside dia.

U.S. Gals. Per Min.	vel. V f.p.s.	vel. head V²/2g feet	frict. loss h_f feet	U.S. Gals. Per Min.	vel. V f.p.s.	vel. head V²/2g feet	frict. loss h_f feet
30000	2.37	0.09	0.0184	120000	9.47	1.39	0.271
35000	2.76	0.12	0.0248	140000	11.04	1.89	0.365
40000	3.16	0.16	0.0320	160000	12.60	2.47	0.475
45000	3.55	0.20	0.0402	180000	14.20	3.13	0.600
50000	3.94	0.24	0.0493	200000	15.80	3.87	0.736
60000	4.73	0.35	0.0700	250000	19.70	6.04	1.14
70000	5.52	0.47	0.0940	300000	23.70	8.70	1.64
80000	6.31	0.62	0.122	350000	27.60	11.80	2.23
90000	7.10	0.78	0.154				
100000	7.89	0.97	0.189				

CAUTION: No allowance has been made for age, differences in diameter resulting from manufacturing tolerances or any abnormal conditions of interior pipe surface. It is recommended that for commercial application a reserve or margin of safety to cover these effects be added to the values shown in the tables. Where no careful analysis of these effects are made a reserve of 15% is recommended.

FRICTION LOSS IN PIPE FITTINGS:

The resistance to flow caused by a valve or fitting may be computed from the equation:

$$h = K \frac{V^2}{2g}$$

where h = frictional resistance in feet of fluid
V = average velocity in feet per second in pipe
of corresponding diameter.
K = resistance coefficient for fitting

Values of K for frequently used fittings may be found in Table 3. Wide differences in the values of K are found in the published literature. Flanged fittings should have lower resistance coefficients than screwed fittings. Resistance coefficients usually decrease with increase in pipe size.

For convenience Table 4 shows the friction loss in fittings ex-

TABLE 3. VALUES OF RESISTANCE COEFFICIENT FOR PIPE FITTINGS†

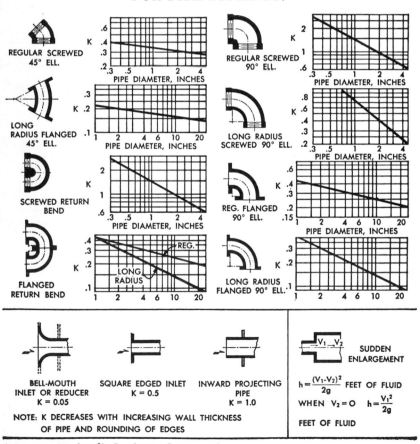

NOTE: K DECREASES WITH INCREASING WALL THICKNESS
OF PIPE AND ROUNDING OF EDGES

†*Courtesy Hydraulic Institute. See page 6.*

TABLE 3. (Cont.)

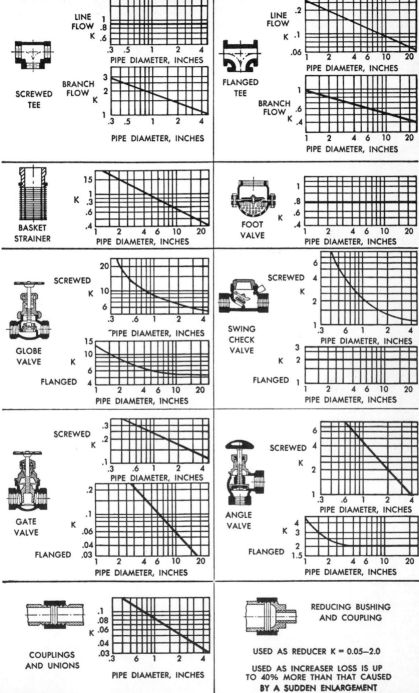

SCREWED TEE — LINE FLOW K — PIPE DIAMETER, INCHES — BRANCH FLOW K — PIPE DIAMETER, INCHES

FLANGED TEE — LINE FLOW K — PIPE DIAMETER, INCHES — BRANCH FLOW K — PIPE DIAMETER, INCHES

BASKET STRAINER — K — PIPE DIAMETER, INCHES

FOOT VALVE — K — PIPE DIAMETER, INCHES

GLOBE VALVE — SCREWED K — PIPE DIAMETER, INCHES — FLANGED K — PIPE DIAMETER, INCHES

SWING CHECK VALVE — SCREWED K — PIPE DIAMETER, INCHES — FLANGED K — PIPE DIAMETER, INCHES

GATE VALVE — SCREWED K — PIPE DIAMETER, INCHES — FLANGED K — PIPE DIAMETER, INCHES

ANGLE VALVE — SCREWED K — PIPE DIAMETER, INCHES — FLANGED K — PIPE DIAMETER, INCHES

COUPLINGS AND UNIONS — K — PIPE DIAMETER, INCHES

REDUCING BUSHING AND COUPLING

USED AS REDUCER K = 0.05—2.0

USED AS INCREASER LOSS IS UP TO 40% MORE THAN THAT CAUSED BY A SUDDEN ENLARGEMENT

TABLE 4. EQUIVALENT LENGTH OF STRAIGHT PIPE FOR VARIOUS FITTINGS TURBULENT FLOW ONLY†

FITTINGS			1/4	3/8	1/2	3/4	1	1 1/4	1 1/2	2	2 1/2	3	4	5	6	8	10	12	14	16	18	20	24
																					PIPE SIZE		
REGULAR 90° ELL	SCREWED	STEEL	2.3	3.1	3.6	4.4	5.2	6.6	7.4	8.5	9.3	11.0	13.0										
		C.I.										9.0	11.0										
	FLANGED	STEEL			.92	1.2	1.6	2.1	2.4	3.1	3.6	4.4	5.9	7.3	8.9	12.0	14.0	17.0	18.0	21.0	23.0	25.0	30.0
		C.I.										3.6	4.8		7.2	9.8	12.0	15.0	17.0	19.0	22.0	24.0	28.0
LONG RADIUS 90° ELL	SCREWED	STEEL	1.5	2.0	2.2	2.3	2.7	3.2	3.4	3.6	3.6	4.0	4.6										
		C.I.										3.3	3.7										
	FLANGED	STEEL			1.1	1.3	1.6	2.0	2.3	2.7	2.9	3.4	4.2	5.0	5.7	7.0	8.0	9.0	9.4	10.0	11.0	12.0	14.0
		C.I.										2.8	3.4		4.7	5.7	6.8	7.8	8.6	9.6	11.0	11.0	13.0
REGULAR 45° ELL	SCREWED	STEEL	.34	.52	.71	.92	1.3	1.7	2.1	2.7	3.2	4.0	5.5										
		C.I.										3.3	4.5										
	FLANGED	STEEL			.45	.59	.81	1.1	1.3	1.7	2.0	2.6	3.5	4.5	5.6	7.7	9.0	11.0	13.0	15.0	16.0	18.0	22.0
		C.I.										2.1	2.9		4.5	6.3	8.1	9.7	12.0	13.0	15.0	17.0	20.0
TEE-LINE FLOW	SCREWED	STEEL	.79	1.2	1.7	2.4	3.2	4.6	5.6	7.7	9.3	12.0	17.0										
		C.I.										9.9	14.0										
	FLANGED	STEEL			.69	.82	1.0	1.3	1.5	1.8	1.9	2.2	2.8	3.3	3.8	4.7	5.2	6.0	6.4	7.2	7.6	8.2	9.6
		C.I.										1.9	2.2		3.1	3.9	4.6	5.2	5.9	6.5	7.2	7.7	8.8
TEE-BRANCH FLOW	SCREWED	STEEL	2.4	3.5	4.2	5.3	6.6	8.7	9.9	12.0	13.0	17.0	21.0										
		C.I.										14.0	17.0										
	FLANGED	STEEL			2.0	2.6	3.3	4.4	5.2	6.6	7.5	9.4	12.0	15.0	18.0	24.0	30.0	34.0	37.0	43.0	47.0	52.0	62.0
		C.I.										7.7	10.0		15.0	20.0	25.0	30.0	35.0	39.0	44.0	49.0	57.0
180° RETURN BEND	REG. FLANGED	STEEL	2.3	3.1	3.6	4.4	5.2	6.6	7.4	8.5	9.3	11.0	13.0	7.3	8.9	12.0	14.0	17.0	18.0	21.0	23.0	25.0	30.0
		C.I.										9.0	11.0		7.2	9.8	12.0	15.0	17.0	19.0	22.0	24.0	28.0
	LONG RAD. FLANGED	STEEL			1.1	1.3	1.6	2.1	2.4	3.1	3.6	3.4	4.2	5.0	5.7	7.0	8.0	9.0	9.4	10.0	11.0	12.0	14.0
		C.I.										2.8	3.4		4.7	5.7	6.8	7.8	8.6	9.6	11.0	11.0	13.0

†*Courtesy of, Hydraulic Institute. See page 6.*

TABLE 4. (Cont.) EQUIVALENT LENGTH OF STRAIGHT PIPE FOR VARIOUS FITTINGS TURBULENT FLOW ONLY

FITTINGS		¼	⅜	½	¾	1	1¼	1½	2	2½	3	4	5	6	8	10	12	14	16	18	20	24
GLOBE VALVE SCREWED	STEEL	21.0	22.0	22.0	24.0	29.0	37.0	42.0	54.0	62.0	79.0	110.0										
GLOBE VALVE SCREWED	C.I.										65.0	86.0										
GLOBE VALVE FLANGED	STEEL			38.0	40.0	45.0	54.0	59.0	70.0	77.0	94.0	120.0	150.0	190.0	260.0	310.0	390.0					
GLOBE VALVE FLANGED	C.I.										77.	99.0		150.0	210.0	270.0	330.0					
GATE VALVE SCREWED	STEEL	.32	.45	.56	.67	.84	1.1	1.2	1.5	1.7	1.9	2.5										
GATE VALVE SCREWED	C.I.										1.6	2.0										
GATE VALVE FLANGED	STEEL								2.6	2.7	2.8	2.9	3.1	3.2	3.2	3.2	3.2	3.2	3.2	3.2	3.2	3.2
GATE VALVE FLANGED	C.I.										2.3	2.4		2.6	2.7	2.8	2.9	2.9	3.0	3.0	3.0	3.0
ANGLE VALVE SCREWED	STEEL	12.8	15.0	15.0	15.0	17.0	18.0	18.0	18.0	18.0	18.0	18.0										
ANGLE VALVE SCREWED	C.I.										15.0	15.0										
ANGLE VALVE FLANGED	STEEL			15.0	15.0	17.0	18.0	18.0	21.0	22.0	28.0	38.0	50.0	63.0	90.0	120.0	140.0	160.0	190.0	210.0	240.0	300.0
ANGLE VALVE FLANGED	C.I.										23.0	31.0		52.0	74.0	98.0	120.0	150.0	170.0	200.0	230.0	280.0
SWING CHECK VALVE SCREWED	STEEL	7.2	7.3	8.0	8.8	11.0	13.0	15.0	19.0	22.0	27.0	38.0	50.0	63.0	90.0	120.0	140.0					
SWING CHECK VALVE FLANGED	STEEL			3.8	5.3	7.2	10.0	12.0	17.0	21.0	27.0	38.0	50.0	63.0	90.0	120.0	140.0					
SWING CHECK VALVE FLANGED	C.I.										22.0	31.0		52.0	74.0	98.0	120.0					
COUPLING OR UNION SCREWED	STEEL	.14	.18	.21	.24	.29	.36	.39	.45	.47	.53	.65										
COUPLING OR UNION SCREWED	C.I.										.44	.52										
BELL MOUTH INLET	STEEL	.04	.07	.10	.13	.18	.26	.31	.43	.52	.67	.95	1.3	1.6	2.3	2.9	3.5	4.0	4.7	5.3	6.1	7.6
BELL MOUTH INLET	C.I.										.55	.77		1.3	1.9	2.4	3.0	3.6	4.3	5.0	5.7	7.0
SQUARE MOUTH INLET	STEEL	.44	.68	.96	1.3	1.8	2.6	3.1	4.3	5.2	6.7	9.5	13.0	16.0	23.0	29.0	35.0	40.0	47.0	53.0	61.0	76.0
SQUARE MOUTH INLET	C.I.										5.5	7.7		13.0	19.0	24.0	30.0	36.0	43.0	50.0	57.0	70.0
RE-ENTRANT PIPE	STEEL	.88	1.4	1.9	2.6	3.6	5.1	6.2	8.5	10.0	13.0	19.0	25.0	32.0	45.0	58.0	70.0	80.0	95.0	110.0	120.0	150.0
RE-ENTRANT PIPE	C.I.										11.0	15.0		26.0	37.0	49.0	61.0	73.0	86.0	100.0	110.0	140.0
SUDDEN ENLARGEMENT																						

$$h = \frac{(V_1 - V_2)^2}{2g} \text{ FEET OF FLUID; IF } V_2 = 0 \quad h = \frac{V_1^2}{2g} \text{ FEET OF FLUID}$$

pressed as an equivalent length of straight pipe. This presentation is simple to use on complicated piping layouts involving an assortment of different fittings and is especially well suited to the preparation of station curves where varying rates of flow are involved.

FRICTION IN OTHER TYPES OF PIPE

The preceding tabulations for friction loss in pipes apply to new schedule #40 steel pipe and new asphalt-dipped cast-iron pipe as noted. Friction loss in other types of pipe vary from these values due to the difference in the average relative roughness of the interior surface of such pipes as commercially manufactured.

The following chart Fig. 26 shows relative roughness factors $\left(\frac{\epsilon}{D}\right)$ for new clean pipes as commercially manufactured plotted against pipe diameter in inches. The curves for schedule #40 steel pipe (absolute roughness 0.00015′) and asphalt-dipped cast-iron pipe (absolute roughness 0.0004′) on which the previous Tables 1 and 2 are based are shown on this curve.

The ratio of the friction factor for any pipe to that for schedule #40 steel pipe may be used as a multiplier to adjust the friction losses shown in Table 1 to apply to the other type of pipe.

It must be recognized that various types of pipe as commercially manufactured are subject to a considerable variation in roughness.

Average values for good clean new pipe however yield the multipliers recommended in the following Table 5.

TABLE 5. MULTIPLIERS TO APPLY TO VALUES FROM TABLE 1 TO OBTAIN FRICTION LOSS IN OTHER TYPES OF PIPE OR CONDUIT.

Type of New Conduit or Pipe	Multiplier to Apply to Table 1 Values of Friction Loss
Rubber lined hose	0.72
Spun cement line pipe	0.76
Spun bitumastic enameled pipe	0.76
Aluminum irrigation pipe	0.81
Transite Pipe	0.85
Copper or Brass pipe	0.86
Seamless steel tubing	0.86
Glass tube or pipe	0.86
Schedule #40 steel pipe	1.00
Wood Stave pipe	1.15
Galvanized iron pipe	1.22
Vitrified pipe	1.36
Spiral riveted pipe (flow with lap)	1.40
Spiral riveted pipe (flow against lap)	1.70
Unlined linen hose	1.80

The multipliers in Table 5 provide for the difference in type of pipe only. They do not include deviations in internal diameter from schedule #40 steel pipe.

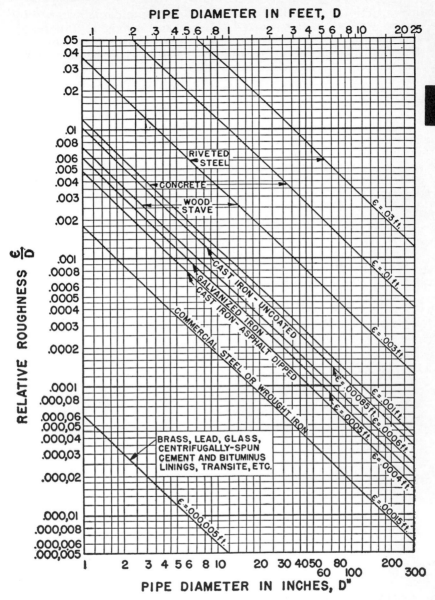

PIPE DIAMETER IN FEET, D

RELATIVE ROUGHNESS $\frac{\epsilon}{D}$

RIVETED STEEL

CONCRETE

WOOD STAVE

CAST IRON - UNCOATED

GALVANIZED IRON

CAST IRON - ASPHALT DIPPED

COMMERCIAL STEEL OR WROUGHT IRON

BRASS, LEAD, GLASS, CENTRIFUGALLY-SPUN CEMENT AND BITUMINUS LININGS, TRANSITE, ETC.

$\epsilon = .03$ ft.

$\epsilon = .01$ ft.

$\epsilon = .003$ ft.

$\epsilon = .00085$ ft.

$\epsilon = .001$ ft.

$\epsilon = .0006$ ft.

$\epsilon = .0005$ ft.

$\epsilon = .0004$ ft.

$\epsilon = .00015$ ft.

$\epsilon = .000,005$ ft.

PIPE DIAMETER IN INCHES, D"

Fig. 26. Relative roughness factors for new clean pipes.†

FRICTION LOSS AS AFFECTED BY AGING OF PIPE

The deterioration of pipes with age depends upon the chemical properties of the liquid flowing and the characteristics of the material from which the pipe is made. In general, the flow carry-

† Courtesy Hydraulic Institute. See page 6.

ing capacity of a pipe line decreases with age due to a roughening of the interior surface caused by corrosive products, tubercules and the like or an actual reduction in area caused by chemical deposits. The effect corresponds to a variation in friction factor due to increasing relative roughness.

A wide variation in waters over the country makes impossible any precise estimation of this aging effect. No reputable authority will go on record to endorse friction factors for other than new pipe. This fact, however, does not eliminate the deterioration of friction factor and some means of estimation is required. Wherever records are available on the aging effect of local or similar waters, it is recommended that they be studied and applied as a correction to the computation of friction loss for new pipe from the previous tables. This is a sound and logical approach for a specific problem.

In many instances either the economics of the project do not warrant the expense of this detailed investigation or there are no available records on local or similar waters. For those occasions, Table 6 may be used with caution and discretion. It is based upon the best known available data.

TABLE 6 INCREASE IN FRICTION LOSS DUE TO AGING OF PIPE

Multipliers for use with Table 1

Age of Pipe in Years	Small Pipes 4″-10″	Large Pipes 12″-60″
New	1.00	1.00
5	1.40	1.30
10	2.20	1.60
15	3.60	1.80
20	5.00	2.00
25	6.30	2.10
30	7.25	2.20
35	8.10	2.30
40	8.75	2.40
45	9.25	2.60
50	9.60	2.86
55	9.80	3.26
60	10.00	3.70
65	10.05	4.25
70	10.10	4.70

It will be obvious that there is no sudden increase in aging effect between 10″ and 12″ pipe as indicated from Table 6. The values shown are composites of many tests grouped by the experimenter. A reasonable amount of interpretation and logic must be used in selecting and applying a multiplier for each specific problem.

It must also be borne in mind that some test data on aging of pipe may vary up to fifty percent from the averages as shown in Table 6.

SECTION III—CONVERSION FACTORS

CONTENTS

TABLE 7. CONVERSION FACTORS—UNITS OF LENGTH

Examples: 2 Yards x 3 = 6 Feet. 3 Feet x 0.333 = 1 Yard

Unit	Inch	Foot	Yard	Centimeter	Meter
Inch	1	.0833	.0278	2.54	.0254
Foot	12	1	.333	30.48	.3048
Yard	36	3	1	91.44	.9144
Centimeters	.3937	.0328	.0109	1	.01
Meter	39.37	3.281	1.094	100	1

1 Rod = 16.5 ft. = 5.5 yards = 5.029 meters
1 Mile = 5280 ft. = 1760 yards = 1609.3 meters = 1.61 Kilometers
1 Kilometer = 1000 meters = 1093.6 yards = .62137 miles

TABLE 8. CONVERSION FACTORS—UNITS OF AREA

Examples: 6 sq. ft. x .1111 = .6666 sq. yds.

3 sq. yds. x 9 = 27 sq. ft.

Unit	Sq. In.	Sq. Ft.	Sq. Yd.	Sq. Cm.	Sq. Meter
Sq. In.	1.00	0.00694	0.000772	6.452	0.000645
Sq. Ft.	144.00	1.00	0.1111	929.00	0.0929
Sq. Yd.	1296.00	9.00	1.00	8360.00	0.836
Sq. Cm.	0.1550	0.001076	0.00012	1.00	0.0001
Sq. M.	1550.00	10.76	1.196	10,000.00	1.00

1 Sq Mile = 640 Acres = 259 Hectares = 2.59 Sq. Kilometers
1 Acre = 43560 Sq. Ft. = 4840 Sq. Yds. = 4047 Sq. Meters
1 Hectare = 107,639 Sq. Ft. = 2.471 Acres = .01 Sq. Km.

TABLE 9. CONVERSION FACTORS—UNITS OF PRESSURE

(Density at 39.2°F)

Example: 15 Ft. Water × .433 = 6.49 Psi

15 Psi × 2.31 = 34.65 Ft. Water

	In. Water	Ft. Water	Psi	In. Hg.	Mm. Hg.	Gr./ Sq. Cm.	Kg./ Sq. Cm.
In. Water	1.0	.0833	.0361	.0736	1.870	2.538	.0025
Ft. Water	12.0	1.0	.433	.883	22.43	30.45	.0304
Psi.	27.72	2.31	1.0	2.040	51.816	70.31	.0703
In. Hg.	13.596	1.133	.4906	1.0	25.40	34.49	.0345
Mm. Hg.	.5353	.0446	.0193	.03937	1.0	1.357	.0014
Gr./Sq. Cm.	.3936	.0328	.0142	.02897	.7360	1.0	.001
Kg./Sq. Cm.	393.6	32.80	14.22	28.97	736.03	1000.0	1.0
Kilopascal	4.0135	.3344	.1451	.2954	7.505	10.20	.0102

TABLE 10. CONVERSION FACTORS: UNITS OF VOLUME

Example: 10 U.S. Gal. × .1337 = 1.337 Cu. Ft. or 5 Cu. Ft. × 7.481 = 37.405 U.S. Gal.

Unit	U.S. Gal.	Imp. Gal.	Cu. In.	Cu. Ft.	Cu. Yd.	Acre In.	Acre Ft.	Lb. Water at 60°F.	Cu. Meter	Qt.	Liter
U.S. Gal.	1.0	.833	231.0	.1337	.00495	....	....	8.33	.003785	4.0	3.785
Imp. Gal.	1.2	1.0	277.4	.1605	.00595	....	....	10.0	.004546	4.8	4.546
Cu. In.	.00433	.00361	1.0	....	....	....	....	.0361	....	.0173	.0164
Cu. Ft.	7.481	6.232	1728.0	1.0	.037	....	....	62.37	.0283	29.92	28.32
Cu. Yd.	202.0	168.4	46,656.0	27.0	1.0	....	....	1684.0	.7646	808.0	764.6
Acre In.	27,157.0	22,611.0	....	3,630.0	....	1.0	.0833	....	....	....	....
Acre Ft.	325,892.0	271,335.0	....	43,560.0	....	12.0	1.0	....	1233.5	....	....
Lb. Water	.120	.10	27.7	.0160	....	....	....	1.0	....	.48	.454
Cu. Meter	264.2	220.0	61,023.0	35.31	1.308	....	.000811	2204.0	1.0	1057.0	1000.0
Qt.	.25	.208	57.75	.0334	....	....	....	2.086	....	1.0	.9464
Liter	.2642	.220	61.023	.0353	....	....	....	2.204	.001	1.057	1.0

Barrel volume differs in different industries: Beer—31 gal., Wine—31½ gal., Oil—42 gal., Whiskey—45 gal.

TABLE 11. CONVERSION FACTORS: UNITS OF FLOW

Examples: 500 U.S. Gpm × .00144 = .72 U.S. Mgd. 10 U.S. Mgd × 694.5 = 6945 U.S. Gpm

Unit	U.S. Gpm	Imp. Gpm	U.S. Mgd (2)	Imperial Mgd (2)	Cu.Ft. /Sec.	Cu. Meters /Hr.	Liters /Sec.	Miners Inch A*	Miners Inch B*	Miners Inch C*	Acre Inches /Hr.	Acre Ft. /24 Hrs.	Barrels /Min. (3)	Barrels /24 Hrs. (3)
U.S. Gal./Min.	1.	.833	.00144	.00120	.00223	.227	.0631	.0891	.1114	.0856	.0022	.00442	.0238	34.25
Imp. Gal./Min.	1.2	1.	.00173	.00144	.00268	.272	.0757	......	......	......	.0026	.00530	.0286	41.09
U.S. Mgd (2)	694.4	578.7	1.	.833	1.547	157.73	43.8	61.89	77.36	59.44	1.535	3.07	16.53	23786.6
Imperial Mgd (2)	833.4	694.5	1.2	1.	1.856	189.28	52.56	......	......	......	1.842	3.68	19.83	28544.0
Cu. Ft./Sec.	448.8	374.	.646	.538	1.	101.9	28.32	40.	50.	38.4	.992	1.984	10.68	15360.4
Cu. Meters/Hr.	4.403	3.67	.00634	.00528	.00981	1.	.2778	......	......	......	.00973	1.946	.1047	150.80
Liters/Sec.	15.85	13.21	.0228	.0190	.0353	3.60	1.	......	......	......	.0350	.0700	.377	542.86
Miners Inch A*	11.22	......	.01618	......	.0250	......	......	1.	1.25	.960	.0248	.0496	......	......
Miners Inch B*	8.98	......	.01294	......	.0200	......	......	.80	1.	.768	.0198	.0396	......	......
Miners Inch C*	11.69	......	.01682	......	.0260	......	......	1.042	1.302	1.	.0258	.0516	......	......
Acre Inches/Hr.	452.4	376.9	.651	.542	1.010	1.030	.286	40.32	50.40	38.71	1.	2.0	......	......
Acre Feet/24 Hrs.	226.2	188.5	.326	.271	.505	.515	.143	20.16	25.20	19.36	.5	1.	......	......
Barrels/Min. (3)	42.	34.99	.0605	.0504	.0937	9.534	2.65	......	......	......	......	......	1.	1440.
Barrels/24 Hrs. (3)	.0292	.0243	.000042	.000035	.000065	.00662	.00184	......	......	......	......	......	.000694	1.

*Miners Inch A established by law in States of Arizona, California(1), Montana, Nevada, Oregon.
*Miners Inch B established by law in States of Idaho, Kansas, Nebraska, New Mexico, North Dakota, South Dakota, Utah.
*Miners Inch C established by law in States of Colorado.

(1) The general practice in Southern California is to use 9 Gpm per miners inch.

(2) US Mgd = Million U.S. gallons per 24 hr. day.   Imp Mgd = Million Imperial gallons per 24 hr. day.

(3) 42 gal. bbl.

TABLE 12.
CONVERSION TABLE—MGD. AND CU. FT./SEC. TO GPM.

Million Gal. per 24 Hrs. Mgd.	Gpm.	Cu. Ft. per Sec.	Million Gal. per 24 Hrs. Mgd.	Gpm.	Cu. Ft. per Sec.
0.100	69	0.15	5.816	4039	9.00
0.129	90	0.20	6.000	4167	9.28
0.200	139	0.31	6.463	4488	10.00
0.259	180	0.40	7.000	4861	10.83
0.300	208	0.46	8.000	5556	12.38
0.388	269	0.60	9.000	6250	13.92
0.400	278	0.62	10.000	6944	15.47
0.500	347	0.77	12.925	8976	20.00
0.517	359	0.80	19.388	13,464	30.00
0.600	417	0.93	20.000	13,889	30.94
0.646	449	1.00	25.851	17,952	40.00
0.700	486	1.08	30.000	20,833	46.41
0.800	556	1.24	32.314	22,440	50.00
0.900	625	1.39	38.776	26,928	60.00
0.969	673	1.50	40.000	27,778	61.88
1.000	694	1.55	45.239	31,416	70.00
1.293	898	2.00	50.000	34,722	77.35
1.616	1122	2.50	51.702	35,904	80.00
1.939	1346	3.00	58.164	40,392	90.00
2.000	1389	3.09	60.000	41,667	92.82
2.262	1571	3.50	64.627	44,880	100.00
2.585	1795	4.00	70.000	48,611	108.29
2.908	2020	4.50	71.090	49,368	110.00
3.000	2083	4.64	77.553	53,856	120.00
3.231	2244	5.00	80.000	55,556	123.76
3.878	2693	6.00	84.015	58,344	130.00
4.000	2778	6.19	90.000	62,500	139.23
4.524	3142	7.00	90.478	62,832	140.00
5.000	3472	7.74	96.941	67,320	150.00
5.170	3590	8.00	100.000	69,444	154.72

TABLE 13.
CONVERSION TABLE—UNITS OF PRESSURE
(DENSITY AT 39.2°F)

In. Water	Ft. Water	In. Hg.	Psi.
1.00	.08	.07	.04
2.00	.17	.15	.07
3.00	.25	.22	.11
4.00	.33	.29	.14
5.00	.42	.37	.18
6.00	.50	.44	.22
7.00	.58	.52	.25
8.00	.67	.59	.29
9.00	.75	.66	.32
10.00	.83	.74	.36
11.00	.92	.81	.40
12.00	**1.00**	.88	.43
13.60	1.13	**1.00**	.49
24.00	**2.00**	1.77	.87
27.19	2.27	**2.00**	.98
27.72	2.31	2.04	**1.00**
36.00	**3.00**	2.65	1.30
40.79	3.40	**3.00**	1.47
48.00	**4.00**	3.53	1.73
54.38	4.53	**4.00**	1.96
55.44	4.62	4.08	**2.00**
60.00	**5.00**	4.42	2.17

Ft. Water	In. Hg.	Psi.	Ft. Water	In. Hg.	Psi.
5.67	**5.00**	2.45	**7.00**	6.18	3.03
6.00	5.30	2.60	7.93	**7.00**	3.43
6.80	**6.00**	2.94	**8.00**	7.06	3.46
6.93	6.12	**3.00**	**9.00**	7.95	3.90

TABLE 13. (Cont.)
CONVERSION TABLE—UNITS OF PRESSURE

Ft. Water	In. Hg.	Psi.	Ft. Water	In. Hg.	Psi.
9.06	**8.00**	3.92	**22.00**	19.43	9.53
9.24	8.16	**4.00**	22.66	**20.00**	9.81
10.00	8.83	4.33	**23.00**	20.31	9.96
10.20	**9.00**	4.42	23.10	20.40	**10.00**
11.00	9.71	4.76	23.79	**21.00**	10.30
11.33	**10.00**	4.91	**24.00**	21.19	10.39
11.55	10.20	**5.00**	24.93	**22.00**	10.79
12.00	10.60	5.20	**25.00**	22.08	10.83
12.46	**11.00**	5.40	25.41	22.44	**11.00**
13.00	11.48	5.63	**26.00**	22.96	11.26
13.60	**12.00**	5.89	26.06	**23.00**	11.28
13.86	12.24	**6.00**	**27.00**	23.84	11.69
14.00	12.36	6.06	27.19	**24.00**	11.77
14.73	**13.00**	6.38	27.72	24.48	**12.00**
15.00	13.25	6.50	**28.00**	24.72	12.12
15.86	**14.00**	6.87	28.33	**25.00**	12.27
16.00	14.13	6.93	**29.00**	25.61	12.56
16.17	14.28	**7.00**	29.46	**26.00**	12.76
17.00	**15.00**	7.36	**30.00**	26.49	12.99
18.00	15.89	7.79	30.03	26.52	**13.00**
18.13	**16.00**	7.85	30.59	**27.00**	13.25
18.48	16.32	**8.00**	**31.00**	27.37	13.42
19.00	16.78	8.23	31.72	**28.00**	13.74
19.26	**17.00**	8.34	**32.00**	28.26	13.86
20.00	17.66	8.66	32.34	28.56	**14.00**
20.39	**18.00**	8.83	32.86	**29.00**	14.23
20.79	18.36	**9.00**	**33.00**	29.14	14.29
21.00	18.54	9.09	33.90	29.92	14.70
21.53	**19.00**	9.32			

TABLE 13. (Cont.)
CONVERSION TABLE — UNITS OF PRESSURE

Ft. Water	Psi.	Ft. Water	Psi.	Ft. Water	Psi.
34.0	14.72	**240.0**	103.96	**550.0**	238.25
34.7	**15.00**	**250.0**	108.29	554.4	**240.00**
40.0	17.32	254.1	**110.00**	577.5	**250.00**
46.2	**20.00**	**260.0**	112.62	**600.0**	259.90
50.0	21.65	**270.0**	116.96	600.6	**260.00**
60.0	25.99	277.2	**120.00**	623.7	**270.00**
69.3	**30.00**	**280.0**	121.29	646.8	**280.00**
70.0	30.32	**290.0**	125.62	**650.0**	281.56
80.0	34.65	**300.0**	129.95	669.9	**290.00**
90.0	38.98	300.3	**130.00**	693.0	**300.00**
92.4	**40.00**	**310.0**	134.28	**700.0**	303.22
100.0	43.31	**320.0**	138.62	716.1	**310.00**
110.0	47.64	323.4	**140.00**	739.2	**320.00**
115.5	**50.00**	**330.0**	142.95	**750.0**	324.88
120.0	51.98	**340.0**	147.28	762.3	**330.00**
130.0	56.31	346.5	**150.00**	785.4	**340.00**
138.6	**60.00**	**350.0**	151.61	**800.0**	346.54
140.0	60.64	**360.0**	155.94	808.5	**350.00**
150.0	64.97	369.6	**160.00**	831.6	**360.00**
160.0	69.31	**370.0**	160.27	**850.0**	368.20
161.7	**70.00**	**380.0**	164.61	854.7	**370.00**
170.0	73.64	**390.0**	168.94	877.8	**380.00**
180.0	77.97	392.7	**170.00**	**900.0**	389.86
184.8	**80.00**	**400.0**	173.27	900.9	**390.00**
190.0	82.30	415.8	**180.00**	924.0	**400.00**
200.0	86.63	438.9	**190.00**	**1000.0**	433.18
207.9	**90.00**	**450.0**	195.00	1039.5	**450.00**
210.0	90.96	462.0	**200.00**	1155.0	**500.00**
220.0	95.30	485.1	**210.00**	1270.5	**550.00**
230.0	99.63	**500.0**	216.58	1386.0	**600.00**
231.0	**100.00**	508.2	**220.00**	**1500.0**	649.70
		531.3	**230.00**		

TABLE 14. CONVERSION FACTORS—WORK—POWER—TORQUE

Examples: 20 Hp Hrs. × .746 = 14.92 Kw Hrs.   20 Kw Hrs. × 1.341 = 26.82 Hp Hrs.

	Hp	Metric Hp	Kw	Ft. Lb.	Kg. M.	Ft. Lbs./Min.	Hp Hr.	Kw Hr.	Btu
Horse Power	1.0	1.014	.746	......	......	33,000.0	......	......	......
Metric Hp	.986	1.0	.736	......	......	32,550.0	......	......	......
Kilowatt	1.341	1.360	1.0	......	......	44,253.0	......	......	......
Ft. Lbs.	......	......	......	1.0	.1383	......	......	......	.001285
Kg. Meter	......	......	......	7.235	1.0	......	......	......	.00930
Ft. Lbs./Min.	.0000303	.0000307	.0000226	......	......	1.0	......	......	......
Hp Hr.	......	......	......	1,980,000.0	273,834.0	......	1.0	.746	2545.0
Kw Hr.	......	......	......	2,656,000.0	367,325.0	......	1.341	1.0	3413.0
Btu	......	......	......	778.4	107.6	......	.000393	.000293	1.0

III

TABLE 15. POWER CONSUMED PUMPING 1000 GALLONS OF CLEAR WATER AT ONE FOOT TOTAL HEAD— VARIOUS EFFICIENCIES

Overall Efficiency Pump Unit	Kwh Per 1000 Gallons at One Ft. Total Head	Overall Efficiency Pump Unit	Kwh Per 1000 Gallons at One Ft. Total Head	Overall Efficiency Pump Unit	Kwh Per 1000 Gallons at One Ft. Total Head
32	.00980	51.5	.00609	71	.00442
32.5	.00958	52	.00603	71.5	.00439
33	.00951	52.5	.00597	72	.00435
33.5	.00937	53	.00592	72.5	.00432
34	.00922	53.5	.00586	73	.00430
34.5	.00909	54	.00581	73.5	.00427
35	.00896	54.5	.00575	74	.00424
35.5	.00884	55	.00570	74.5	.00421
36	.00871	55.5	.00565	75	.00418
36.5	.00860	56	.00560	75.5	.00415
37	.00848	56.5	.00555	76	.00413
37.5	.00837	57	.00550	76.5	.00410
38	.00826	57.5	.00545	77	.00407
38.5	.00815	58	.00541	77.5	.00405
39	.00804	58.5	.00536	78	.00402
39.5	.00794	59	.00532	78.5	.00399
40	.00784	59.5	.00527	79	.00397
40.5	.00775	60	.00523	79.5	.00394
41	.00765	60.5	.00518	80	.00392
41.5	.00756	61	.00514	80.5	.00389
42	.00747	61.5	.00510	81	.00387
42.5	.00738	62	.00506	81.5	.00385
43	.00730	62.5	.00502	82	.00382
43.5	.00721	63	.00498	82.5	.00380
44	.00713	63.5	.00494	83	.00378
44.5	.00705	64	.00490	83.5	.00375
45	.00697	64.5	.00486	84	.00373
45.5	.00689	65	.00482	84.5	.00371
46	.00682	65.5	.00479	85	.00369
46.5	.00675	66	.00475	85.5	.00367
47	.00667	66.5	.00472	86	.00365
47.5	.00660	67	.00468	86.5	.00362
48	.00653	67.5	.00465	87	.00360
48.5	.00647	68	.00461	87.5	.00358
49	.00640	68.5	.00458	88	.00356
49.5	.00634	69	.00454	88.5	.00354
50	.00627	69.5	.00451	89	.00352
50.5	.00621	70	.00448	89.5	.00350
51	.00615	70.5	.00445	90	.00348

Overall efficiency = true Input-Output efficiency of motor x pump efficiency.

$Kwh/1000$ gal. $= K \cdot H$

Where $K = Kwh/1000$ gal. at one ft. head. $H = $ Total Head.

Example: Overall efficiency = 72%. Total Head at the rated capacity = 150 ft.

$Kwh/1000$ gal. $= .00435$ x $150 = 0.653$

$$\text{Deg. F.} = \frac{9}{5} \text{ Deg. C.} + 32. \qquad \text{Deg. C.} = \frac{5}{9} (\text{Deg. F.} - 32)$$

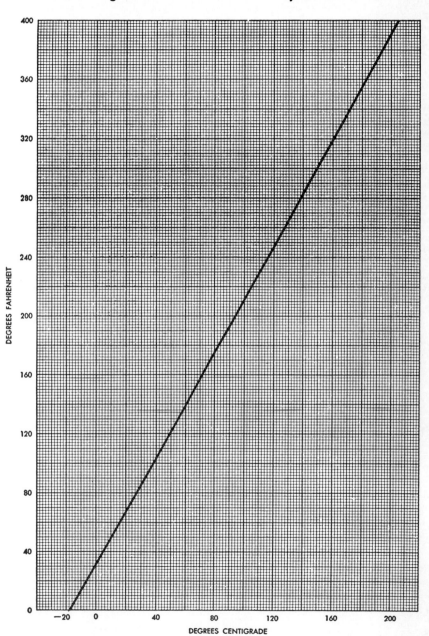

FIG. 27. Conversion chart. Fahrenheit - Centigrade.

TABLE 16. UNITED STATES STANDARD BAUME SCALES

Relation Between Baume Degrees and Specific Gravity

LIQUIDS HEAVIER THAN WATER

$$\text{Formula—sp gr} = \frac{145}{145 - °\text{ Baume}}$$

Baume degrees	Sp Gr 60°—60°F	Baume degrees	Sp Gr 60°—60°F	Baume degrees	Sp Gr 60°—60°F	Baume degrees	Sp Gr 60°—60°F
0	1.00000	20	1.16000	40	1.38095	60	1.70588
1	1.00694	21	1.16935	41	1.39423	61	1.72619
2	1.01399	22	1.17886	42	1.40777	62	1.74699
3	1.02113	23	1.18852	43	1.42157	63	1.76829
4	1.02837	24	1.19835	44	1.43564	64	1.79012
5	1.03571	25	1.20833	45	1.45000	65	1.81250
6	1.04317	26	1.21849	46	1.46465	66	1.83544
7	1.05072	27	1.22881	47	1.47959	67	1.85897
8	1.05839	28	1.23932	48	1.49485	68	1.88312
9	1.06618	29	1.25000	49	1.51042	69	1.90789
10	1.07407	30	1.26087	50	1.52632	70	1.93333
11	1.08209	31	1.27193	51	1.54255	71	1.95946
12	1.09023	32	1.28319	52	1.55914	72	1.98630
13	1.09848	33	1.29464	53	1.57609	73	2.01389
14	1.10687	34	1.30631	54	1.59341	74	2.04225
15	1.11538	35	1.31818	55	1.61111	75	2.07143
16	1.12403	36	1.33028	56	1.62921	76	2.10145
17	1.13281	37	1.34259	57	1.64773	77	2.13235
18	1.14173	38	1.35514	58	1.66667	78	2.16418
19	1.15079	39	1.36792	59	1.68605	79	2.19697

LIQUIDS LIGHTER THAN WATER

$$\text{Formula—sp gr} = \frac{140}{130 + °\text{ Baume}}$$

Baume	Sp Gr	Baume	Sp Gr	Baume	Sp Gr	Baume	Sp Gr
10	1.00000	30	0.87500	50	0.77778	70	0.70000
11	.99291	31	.86957	51	.77348	71	.69652
12	.98592	32	.86420	52	.76923	72	.69307
13	.97902	33	.85890	53	.76503	73	.68966
14	.97222	34	.85366	54	.76087	74	.68627
15	.96552	35	.84848	55	.75676	75	.68293
16	.95890	36	.84337	56	.75269	76	.67961
17	.95238	37	.83832	57	.74866	77	.67633
18	.94595	38	.83333	58	.74468	78	.67308
19	.93960	39	.82840	59	.74074	79	.66986
20	.93333	40	.82353	60	.73684	80	.66667
21	.92715	41	.81871	61	.73298	81	.66351
22	.92105	42	.81395	62	.72917	82	.66038
23	.91503	43	.80925	63	.72539	83	.65728
24	.90909	44	.80460	64	.72165	84	.65421
25	.90323	45	.80000	65	.71795	85	.65117
26	.89744	46	.79545	66	.71428	86	.64815
27	.89172	47	.79096	67	.71066	87	.64516
28	.88608	48	.78652	68	.70707	88	.64220
29	.88050	49	.78212	69	.70352	89	.63927

From Circular No. 59 Bureau of Standards.

TABLE 17. RELATION BETWEEN SPECIFIC GRAVITY AND DEG. API AT 60°F.

$$\text{Specific Gravity} = \frac{141.5}{131.5 + °\text{API}}$$

Degrees A.P.I.	Specific Gravity	Degrees A.P.I.	Specific Gravity	Degrees A.P.I.	Specific Gravity
10	1.0000	40	.8251	70	.7022
11	.9930	41	.8203	71	.6988
12	.9861	42	.8155	72	.6952
13	.9792	43	.8109	73	.6919
14	.9725	44	.8063	74	.6886
15	.9659	45	.8017	75	.6852
16	.9593	46	.7972	76	.6819
17	.9529	47	.7927	77	.6787
18	.9465	48	.7883	78	.6754
19	.9402	49	.7839	79	.6722
20	.9340	50	.7796	80	.6690
21	.9279	51	.7753	81	.6659
22	.9218	52	.7711	82	.6628
23	.9159	53	.7669	83	.6597
24	.9100	54	.7628	84	.6566
25	.9042	55	.7587	85	.6536
26	.8984	56	.7547	86	.6506
27	.8927	57	.7507	87	.6476
28	.8871	58	.7467	88	.6446
29	.8816	59	.7428	89	.6417
30	.8762	60	.7389	90	.6388
31	.8708	61	.7351	91	.6360
32	.8654	62	.7313	92	.6331
33	.8602	63	.7275	93	.6303
34	.8550	64	.7238	94	.6275
35	.8498	65	.7201	95	.6247
36	.8448	66	.7165	96	.6220
37	.8398	67	.7128	97	.6193
38	.8348	68	.7093	98	.6166
39	.8299	69	.7057	99	.6139
				100	.6112

TABLE 18. DEGREES BRIX†
Per Cent Sugar (Degrees Balling's or Brix) with Corresponding Specific Gravity and Degrees Baume. Temperature 60°F

Per cent sugar Balling's or Brix 60°F— 15.56°C	Specific gravity 60°/60°F	Degrees Baume 60°F	Per cent sugar Balling's or Brix 60°F— 15.56°C	Specific gravity 60°/60°F	Degrees Baume 60°F
0	1.0000	0.00	50	1.2328	27.38
1	1.0039	0.56	51	1.2384	27.91
2	1.0078	1.13	52	1.2439	28.43
3	1.0118	1.68	53	1.2496	28.96
4	1.0157	2.24	54	1.2552	29.48
5	1.0197	2.80	55	1.2609	30.00
6	1.0238	3.37	56	1.2667	30.53
7	1.0278	3.93	57	1.2724	31.05
8	1.0319	4.49	58	1.2782	31.56
9	1.0360	5.04	59	1.2841	32.08
10	1.0402	5.60	60	1.2900	32.60
11	1.0443	6.15	61	1.2959	33.11
12	1.0485	6.71	62	1.3019	33.63
13	1.0528	7.28	63	1.3079	34.13
14	1.0570	7.81	64	1.3139	34.64
15	1.0613	8.38	65	1.3200	35.15
16	1.0657	8.94	66	1.3261	35.66
17	1.0700	9.49	67	1.3323	36.16
18	1.0744	10.04	68	1.3384	36.67
19	1.0788	10.59	69	1.3447	37.17
20	1.0833	11.15	70	1.3509	37.66
21	1.0878	11.70	71	1.3573	38.17
22	1.0923	12.25	72	1.3636	38.66
23	1.0968	12.80	73	1.3700	39.16
24	1.1014	13.35	74	1.3764	39.65
25	1.1060	13.90	75	1.3829	40.15
26	1.1107	14.45	76	1.3894	40.64
27	1.1154	15.00	77	1.3959	41.12
28	1.1201	15.54	78	1.4025	41.61
29	1.1248	16.19	79	1.4091	42.10
30	1.1296	16.63	80	1.4157	42.58
31	1.1345	17.19	81	1.4224	43.06
32	1.1393	17.73	82	1.4291	43.54
33	1.1442	18.28	83	1.4359	44.02
34	1.1491	18.81	84	1.4427	44.49
35	1.1541	19.36	85	1.4495	44.96
36	1.1591	19.90	86	1.4564	45.44
37	1.1641	20.44	87	1.4633	45.91
38	1.1692	20.98	88	1.4702	46.37
39	1.1743	21.52	89	1.4772	46.84
40	1.1794	22.06	90	1.4842	47.31
41	1.1846	22.60	91	1.4913	47.77
42	1.1898	23.13	92	1.4984	48.23
43	1.1950	23.66	93	1.5055	48.69
44	1.2003	24.20	94	1.5126	49.14
45	1.2057	24.74	95	1.5198	49.59
46	1.2110	25.26	96	1.5270	50.04
47	1.2164	25.80	97	1.5343	50.49
48	1.2218	26.32	98	1.5416	50.94
49	1.2273	26.86	99	1.5489	51.39
			100	1.5563	51.93

The above table is from the determinations of Dr. F. Plato, and has been adopted as standard by the United States Bureau of Standards.

†*Courtesy Ingersoll-Rand Co. See page 6.*

TABLE 19. CONVERSION FACTORS—WATER ANALYSIS

Examples: 5 Gr./gal. × 17.1 = 85.5 Ppm   103 Ppm × .07 = 7.21 Gr./Imp. Gal.

	Grains per U.S. Gallon	Grains per Imp. Gallon	Parts per Million or Mg./liter
Grains per U.S. Gal.	1.00	1.20	17.1
Grains per Imp. Gal.	0.835	1.00	14.3
Parts/Million or Milligrams/liter	0.0585	0.07	1.0

TABLE 20. POUNDS PER CUBIC FOOT AT VARIOUS SPECIFIC GRAVITIES

Specific Gravity	Lb. Per Cu. Ft.	Specific Gravity	Lb. Per Cu. Ft.	Specific Gravity	Lb. Per Cu. Ft.
.90	56.16	1.40	87.36	1.90	118.56
.91	56.78	1.41	87.98	1.91	119.18
.92	57.41	1.42	88.61	1.92	119.81
.93	58.03	1.43	89.23	1.93	120.43
.94	58.66	1.44	89.86	1.94	121.06
.95	59.28	1.45	90.48	1.95	121.68
.96	59.90	1.46	91.10	1.96	122.30
.97	60.53	1.47	91.73	1.97	122.93
.98	61.15	1.48	92.35	1.98	123.55
.99	61.78	1.49	92.98	1.99	124.18
1.00	62.40	1.50	93.60	2.00	124.80
1.01	63.02	1.51	94.22	2.01	125.42
1.02	63.65	1.52	94.85	2.02	126.05
1.03	64.27	1.53	95.47	2.03	126.67
1.04	64.90	1.54	96.10	2.04	127.30
1.05	65.52	1.55	96.72	2.05	127.92
1.06	66.14	1.56	97.34	2.06	128.54
1.07	66.77	1.57	97.97	2.07	129.17
1.08	67.39	1.58	98.59	2.08	129.79
1.09	68.02	1.59	99.22	2.09	130.42
1.10	68.64	1.60	99.84	2.10	131.04
1.11	69.26	1.61	100.46	2.11	131.66
1.12	69.89	1.62	101.09	2.12	132.29
1.13	70.51	1.63	101.71	2.13	132.91
1.14	71.14	1.64	102.34	2.14	133.54
1.15	71.76	1.65	102.96	2.15	134.16
1.16	72.38	1.66	103.58	2.16	134.78
1.17	73.01	1.67	104.21	2.17	135.41
1.18	73.63	1.68	104.83	2.18	136.03
1.19	74.26	1.69	105.46	2.19	136.66
1.20	74.88	1.70	106.08	2.20	137.28
1.21	75.50	1.71	106.70	2.21	137.90
1.22	76.13	1.72	107.33	2.22	138.53
1.23	76.75	1.73	107.95	2.23	139.15
1.24	77.38	1.74	108.58	2.24	139.78
1.25	78.00	1.75	109.20	2.25	140.40
1.26	78.62	1.76	109.82	2.26	141.02
1.27	79.25	1.77	110.45	2.27	141.65
1.28	79.87	1.78	111.07	2.28	142.27
1.29	80.50	1.79	111.70	2.29	142.90
1.30	81.12	1.80	112.32	2.30	143.52
1.31	81.74	1.81	112.94	2.31	144.14
1.32	82.37	1.82	113.57	2.32	144.77
1.33	82.99	1.83	114.19	2.33	145.39
1.34	83.62	1.84	114.82	2.34	146.02
1.35	84.24	1.85	115.44	2.35	146.64
1.36	84.86	1.86	116.06	2.36	147.26
1.37	85.49	1.87	116.69	2.37	147.89
1.38	86.11	1.88	117.31	2.38	148.51
1.39	86.74	1.89	117.94	2.39	149.14

DECIMAL EQUIVALENTS

32nds	64ths	0"	1"	2"	3"	4"	5"	6"	7"	8"	9"	10"	11"	64ths	32nds	Decimals of an Inch
0		0.0000	0.0833	0.1667	0.2500	0.3333	0.4167	0.5000	0.5833	0.6667	0.7500	0.8333	0.9167		0	
	1	0.0013	0.0846	0.1680	0.2513	0.3346	0.4180	0.5013	0.5846	0.6680	0.7513	0.8346	0.9180	1		0.015625
1/32		0.0026	0.0859	0.1693	0.2526	0.3359	0.4193	0.5026	0.5859	0.6693	0.7526	0.8359	0.9193		1/32	0.031250
	3	0.0039	0.0872	0.1706	0.2539	0.3372	0.4206	0.5039	0.5872	0.6706	0.7539	0.8372	0.9206	3		0.046875
1/16		0.0052	0.0885	0.1719	0.2552	0.3385	0.4219	0.5052	0.5885	0.6719	0.7552	0.8385	0.9219		1/16	0.062500
	5	0.0065	0.0898	0.1732	0.2565	0.3398	0.4232	0.5065	0.5898	0.6732	0.7565	0.8398	0.9232	5		0.078125
3/32		0.0078	0.0911	0.1745	0.2578	0.3411	0.4245	0.5078	0.5911	0.6745	0.7578	0.8411	0.9245		3/32	0.093750
	7	0.0091	0.0924	0.1758	0.2591	0.3424	0.4258	0.5091	0.5924	0.6758	0.7591	0.8424	0.9258	7		0.109375
1/8		0.0104	0.0937	0.1771	0.2604	0.3437	0.4271	0.5104	0.5937	0.6771	0.7604	0.8437	0.9271		1/8	0.125000
	9	0.0117	0.0951	0.1784	0.2617	0.3451	0.4284	0.5117	0.5951	0.6784	0.7617	0.8451	0.9284	9		0.140625
5/32		0.0130	0.0964	0.1797	0.2630	0.3464	0.4297	0.5130	0.5964	0.6797	0.7630	0.8464	0.9297		5/32	0.156250
	11	0.0143	0.0977	0.1810	0.2643	0.3477	0.4310	0.5143	0.5977	0.6810	0.7643	0.8477	0.9310	11		0.171875
3/16		0.0156	0.0990	0.1823	0.2656	0.3490	0.4323	0.5156	0.5990	0.6823	0.7656	0.8490	0.9323		3/16	0.187500
	13	0.0169	0.1003	0.1836	0.2669	0.3503	0.4336	0.5169	0.6003	0.6836	0.7669	0.8503	0.9336	13		0.203125
7/32		0.0182	0.1016	0.1849	0.2682	0.3516	0.4349	0.5182	0.6016	0.6849	0.7682	0.8516	0.9349		7/32	0.218750
	15	0.0195	0.1029	0.1862	0.2695	0.3529	0.4362	0.5195	0.6029	0.6862	0.7695	0.8529	0.9362	15		0.234375
1/4		0.0208	0.1042	0.1875	0.2708	0.3542	0.4375	0.5208	0.6042	0.6875	0.7708	0.8542	0.9375		1/4	0.250000
	17	0.0221	0.1055	0.1888	0.2721	0.3555	0.4388	0.5221	0.6055	0.6888	0.7721	0.8555	0.9388	17		0.265625
9/32		0.0234	0.1068	0.1901	0.2734	0.3568	0.4401	0.5234	0.6068	0.6901	0.7734	0.8568	0.9401		9/32	0.281250
	19	0.0247	0.1081	0.1914	0.2747	0.3581	0.4414	0.5247	0.6081	0.6914	0.7747	0.8581	0.9414	19		0.296875
5/16		0.0260	0.1094	0.1927	0.2760	0.3594	0.4427	0.5260	0.6094	0.6927	0.7760	0.8594	0.9427		5/16	0.312500
	21	0.0273	0.1107	0.1940	0.2773	0.3607	0.4440	0.5273	0.6107	0.6940	0.7773	0.8607	0.9440	21		0.328125
11/32		0.0286	0.1120	0.1953	0.2786	0.3620	0.4453	0.5286	0.6120	0.6953	0.7786	0.8620	0.9453		11/32	0.343750
	23	0.0299	0.1133	0.1966	0.2799	0.3633	0.4466	0.5299	0.6133	0.6966	0.7799	0.8633	0.9466	23		0.359375
3/8		0.0312	0.1146	0.1979	0.2812	0.3646	0.4479	0.5312	0.6146	0.6979	0.7812	0.8646	0.9479		3/8	0.375000
	25	0.0326	0.1159	0.1992	0.2826	0.3659	0.4492	0.5326	0.6159	0.6992	0.7826	0.8659	0.9492	25		0.390625
13/32		0.0339	0.1172	0.2005	0.2839	0.3672	0.4505	0.5339	0.6172	0.7005	0.7839	0.8672	0.9505		13/32	0.406250

DECIMALS OF A FOOT

Decimal	No.	Fraction													Fraction	No.
0.453125	29		0.9544	0.8711	0.7878	0.7044	0.6211	0.5378	0.4544	0.3711	0.2878	0.2044	0.1211	0.0378		29
0.468750		15/32	0.9557	0.8724	0.7891	0.7057	0.6224	0.5391	0.4557	0.3724	0.2891	0.2057	0.1224	0.0391	15/32	
0.484375	31		0.9570	0.8737	0.7904	0.7070	0.6237	0.5404	0.4570	0.3737	0.2904	0.2070	0.1237	0.0404		31
0.500000		1/2	0.9583	0.8750	0.7917	0.7083	0.6250	0.5417	0.4583	0.3750	0.2917	0.2083	0.1250	0.0417	1/2	
0.515625	33		0.9596	0.8763	0.7930	0.7096	0.6263	0.5430	0.4596	0.3763	0.2930	0.2096	0.1263	0.0430		33
0.531250		17/32	0.9609	0.8776	0.7943	0.7109	0.6276	0.5443	0.4609	0.3776	0.2943	0.2109	0.1276	0.0443	17/32	
0.546875	35		0.9622	0.8789	0.7956	0.7122	0.6289	0.5456	0.4622	0.3789	0.2956	0.2122	0.1289	0.0456		35
0.562500		9/16	0.9635	0.8802	0.7969	0.7135	0.6302	0.5469	0.4635	0.3802	0.2969	0.2135	0.1302	0.0469	9/16	
0.578125	37		0.9648	0.8815	0.7982	0.7148	0.6315	0.5482	0.4648	0.3815	0.2982	0.2148	0.1315	0.0482		37
0.593750		19/32	0.9661	0.8828	0.7995	0.7161	0.6328	0.5495	0.4661	0.3828	0.2995	0.2161	0.1328	0.0495	19/32	
0.609375	39		0.9674	0.8841	0.8008	0.7174	0.6341	0.5508	0.4674	0.3841	0.3008	0.2174	0.1341	0.0508		39
0.625000		5/8	0.9688	0.8854	0.8021	0.7188	0.6354	0.5521	0.4688	0.3854	0.3021	0.2188	0.1354	0.0521	5/8	
0.640625	41		0.9701	0.8867	0.8034	0.7201	0.6367	0.5534	0.4701	0.3867	0.3034	0.2201	0.1367	0.0534		41
0.656250		21/32	0.9714	0.8880	0.8047	0.7214	0.6380	0.5547	0.4714	0.3880	0.3047	0.2214	0.1380	0.0547	21/32	
0.671875	43		0.9727	0.8893	0.8060	0.7227	0.6393	0.5560	0.4727	0.3893	0.3060	0.2227	0.1393	0.0560		43
0.687500		11/16	0.9740	0.8906	0.8073	0.7240	0.6406	0.5573	0.4740	0.3906	0.3073	0.2240	0.1406	0.0573	11/16	
0.703125	45		0.9753	0.8919	0.8086	0.7253	0.6419	0.5586	0.4753	0.3919	0.3086	0.2253	0.1419	0.0586		45
0.718750		23/32	0.9766	0.8932	0.8099	0.7266	0.6432	0.5599	0.4766	0.3932	0.3099	0.2266	0.1432	0.0599	23/32	
0.734375	47		0.9779	0.8945	0.8112	0.7279	0.6445	0.5612	0.4779	0.3945	0.3112	0.2279	0.1445	0.0612		47
0.750000		3/4	0.9792	0.8958	0.8125	0.7292	0.6458	0.5625	0.4792	0.3958	0.3125	0.2292	0.1458	0.0625	3/4	
0.765625	49		0.9805	0.8971	0.8138	0.7305	0.6471	0.5638	0.4805	0.3971	0.3138	0.2305	0.1471	0.0638		49
0.781250		25/32	0.9818	0.8984	0.8151	0.7318	0.6484	0.5651	0.4818	0.3984	0.3151	0.2318	0.1484	0.0651	25/32	
0.796875	51		0.9831	0.8997	0.8164	0.7331	0.6497	0.5664	0.4831	0.3997	0.3164	0.2331	0.1497	0.0664		51
0.812500		13/16	0.9844	0.9010	0.8177	0.7344	0.6510	0.5677	0.4844	0.4010	0.3177	0.2344	0.1510	0.0677	13/16	
0.828125	53		0.9857	0.9023	0.8190	0.7357	0.6523	0.5690	0.4857	0.4023	0.3190	0.2357	0.1523	0.0690		53
0.843750		27/32	0.9870	0.9036	0.8203	0.7370	0.6536	0.5703	0.4870	0.4036	0.3203	0.2370	0.1536	0.0703	27/32	
0.859375	55		0.9883	0.9049	0.8216	0.7383	0.6549	0.5716	0.4883	0.4049	0.3216	0.2383	0.1549	0.0716		55
0.875000		7/8	0.9896	0.9062	0.8229	0.7396	0.6562	0.5729	0.4896	0.4062	0.3229	0.2396	0.1562	0.0729	7/8	
0.890625	57		0.9909	0.9076	0.8242	0.7409	0.6576	0.5742	0.4909	0.4076	0.3242	0.2409	0.1576	0.0742		57
0.906250		29/32	0.9922	0.9089	0.8255	0.7422	0.6589	0.5755	0.4922	0.4089	0.3255	0.2422	0.1589	0.0755	29/32	
0.921875	59		0.9935	0.9102	0.8268	0.7435	0.6602	0.5768	0.4935	0.4102	0.3268	0.2435	0.1602	0.0768		59
0.937500		15/16	0.9948	0.9115	0.8281	0.7448	0.6615	0.5781	0.4948	0.4115	0.3281	0.2448	0.1615	0.0781	15/16	
0.953125	61		0.9961	0.9128	0.8294	0.7461	0.6628	0.5794	0.4961	0.4128	0.3294	0.2461	0.1628	0.0794		61
0.968750		31/32	0.9974	0.9141	0.8307	0.7474	0.6641	0.5807	0.4974	0.4141	0.3307	0.2474	0.1641	0.0807	31/32	
0.984375	63		0.9987	0.9154	0.8320	0.7487	0.6654	0.5820	0.4987	0.4154	0.3320	0.2487	0.1654	0.0820		63

TABLE 21a. CONVERSION TABLE FOR APPROXIMATE HARDNESS NUMBERS OBTAINED BY DIFFERENT METHODS†

(Compiled mainly from manufacturers' tables)

Brinell, 3000-kg load, 10 mm ball		Rockwell Number			
Diameter of Indentation, d mm	Hardness Number	C Scale, 150 kg load, 120° diamond cone	B Scale, 100 kg load, 1/16 in. ball	Shore Sclero-scope Number	Vickers Pyramid Number
2.40	653	62	....	86	783
2.60	555	55	....	75	622
2.80	477	49	....	66	513
3.00	415	44	....	58	439
3.10	388	41	....	54	404
3.20	363	39	....	51	374
3.30	341	37	....	48	352
3.40	321	35	....	45	329
3.50	302	32	....	42	303
3.60	285	30	....	40	285
3.70	269	27	....	37	269
3.80	255	25	....	35	255
3.90	241	23	99	33	241
4.00	229	20	98	32	229
4.10	217	....	96	30	217
4.20	207	....	95	29	207
4.30	197	....	93	28	197
4.40	187	....	91	27	187
4.50	179	....	89	25	179
4.60	170	....	87	24	170
4.70	163	....	85	23	163
4.80	156	....	82	23	156
4.90	149	....	80	22	149
5.00	143	....	78	21	143
5.10	137	....	75	20	137
5.20	131	....	73	19	131
5.30	126	....	70	18	126
5.40	121	....	68	17	121
5.50	116	....	65	16	116
5.60	111	....	62	....	111
5.70	107	....	60	....	107
5.80	103	....	57	....	103
5.90	99.2	....	55	....	99.2
6.00	95.5	....	52	....	95.5
6.10	92.0	....	49	....	92.0
6.20	88.7	....	47	....	88.7
6.30	85.5	....	44	....	85.5
6.40	82.5	....	42	....	82.5

†*Courtesy John Wiley and Sons. See page 6.*

SECTION IV—WATER DATA

CONTENTS

IV

SECTION IV—WATER DATA

PROPERTIES OF WATER—VISCOSITY

In this handbook, the specific gravity is referred to water at 39.2°F (4°C) as 1.000. This is its point of maximum density. Quite often, however, it is referred to water at 60°F (15.6°C) as 1.000. Based on water at 39.2°F as 1.000, water at 60°F has a specific gravity of 0.999+. Therefore, the base which is selected for use makes no practical difference in pumping problems.

TABLE 22. VISCOSITY OF WATER

Temp— °F.	Absolute Viscosity	Kinematic Viscosity		
	Centipoises	Centistokes	SSU	ft²/sec
32	1.79	1.79	33.0	0.00001931
50	1.31	1.31	31.6	0.00001410
60	1.12	1.12	31.2	0.00001217
70	0.98	0.98	30.9	0.00001059
80	0.86	0.86	30.6	0.00000930
85	0.81	0.81	30.4	0.00000869
100	0.68	0.69	30.2	0.00000739
120	0.56	0.57	30.0	0.00000609
140	0.47	0.48	29.7	0.00000514
160	0.40	0.41	29.6	0.00000442
180	0.35	0.36	29.5	0.00000385
212	0.28	0.29	29.3	0.00000319

TABLE 23. PROPERTIES OF WATER

Temp. °F.	Absolute Vapor Pressure		Specific Gravity (Water at 39.2°F = 1.000)	Temp. °F.	Absolute Vapor Pressure		Specific Gravity (Water at 39.2°F = 1.000)
	Psi.	Ft. Water			Psi.	Ft. Water	
60	0.26	0.59	0.999	160	4.74	11.2	0.977
70	0.36	0.89	0.998	161	4.85	11.5	0.977
80	0.51	1.2	0.997	162	4.97	11.7	0.977
85	0.60	1.4	0.996	163	5.09	12.0	0.976
90	0.70	1.6	0.995	164	5.21	12.3	0.976
100	0.95	2.2	0.993	165	5.33	12.6	0.976
110	1.27	3.0	0.991	166	5.46	12.9	0.975
120	1.69	3.9	0.989	167	5.59	13.3	0.975
130	2.22	5.0	0.986	168	5.72	13.6	0.974
140	2.89	6.8	0.983	169	5.85	13.9	0.974
150	3.72	8.8	0.981	170	5.99	14.2	0.974
151	3.81	9.0	0.981	171	6.13	14.5	0.973
152	3.90	9.2	0.980	172	6.27	14.9	0.973
153	4.00	9.4	0.980	173	6.42	15.2	0.973
154	4.10	9.7	0.979	174	6.56	15.6	0.972
155	4.20	9.9	0.979	175	6.71	15.9	0.972
156	4.31	10.1	0.979	176	6.87	16.3	0.972
157	4.41	10.4	0.978	177	7.02	16.7	0.971
158	4.52	10.7	0.978	178	7.18	17.1	0.971
159	4.63	10.9	0.978	179	7.34	17.4	0.971

TABLE 23. (Cont.) PROPERTIES OF WATER

Temp. °F.	Absolute Vapor Pressure		Specific Gravity (Water at 39.2°F = 1.000)	Temp. °F.	Absolute Vapor Pressure		Specific Gravity (Water at 39.2°F = 1.000)
	Psi.	Ft. Water			Psi.	Ft. Water	
180	7.51	17.8	0.970	225	18.92	45.9	0.953
181	7.68	18.3	0.970	226	19.28	46.8	0.953
182	7.85	18.7	0.970	227	19.65	47.7	0.952
183	8.02	19.1	0.969	228	20.02	48.6	0.952
184	8.20	19.5	0.969	229	20.40	49.5	0.951
185	8.38	20.0	0.969	230	20.78	50.5	0.951
186	8.57	20.4	0.968	231	21.17	51.4	0.951
187	8.76	20.9	0.968	232	21.57	52.5	0.950
188	8.95	21.4	0.967	233	21.97	53.5	0.950
189	9.14	21.8	0.967	234	22.38	54.5	0.950
190	9.34	22.3	0.966	235	22.80	55.5	0.949
191	9.54	22.8	0.966	236	23.22	56.6	0.949
192	9.75	23.3	0.965	237	23.65	57.8	0.948
193	9.96	23.8	0.965	238	24.09	58.8	0.948
194	10.17	24.3	0.965	239	24.53	59.8	0.948
195	10.38	24.9	0.964	240	24.97	61.0	0.947
196	10.60	25.4	0.964	241	25.43	62.1	0.947
197	10.83	25.9	0.963	242	25.89	63.3	0.946
198	11.06	26.6	0.963	243	26.36	64.5	0.946
199	11.29	27.1	0.963	244	26.83	65.6	0.946
200	11.53	27.6	0.963	245	27.31	66.8	0.945
201	11.77	28.2	0.962	250	29.83	73.2	0.943
202	12.01	28.8	0.962	260	35.44	87.4	0.938
203	12.26	29.4	0.962	270	41.87	103.6	0.933
204	12.51	30.0	0.961	280	49.22	122.8	0.927
205	12.77	30.6	0.961	290	57.57	144.0	0.923
206	13.03	31.2	0.960	300	67.0	168.6	0.918
207	13.30	32.0	0.960	310	77.7	197.0	0.913
208	13.57	32.6	0.960	320	89.7	228.4	0.908
209	13.84	33.2	0.959	330	103.0	264.0	0.902
210	14.12	33.9	0.959	340	118.0	305.0	0.896
211	14.41	34.6	0.958	350	134.6	349.0	0.891
212	14.70	35.4	0.958	360	153.0	399.2	0.886
213	14.99	36.2	0.957	380	195.8	517.7	0.874
214	15.29	37.0	0.957	400	247.3	663.9	0.861
215	15.59	37.7	0.957	420	308.8	842.4	0.847
216	15.90	38.4	0.956	440	381.6	1058.5	0.833
217	16.22	39.2	0.956	460	466.9	1318.0	0.818
218	16.54	40.0	0.956	480	566.1	1630.5	0.802
219	16.86	40.8	0.955	500	680.8	2000.1	0.786
220	17.19	41.6	0.955	520	812.4	2445.5	0.767
221	17.52	42.5	0.955	540	962.5	2980.4	0.746
222	17.86	43.3	0.954				
223	18.21	44.2	0.954				
224	18.56	45.0	0.953				

IV

TABLE 24. ATMOSPHERIC PRESSURE, BAROMETER READING AND BOILING POINT OF WATER AT VARIOUS ALTITUDES

Altitude		Barometer Reading		Atmos. Press.		Boiling Point of Water
Feet	Meters	In. Hg.	Mm. Hg.	psia	Ft. Water	° F
− 1000	− 304.8	31.0	788	15.2	35.2	213.8
− 500	− 152.4	30.5	775	15.0	34.6	212.9
0	0.0	29.9	760	14.7	33.9	212.0
+ 500	+ 152.4	29.4	747	14.4	33.3	211.1
+ 1000	304.8	28.9	734	14.2	32.8	210.2
1500	457.2	28.3	719	13.9	32.1	209.3
2000	609.6	27.8	706	13.7	31.5	208.4
2500	762.0	27.3	694	13.4	31.0	207.4
3000	914.4	26.8	681	13.2	30.4	206.5
3500	1066.8	26.3	668	12.9	29.8	205.6
4000	1219.2	25.8	655	12.7	29.2	204.7
4500	1371.6	25.4	645	12.4	28.8	203.8
5000	1524.0	24.9	633	12.2	28.2	202.9
5500	1676.4	24.4	620	12.0	27.6	201.9
6000	1828.8	24.0	610	11.8	27.2	201.0
6500	1981.2	23.5	597	11.5	26.7	200.1
7000	2133.6	23.1	587	11.3	26.2	199.2
7500	2286.0	22.7	577	11.1	25.7	198.3
8000	2438.4	22.2	564	10.9	25.2	197.4
8500	2590.8	21.8	554	10.7	24.7	196.5
9000	2743.2	21.4	544	10.5	24.3	195.5
9500	2895.6	21.0	533	10.3	23.8	194.6
10000	3048.0	20.6	523	10.1	23.4	193.7
15000	4572.0	16.9	429	8.3	19.2	184.0

TABLE 25. WATER REQUIRED TO
FEED BOILERS, U. S. GPM.

Boiler Hp	gpm	lb./hr.	Boiler Hp	gpm	lb./hr.
10	0.7	345	175	12.1	6037
20	1.4	690	200	13.8	6900
30	2.1	1035	225	15.5	7762
40	2.8	1380	250	17.2	8625
50	3.5	1725	300	20.7	10350
60	4.1	2070	350	24.1	12075
70	4.8	2415	400	27.6	13800
80	5.5	2760	450	31.1	15525
90	6.2	3105	500	34.5	17250
100	6.9	3450	600	41.4	20700
125	8.6	4312	750	51.8	25875
150	10.4	5175	1000	69.0	34500

IV

A Boiler horsepower is equivalent to the evaporation of 34.5 lbs. of water per hour from a feed water temperature of 212°F into steam at 212°F or, in other terms, is equal to the evaporation of 0.069 gpm per Boiler hp. The accompanying table of water requirements is based on these values.

In selecting a Boiler Feed Pump it should be remembered that most Boilers are operated at more than 100% of their rating. With modern firing methods 200% to 300% is not uncommon even with small Boilers. For example a 200 Hp Boiler operating at 300% of rating will actually evaporate 600 Boiler Hp or 41.4 gpm.

A Boiler Feed pump should always develop a pressure higher than the Boiler pressure. The amount the pump pressure exceeds the Boiler pressure is called the Excess Pressure. This excess pressure is needed to overcome the friction losses in the check valve, regulating valve, piping and in the static elevation difference between the pump location and the water level in the boiler. The amount of excess pressure required should be determined from the layout of the installation. Generally, for estimating purposes, excess pressures of 25 lbs. for 100 lb. pressure Boilers to 50 lbs. for 300 lb. Boilers can be used.

TABLE 26. WATER REQUIREMENTS—INDUSTRIAL

The quantities reported below are clearly those of water intake—that is, the amount which is piped into an establishment—rather than consumptive use—the amount discharged to the atmosphere or incorporated into the products of a process. Thus, the wide ranges sometimes given reflect not only differences in processes or products, but differences in the use of water. In arid areas, where even the most rigorous conservation methods are economically feasible, "intake" is only a fraction of what it may be in areas where water is abundant, although "consumptive use" is virtually the same.

CHEMICALS	UNIT	WATER REQUIRED gal
Alcohol, industrial, (100 proof)	gal	120
Alumina (Bayer process)	ton	6,300
Ammonium sulfate	ton	200,000
Butadiene	ton	20,000-660,000*
Calcium carbide	ton	30,000
Carbon dioxide (from flue gas)	ton	20,000
Cottonseed oil	gal	20
Gunpowder or explosives	ton	200,000
Hydrogen	ton	660,000
Oxygen, liquid	1,000 cu ft	2,000
Soap (laundry)	ton	500
Soda ash (ammonia soda process) 58%	ton	18,000
Sodium chlorate	ton	60,000
Sulfuric acid (contact process) 100%	ton	650-4,875*

FOODS		
Bread	ton	500-1,000†
Canning	100 cases #2 cans	750-25,000†
Corn (wet-milling)	bu. corn	140-240†
Corn syrup	bu. corn	30-40†
Gelatin (edible)	ton	13,200-20,000†
Meat:		
Packing	ton live animals	4,130
Packing house operation	100 hog units	55,000
Milk and milk products:		
Butter	ton	5,000
Cheese	ton	4,000
Receiving & bottling	ton	9,000
Sugar:		
Beet sugar	ton	2,160
Cane sugar	ton	1,000

PAPER & PULP		
Ground wood pulp	ton dry	4,000-50,000*
Kraft pulp	ton dry	93,000
Soda pulp	ton dry	85,000
Sulfate pulp	ton dry	70,000
Sulfite pulp	ton dry	70,000-133,000*
Paper	ton	39,000

TABLE 26.   (Continued)

PAPER & PULP (Cont.)

	UNIT	WATER REQUIRED *gal*
Paperboard	ton	15,000-90,000*
Strawboard	ton	26,000

PETROLEUM

	UNIT	WATER REQUIRED
Gasoline, natural	gal	20
Oil refining	100 bbl.	77,000
Refined products	100 bbl.	15,000-1,500,000*

SYNTHETIC FUEL

By coal hydrogenation	100 bbl.	728,600
From coal	100 bbl.	1,115,000
From natural gas	100 bbl.	373,600
From shale	100 bbl.	87,300

TEXTILES

Cotton:		
Bleaching	ton produced	60,000-80,000
Dyeing	ton produced	8,000-16,000
Rayon:		
Cuprammonium (11% moisture)	ton yarn	90,000-160,000†
Viscose	ton yarn	200,000
Weave, dye & finish	1,000 yard	15,000
Woolens	ton produced	140,000

MISCELLANEOUS

Cement, portland	ton	750
Coal & coke:		
By product coke	ton	1,500-3,600†
Washing	ton	200
Electric power, steam generated	kwhr	80-170*
Hospitals	bed per day	135-150
Iron ore (brown)	ton	1,000
Laundries:		
Commercial	ton work	8,600-11,400†
Institutional	ton work	6,000
Leather tanning:		
Vegetable	100 bbl. raw hide	800
Chrome	100 bbl. raw hide	800
Rock wool	ton	5,000
Rubber, synthetic:		
Buna S	ton	631,450
GR-S	ton	28,000-670,000*
Steel (rolled)	net ton	15,000-110,000*
Sulfur mining	ton	3,000

—*Compiled* by the American Water Works Assn., New York (Dec. 1953).
*Range from no reuse to maximum recycling.
†Range covers various products or processes involved.

TABLE 27. WATER REQUIREMENTS—PUBLIC BUILDINGS

Kind of Building		Number of Fixtures							See Notes
		0-50	51-100	101-200	201-400	401-800	801-1200	Over 1200	
Hotels and Clubs	Gpm per Fixture	.65	.55	.45	.35	.27	.25	.20	A B
	Min. Capacity, Gpm	25	35	60	100	150	225	300	
	Max. Capacity Gpm	33	55	90	140	210	300	-----	
Hospitals	Gpm per Fixture	1.0	.8	.6	.5	.4	.4	.4	A B
	Min. Capacity, Gpm	25	55	85	125	210	330	500	
	Max. Capacity Gpm	50	80	120	200	320	480	-----	
Apartments and Apartment Hotels	Gpm per Fixture	.5	.35	.30	.28	.25	.24	.24	A
	Min. Capacity, Gpm	16	30	40	65	120	210	300	
	Max. Capacity Gpm	25	35	60	115	200	290	-----	
Mercantile	Gpm per Fixture	1.3	.75	.70	.60	.55	.50	.50	A C
	Min. Capacity, Gpm	40	70	80	150	250	460	620	
	Max. Capacity Gpm	65	75	140	240	440	600	-----	
Office	Gpm per Fixture	1.1	.70	.60	.50	.37	.30	.27	A C
	Min. Capacity, Gpm	35	60	80	140	210	320	380	
	Max. Capacity Gpm	55	70	120	200	300	360	-----	
Schools	Gpm per Fixture	1.0	.60	.50	.40	.40	.40	.40	A
	Min. Capacity, Gpm	20	50	70	110	180	340	500	
	Max. Capacity Gpm	50	60	100	160	323	480	-----	

A. Tables are based on equal number men and women. If major number of occupants are women increase capacity 15%.

B. Where laundry is operated in connection with building increase capacity 10%.

C. These estimates do not include water for special process work. The extra amount should be determined and added to the total capacity.

WATER REQUIREMENTS — SWIMMING POOLS†

Table 28. indicates capacity required for swimming pools, depending upon the number of bathers accommodated per day. Many localities require that the period of recirculation must not exceed 8 hr.; others are less exacting. The period of refiltration of the pool takes into account the amount of water per bather per day, determined empirically.

The pump requirements depend upon various factors comprising the head, and upon the rate of refiltration and backwash of filter. The head is comprised of total friction in the pipes leaving the pool and draining it into the filters, as well as of the back pressure at inlets, strainers, and the resistance to filter beds. Total head is usually figured between 40 and 60 ft., depending upon pool size.

In selecting the capacity of pump, the local requirement of the minimum period of refiltration is used. In addition to the duty of recirculating, the pump must also be capable of supplying water for backwash. The flow through each filter when backwashing is four times the normal flow.

When the filter installation consists of three or more filters, and only one is backwashed at a time, then the pool circulating pump will have ample capacity for backwashing.

If a single filter is used, a separate backwash pump should be provided with a capacity aproximately four times that of the circulating pump.

TABLE 28. WATER REQUIREMENTS—SWIMMING POOLS

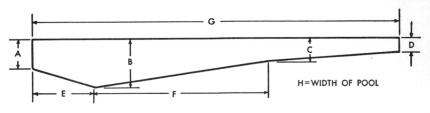

Holding Capacity, Gallons	A	B	C	D	E	F	G	H
55,500	8′	9′	5′	3′3″	15″	20′	60′	20′
80,800	8′	9′	5′	3′3″	15″	20′	75′	25′
120,000	8′	9′6″	5′	3′3″	18″	25′	90′	30′
155,600	8′	10′	5′	3′3″	18″	25′	105′	35′
207,600	8′	10′	5′	3′3″	20″	30′	120′	40′
254,000	8′	10′	5′	3′3″	20″	30′	135′	45′
306,000	8′	10′	5′	3′3″	20″	30′	150′	50′
422,400	8′	10′	5′	3′3″	20″	30′	180′	60′
558,000	8′	10′	5′	3′3″	20″	30′	210′	70′

†*Courtesy McGraw-Hill Book Co. See page 6.*

BATHING CAPACITY PER DAY ASSUMING 24-HOUR OPERATION
ON BASIS OF REFILTRATION IN—

Holding Capacity, Gallons	8 Hours 400 Gallons Per Bather		10 Hours 625 Gallons Per Bather		12 Hours 900 Gallons Per Bather		16 Hours 1600 Gallons Per Bather	
	Bathers	Pump Capacity Gpm	Bathers	Pump Capacity Gpm	Bathers	Pump Capacity Gpm	Bathers	Pump Capacity Gpm
55,500	418	116	214	93	124	72	53	58
80,800	606	168	311	135	180	112	76	84
120,000	900	250	461	200	267	167	113	125
155,600	1170	324	597	260	346	216	146	162
207,600	1555	432	796	346	461	288	195	216
254,000	1905	530	975	423	565	353	238	264
306,000	2300	638	1177	510	681	425	288	318
422,400	3170	880	1623	705	950	586	397	440
558,000	4180	1160	2145	930	1242	775	524	581

WATER REQUIREMENTS:
DOMESTIC HOT WATER SERVICE

Where a hot water system has long runs of pipe with numerous elbows, the friction may be sufficient to prevent the normal and natural circulation of the hot water. In which event, a pump is installed to supply the circulation.

When a pump is installed, it is connected in the return end of the system where the return pipe connects to the cold water side of the heater.

The purpose of the pump is not to pump the hot water to the fixtures, but to circulate the water in the system rapidly enough so that when a faucet is opened, hot water may be almost instantly drawn. Therefore, the capacity of the pump should be such that it moves the water through the pipes sufficiently fast to prevent it from cooling.

The capacity of a pump, determined by the following rule, will insure proper circulation so that a supply of hot water may always be available at the faucet.

ONE gallon per minute for each twenty fixtures using hot water where hot water pipes are covered.

ONE gallon per minute for each four fixtures using hot water where hot water pipes are not covered.

The friction in a domestic hot water system is usually nominal; therefore, the head against which the pump must discharge will very rarely exceed fifteen to twenty feet.

FIG. 28. PUMP CAPACITY FOR FORCED HOT WATER
CIRCULATION AT VARIOUS TEMPERATURE
DROPS IN HEATING SYSTEM

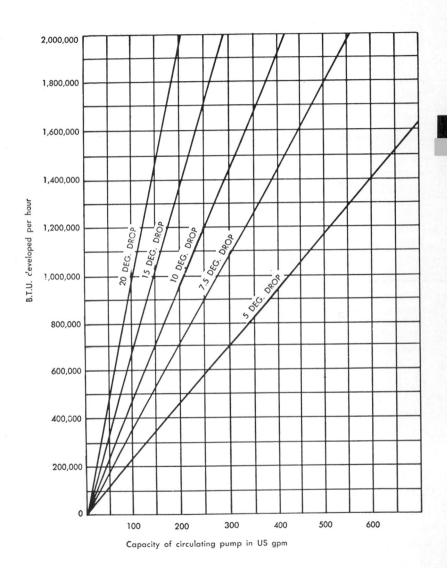

IV

Example: 1,000,000 B.T.U. are being dissipated hourly and the
temperature drop in the system is 15 deg. F. The pump must
handle 150 U.S. g.p.m.

TABLE 29.

WATER REQUIREMENTS — RURAL & DOMESTIC

Residence—Rural:

Each person per day, for all purposes..................60 gal.
Each horse, dry cow or beef animal per day.............12 gal.
Each milking cow per day..............................35 gal.
Each hog per day...................................... 4 gal.
Each sheep per day.................................... 2 gal.
Each 100 chickens per day............................. 6 gal.

Residence—Urban:

Drinking fountain, continuously flowing......50 to 100 gal. per day
Each shower bath.............................25 to 60 gal.
To fill bathtub...................................35 gal.
To flush toilet............................3 to 7 gal.
To fill lavatory...........................1 to 2 gal.
To sprinkle $\frac{1}{4}''$ of water on each 1000 square feet of lawn....160 gal.
Dish Washing Machine — per load...................10 to 20 gal.
Automatic washer — per load........................30 to 50 gal.
Regeneration of Domestic Water Softener...............50-150 gal.

By Fixtures:

Shower...4 to 6 gpm
Bathtub..4 to 8 gpm
Toilet...4 to 5 gpm
Lavatory...1 to 4 gpm
Kitchen sink...2 to 5 gpm
$\frac{1}{2}''$ hose and nozzle.......................200 gph
$\frac{3}{4}''$ hose and nozzle.......................360 gph
Lawn sprinkler......................................3 to 7 gpm

Above requirements are average and consumption or use will vary with location, persons, animals and weather.

WATER REQUIRED — IRRIGATION†

In the spring of the year after the heavy rains have ceased, the soil is wet to its maximum water holding capacity but it cannot be maintained in this condition through the summer growing season without the addition of water. The purpose of irrigation is to supplement natural rainfall and to supply the requisite amount of water to a cropped soil. The correct amount of water to apply will depend upon the type of crop—which determines the depth of penetration required—and upon the type of soil—which determines the amount of water that the soil can hold.

†*Courtesy Armco Drainage and Metal Products, Inc. See page 6.*

TABLE 30.

AMOUNT OF WATER NECESSARY TO IRRIGATE A SOIL TO A FIVE-FOOT DEPTH

Soil Type	Inches of water required to increase moisture content from permanent wilting percentage to maximum field capacity.
Sandy Soils	3 to 5 inches
Medium Soils	6 to 10 inches
Heavy Soils	12 to 15 inches

Permanent wilting percentage is the percentage of moisture at which crop plants commence to wilt and below which moisture should not be allowed to fall.

Maximum field capacity is the maximum percentage of moisture a soil will retain after irrigation.

IV

Clay soils may hold as much as 40 per cent of their dry weight in moisture, whereas sandy soils may retain only 8 per cent. Not all of this moisture, however, is available to plants. A certain percentage is held tightly by the soil particles and can not be taken up by the plant roots. The percentage so held may be as low as 2 per cent in sandy soils, but as high as 25 per cent in clay soils. When the water contents of these soils are permitted to fall to these percentages, plants will wilt and will perish unless water is added. Water should be applied before these wilting percentages are reached, to prevent damage to crops.

In applying water, best results are obtained when just enough water is applied to increase the moisture content of the root zone to the maximum water holding capacity of the soil. If more than this amount is applied it will move downward below the reach of the plant roots and will be lost. On the other hand, too shallow an irrigation should be avoided to eliminate high evaporation losses.

Since light sandy soils retain little moisture they require more frequent irrigations with relatively smaller amounts of water. A one-inch application on a sandy soil will penetrate twelve inches or more. Medium loam soils retain more moisture than sandy soils so may be irrigated at greater intervals, but with larger amounts. A one-inch application on a loam soil will penetrate six to ten inches.

Since heavy clay soils will hold a higher percentage of water than the other types, when once well moistened throughout the root zone they will retain moisture for a longer time and therefore require less frequent irrigations. The rate of application of water to clay soils must be much slower than for the lighter types, however, since water penetrates such soils slowly. One inch of water slowly applied to a heavy clay soil will penetrate 4 or 5 inches.

TABLE 31.

AMOUNT OF WATER AND FREQUENCY OF IRRIGATION REQUIRED FOR VARIOUS CROPS

Crop	Amount of Water to be Applied at Each Irrigation, Inches	Time Between Irrigation, Days
Pastures	2 to 3	14 to 21
Alfalfa	3 to 6	30 to 45
Root Crops	2 to 3	15 to 30
Vegetables	2 to 3	14 to 21
Berries	2 to 3	15 to 30
Orchards	4 to 6	30 to 60
Ladino Clover	2 to 3	14 to 21

The number of irrigations required will depend upon the time of planting, the time of harvest and the occurence of natural rainfall.

Generally speaking at most any place in the world 4″ of precipitation per month will produce a crop. Irrigation should add the amount natural rainfall lacks. Water should never be put on the soil faster than the soil can absorb it.

TABLE 32. PEAK MOISTURE USE FOR COMMON IRRIGATED CROPS AND OPTIMUM YIELDS*†

Crop	Cool Climate		Moderate Climate		Hot Climate	
	Acre Inches /Acre/Day	Gpm/ Acre (1)	Acre Inches /Acre/Day	Gpm/ Acre	Acre Inches /Acre/Day	Gpm/ Acre
Alfalfa	.15	2.8	.20	3.8	.30	5.7
Pasture	.12	2.3	.16	3.0	.25	4.7
Grain	.15	2.8	.20	3.8	.22	4.2
Potatoes	.10	1.9	.12	2.3	.14	2.6
Beets	.12	2.3	.15	2.8	.20	3.8
Deciduous Orchard	.15	2.8	.20	3.8	.25	4.7
Orchard with Cover	.20	3.8	.25	4.7	.30	5.7

*A. W. McCulloch, S.D.S. U.S.D.A.

(1) Continuous flow required per acre at 100% irrigation efficiency. Multiply values given by the following factors:

For Hot dry climate   1.67
For Moderate climate   1.43
For Humid or Cool climate   1.25

Maximum precipitation rates for overhead irrigation on level ground:

Light sandy soils—1.5″ to 0.75″ per hr.—679 to 339 gpm per acre.
Medium textured soils—0.75″ to 0.50″ per hr.—339 to 226 gpm per acre.
Heavy textured soils—0.50″ to 0.20″ per hr.—226 to 90 gpm per acre.

Allowable rates increase with adequate cover and decrease with land slopes.

†*Courtesy Rain Bird Sprinkler Mfg. Corp. See page 6.*

Table 33 is based on 100% irrigation efficiency and 24 hour per day operation.

Example: 2″ of precipitation is to be applied every 15 days, sprinkler system operated 8 hours per day in a moderate climate.

2.55 × 3 × 1.43 = 10.94 gpm per acre.

1.43 = factor obtained from footnote (1) of Table 32.

TABLE 33. G.P.M. PER ACRE REQUIRED FOR OVERHEAD IRRIGATION—24 HOUR OPERATION†

Fre-quency	Inches per Irrigation							
	1	1½	2	2½	3	4	5	6
7 days	2.69	4.03	5.37	6.70	8.06	10.75	13.43	16.1
8 ″	2.36	3.52	4.70	5.88	7.05	9.40	11.75	14.1
9 ″	2.10	3.14	4.19	5.23	6.28	8.36	10.47	12.58
10 ″	1.88	2.82	3.76	4.70	5.65	7.54	9.40	11.3
11 ″	1.71	2.56	3.42	4.27	5.13	6.84	8.55	10.28
12 ″	1.57	2.36	3.14	3.92	4.71	6.27	7.85	9.40
13 ″	1.45	2.18	2.90	3.62	4.35	5.80	7.25	8.70
14 ″	1.35	2.02	2.69	3.36	4.04	5.38	6.73	8.08
15 ″	1.26	1.88	2.55	3.14	3.76	5.02	6.28	7.54
16 ″	1.18	1.77	2.36	2.94	3.54	4.71	5.90	7.06
17 ″	1.11	1.66	2.22	2.77	3.33	4.44	5.55	6.65
18 ″	1.05	1.57	2.09	2.62	3.14	4.18	5.24	6.28
19 ″	0.99	1.49	1.98	2.48	2.98	3.97	4.96	5.95
20 ″	0.94	1.41	1.88	2.36	2.83	3.77	4.71	5.66
21 ″	0.90	1.35	1.80	2.24	2.69	3.59	4.49	5.39
22 ″	0.86	1.28	1.71	2.14	2.57	3.43	4.28	5.14
23 ″	0.82	1.23	1.64	2.05	2.46	3.28	4.09	4.91
24 ″	0.78	1.18	1.57	1.96	2.36	3.14	3.92	4.71
25 ″	0.75	1.13	1.51	1.88	2.26	3.02	3.76	4.52
26 ″	0.72	1.09	1.45	1.81	2.18	2.90	3.62	4.35
27 ″	0.70	1.05	1.40	1.75	2.10	2.78	3.49	4.18
28 ″	0.67	1.01	1.35	1.68	2.02	2.69	3.36	4.03
29 ″	0.65	0.97	1.30	1.62	1.95	2.60	3.25	3.90
30 ″	0.63	0.94	1.26	1.57	1.88	2.51	3.14	3.76

For 12 hour operation multiply by 2.   For 8 hour operation multiply by 3, etc.

WATER REQUIREMENTS — IRRIGATION OF TURF— GOLF COURSES, PARKS, AIRPORTS, CEMETERIES

The U. S. Department of Agriculture estimates that good healthy turf requires *one inch of water per week* but that no stand of turf can use more than a quarter inch of water per hour. (If water is applied at a faster rate, flooding occurs). This one

†*Courtesy Rain Bird Sprinkler Mfg. Corp. See page 6.*

TABLE 34.　IRRIGATION TABLE†

| Gal. min. | Cu. ft. sec. | Cu. ft. min. | Number of Acres covered in twelve hours pumping. | | | | | | | |
			1 in. deep	2 in. deep	3 in. deep	4 in. deep	6 in. deep	8 in. deep	10 in. deep	12 in. deep
20	.0446	2.675	.529	.2645	.1765	.1324	.08825	.06625	.0529	.04415
50	.1112	6.68	1.328	.664	.4425	.332	.2213	.166	.1328	.1105
100	.2225	13.37	2.96	1.325	.883	.6625	.442	.3313	.265	.221
150	.3345	20.05	3.98	1.991	1.328	.995	.664	.4975	.398	.332
225	.502	30.05	5.97	2.985	1.990	1.492	.994	.747	.597	.4975
300	.668	40.01	7.96	3.980	2.655	1.99	1.327	.995	.796	.663
400	.891	53.40	10.61	5.305	3.535	2.652	1.770	1.328	1.061	.884
700	1.560	93.50	18.58	9.28	6.18	4.64	3.095	2.32	1.858	1.548
900	2.008	120.40	23.85	11.95	7.96	5.97	3.98	2.975	2.385	1.99
1200	2.675	160.50	31.82	15.92	10.61	7.95	5.305	3.975	3.182	2.65
1600	3.565	213.50	42.35	21.20	14.15	10.61	7.075	5.305	4.235	3.536
3000	6.68	400.50	79.50	39.75	26.50	19.88	13.25	9.94	7.95	6.625
4500	10.03	602.00	119.30	59.70	39.75	29.85	19.90	14.93	11.93	9.95
6000	13.36	802.00	159.10	79.60	53.00	39.75	26.52	18.89	15.91	13.26
7000	15.61	936.00	185.70	92.80	61.90	46.45	30.95	23.20	18.57	15.47
8500	18.95	1137.00	225.50	112.80	75.20	56.35	37.60	28.19	22.55	18.79
10000	22.25	1337.00	266.00	132.50	88.30	66.25	44.20	33.15	26.50	22.10
14000	31.15	1871.00	371.00	185.50	123.70	92.75	61.80	46.35	37.10	30.95

1 Acrefoot = 1 acre covered to a depth of 1 ft. = 43,560 cubic feet.

†*Courtesy Ingersoll-Rand Co. See page 6.*

TABLE 35. IRRIGATION QUANTITY TABLES

Amount of water required to cover one acre to given depths.

Depth in feet and inches (Acre feet and acre inches)	Cubic feet contained in one acre to depths given in first column	Gallons
0'- 1"	3,630	27,154
0'- 2"	7,260	54,309
0'- 3"	10,890	81,463
0'- 4"	14,520	108,617
0'- 5"	18,150	135,771
0'- 6"	21,780	162,826
0'- 7"	25,410	190,080
0'- 8"	29,040	217,234
0'- 9"	32,670	244,389
0'-10"	36,300	271,542
0'-11"	39,930	298,697
1'-00"	43,560	325,851
1'- 2"	50,820	380,160
1'- 4"	58,080	434,469
1'- 6"	65,340	488,777
1'- 8"	72,600	543,086
1'-10"	79,860	597,394
2'-00"	87,120	651,703

*Second Feet and gallons per minute reduced to Gallons and Acre Feet.

Second feet	Gallons per minute	Gallons per pumping day of 12 hours	Acre feet per pumping day of 12 hours
1/4	112.2	80,790	.2479
1/2	224.4	161,579	.4959
3/4	336.6	242,369	.7438
1	448.8	323,158	.9917
1 1/4	561.0	403,948	1.2397
1 1/2	673.2	484,738	1.4876
1 3/4	785.5	565,527	1.7355
2	897.7	646,317	1.9835
2 1/2	1,122.1	807,896	2.4793
3	1,346.5	969,475	2.9752
4	1,795.3	1,292,634	3.9669
5	2,244.2	1,615,792	4.9586
6	2,693.0	1,938,951	5.9503
7	3,141.8	2,262,109	6.9421
8	3,590.6	2,585,268	7.9338
9	4,039.5	2,908,426	8.9255
10	4,488.3	3,231,585	9.9173
20	8,976.6	6,463,170	19.8345

Gallons required to cover a given number of acres to a depth of one foot (Acre foot)

Acres (or number of acre feet)	Gallons
1	325,851
2	651,703
3	977,554
4	1,303,406
5	1,629,257
6	1,955,109
7	2,280,960
8	2,606,812
9	2,932,663
10	3,258,515
15	4,887,772
20	6,512,029
25	8,146,286
30	9,775,544
40	13,034,058
60	19,551,087
80	26,068,116
160	52,136,232

*One cubic foot of water per second (exact 7.48052 gallons) constant flow is known as the "Second Foot." The "Acre Foot" is the quantity of water required to cover one acre to a depth of one foot.

IV

inch of water per week can fall in the form of rain, heavy dews, or be mechanically applied by sprinkling systems. The sprinkling system should be of ample capacity to supply sufficient water without rain or dew. One inch of water per week on an acre represents 27,150 gallons of water weekly. One acre is equal to 43,560 square feet.

The best results are obtained with water at atmospheric temperature. For this reason, if the water supply is from a deep well, it is usually brought to the surface with deep well pumps and discharged into artificial lakes or ponds. From the lakes or ponds the water is taken by the sprinkler pump.

On the average 18 hole golf course the greens and tees are always watered and in the majority of cases a pump with a capacity of 150 to 175 Gpm is ample. The fairways averaging 300 yards long and approximately 60 yards wide represent 52 acres of fairway. If we figure 27,150 gallons per acre per week, the 52 acres of fairway will require approximately 1,415,000 gallons of water per week. If it is estimated that the sprinkler pumping will be done in fifty hours per week (3000 minutes) the pumping rate will be 472 Gpm. This is about the usual practice, the sprinkling is done in a little over seven hours per night, seven nights a week. The average eighteen hole golf course requires a pump approximately 500 Gpm for fairway watering.

LAND DRAINAGE — PUMPED OUTLETS

Each installation must be analized before determining the pump capacity. For preliminary estimates the following factors may be found helpful.

Multiply the land area to be drained in acres by the factor below to obtain the pump capacity in gpm:

Tile systems, subsurface drainage only—7 gpm per acre.

Surface drainage by ditch or tile, field crops—10 gpm per acre.

Surface drainage by ditch or tile, truck crops—15 gpm per acre.

SECTION V—VISCOUS LIQUIDS

CONTENTS

V

SECTION V — PUMPING VISCOUS LIQUIDS

PROPERTIES OF LIQUIDS

In order to solve problems involving liquids other than water, it is essential that certain liquid properties, and their relations to each other, be understood and utilized correctly. These are specific gravity, sg; density, ρ (Greek letter Rho); absolute viscosity, μ (Greek letter mu); and kinematic viscosity, ν (Greek letter nu).

SPECIFIC GRAVITY (sg)

The specific gravity of a liquid is a relative term, which shows the fluid's density with reference to fresh water at 39.2 deg. F, the point at which its density is 1.0 gr. per cu. cm.

Gravity of liquids may be given in either specific gravity directly, degrees Baume, degrees API (for oils) or Degrees Brix (for sugar) and many others, all of which are definitely related. Some of these relations are given in Section III.

DENSITY ρ (Greek Letter rho)

The density of a liquid is the mass per unit volume and in the English system is expressed as w/g where w is always the weight in lbs./cu. ft. and g is the acceleration caused by gravity and is taken as 32.2 ft./sec./sec., or ft./sec^2. Density may also be computed for any liquid as follows.

Density, $(\rho) = sg \times 62.4/32.2$ slugs/cu. ft.

VISCOSITY

The viscosity of a liquid is a measure of the internal friction tending to resist flow. This resistance to flow, expressed as a coefficient of absolute viscosity, is the force required to overcome the unit shear stress at a unit rate of shearing strain.

Viscosity is expressed in two ways, namely Absolute or Dynamic viscosity, μ (Greek letter mu) and Kinematic viscosity ν (Greek letter nu).

(1) The unit of Absolute viscosity in the metric system is the dyne-second per square centimeter. This unit is called a poise. The unit of Absolute viscosity in the English system has no name but is measured in pound seconds per square foot which may also be expressed as slugs per foot-second. To convert from one system of measurement to another:

100 centipoises = 1 poise = .00209 lb. sec./ft.^{2}

(2) Kinematic viscosity in the metric system is measured in stokes, the unit of which is centimeters squared per second. In the English system the unit is feet squared per second. To convert:

100 centistokes = 1 stoke = .00108 ft.^{2}/sec.

The above two expressions of viscosity are related for any liquid because the Kinematic viscosity is the ratio of the Absolute viscosity to the density. Hence Kinematic viscosity equals μ/ρ (mu/rho).

When the English system is used it is recommended that the Kinematic viscosity (ft.²/sec.) always be determined by dividing the Absolute viscosity (lb. sec./sq.ft.) by the Density expressed as w/g (lbs. per ft.³ divided by 32.2 ft./sec.²).

Engineers often prefer the use of centistokes because arithmetical errors are reduced as the numerical values in centistokes are almost always whole numbers rather than decimals. When using $v = $ ft.²/sec. decimal point errors must be guarded against.

VISCOSITY, SSU

In many tables and diagrams the variables are shown in relation to Kinematic viscosity expressed as Seconds Saybolt Universal (SSU) directly. In others the Kinematic viscosity, v (nu), is expressed at ft.²/sec. The relation between the two is shown in Fig. 32. It may be computed approximately as follows:

$$v \text{ (ft.}^2/\text{sec.)} = 0.000002433 \text{ SSU} - 0.00210/\text{SSU}$$

SSU in this equation being 100 or less

$$v \text{ (ft.}^2/\text{sec.)} = 0.000002368 \text{ SSU} - 0.00145/\text{SSU}$$

SSU in this equation being greater than 100.

For conversion to ft.²/sec. from other viscosity determinations such as Saybolt Furol, Redwood, Engler, Barbey and centistokes see Table 36A.

TABLE 36.
KINEMATIC VISCOSITY OF COMMON LIQUIDS‡

Liquid	*Sg. at 60° F	VISCOSITY SSU	At ° F
ASPHALTS:			
Unblended or virgin asphalts	1.1 to 1.5	2,500 to 12,000	250
		600 to 3,600	300
Blended Asphalt RS-1, MS-1 or SS-1 emulsified primer or binder	Approx 1.0	155 to 1,000	77
		90 to 350	100
RC-O, MC-O or SC-O cutbacks or binders	Approx 1.0	737 to 1,500	77
		280 to 500	100
RC-1, MC-1 or SC-1 cutbacks or binders	Approx 1.0	2,400 to 5,000	100
		737 to 1,500	122
RC-2, MC-2 or SC-2 cutbacks or binders	Approx 1.0	2,400 to 5,000	122
		1,000 to 2,000	140
RC-3, MC-3 or SC-3 cutbacks or binders	Approx 1.0	6,000 to 13,000	122
		2,500 to 5,000	140
RC-4, MC-4 or SC-4 cutbacks or binders	Approx 1.0	8,000 to 20,000	140
		1,250 to 2,500	180
RC-5, MC-5 or SC-5 cutbacks or binders	Approx 1.0	28,000 to 85,000	140
		3,000 to 6,000	180
Asphalt Emulsion Type I Federal Specification	Approx 1.0	1,000 to 7,000	77
		350 to 1,700	100
Asphalt Emulsion Types II, V and VI Federal Specification	Approx 1.0	155 to 1,000	77
		90 to 350	100
CHEMICALS:			
Acetic Acid (100%)	1.05	31.2†	68
Acetone (100%)	.79	29.6†	68

*Unless otherwise noted.
†Data added from other sources.

‡*Courtesy Hydraulic Institute. See page 6.*

TABLE 36. (Cont.)
KINEMATIC VISCOSITY OF COMMON LIQUIDS

Liquid	*Sg. at 60° F	VISCOSITY SSU	At ° F
Alcohol-Ethyl (100%)	.79	32.3†	68
Benzol	.88 @ 68° F	30.3†	68
Black Liquor (typical)	1.30	5.000	122
		2.500	130
Carbon Tetrachloride	1.59 @ 68° F	30.1†	68
Caustic Soda Solutions:			
20% Na OH	1.22	39.4	65
30% Na OH	1.33	58.1	65
40% Na OH	1.43	110.1	65
Ethyl Acetate	.90 @ 68° F	29.7†	68
Formic Acid	1.22 @ 68° F	32.4†	68
Freon	1.37 to 1.49 @ 70° F	29.3†	70
Glycerine (100%)	1.26 @ 68° F	2,950	68.6
		813	100
Glycol:			
Propylene	1.04†	240.6	70
Triethylene	1.13†	185.7	70
Diethylene	1.12	149.7	70
Ethylene	1.13	88.4	70
Hydrochloric Acid (31.5%)	1.15†	33†	68
Mercury	13.6		70
Nitric Acid†	1.41	31.5	68
Phenol (Carbolic Acid)	.95 to 1.08	65	65
Silicate of Soda	1.38	365	100
	1.41	637.6	100
Sulfuric Acid (100%)	1.83	75.7	68
FISH AND ANIMAL OILS:			
Bone Oil	.92	220	130
		65	212
Cod Oil	.93	150	100
		95	130
Lard	.96	287	100
		160	130
Lard Oil	.91 to .93	190 to 220	100
		112 to 128	130
Menhadden Oil	.93	140	100
		90	130
Neatsfoot Oil	.92	230	100
		130	130
Sperm Oil	.88	110	100
		78	130
Whale Oil	.93	163 to 184	100
		97 to 112	130
MINERAL OILS			
Automobile Cranckcase Oils (Average Midcontinent Paraffin Base):			
SAE 10	**.88 to .94	165 to 240	100
		90 to 120	130
SAE 20	**.88 to .94	240 to 400	100
		120 to 185	130
SAE 30	**.88 to .94	400 to 580	100
		185 to 255	130
SAE 40	**.88 to .94	580 to 950	100
		255 to	130
		80	210
SAE 50	**.88 to .94	950 to 1,600	100
		80 to 105	210
SAE 60	**.88 to .94	1,600 to 2,300	100
		105 to 125	210
SAE 70	**.88 to .94	2,300 to 3,100	100
		125 to 150	210

*Unless otherwise noted.
**Depends on origin or percent and type of solvent.
†Data added from other sources.

TABLE 36. (Cont.)
KINEMATIC VISCOSITY OF COMMON LIQUIDS

Liquid	*Sg. at 60° F	VISCOSITY SSU	At ° F
SAE 10W	**.88 to .94	5,000 to 10,000	0
SAE 20W	**.88 to .94	10,000 to 40,000	0
Automobile Transmission Lubricants:			
SAE 80	**.88 to .94	100,000 max	0
SAE 90	**.88 to .94	800 to 1,500	100
		300 to 500	130
SAE 140	**.88 to .94	950 to 2,300	130
		120 to 200	210
SAE 250	**.88 to .94	Over 2,300	130
		Over 200	210
Crude Oils:			
Texas, Oklahoma	.81 to .92	40 to 783	60
		34.2 to 210	100
Wyoming, Montana	.86 to .88	74 to 1,215	60
		46 to 320	100
California	.78 to .92	40 to 4,840	60
		34 to 700	100
Pennsylvania	.8 to .85	46 to 216	60
		38 to 86	100
Diesel Engine Lubricating Oils (Based on Average Midcontinent Paraffin Base):			
Federal Specification No. 9110	**.88 to .94	165 to 240	100
		90 to 120	130
Federal Specification No. 9170	**.88 to .94	300 to 410	100
		140 to 180	130
Federal Specification No. 9250	**.88 to .94	470 to 590	100
		200 to 255	130
Federal Specification No. 9370	**.88 to .94	800 to 1,100	100
		320 to 430	130
Federal Specification No. 9500	**.88 to .94	490 to 600	130
		92 to 105	210
Diesel Fuel Oils:			
No. 2 D	**.82 to .95	32.6 to 45.5	100
		39	130
No. 3 D	**.82 to .95	45.5 to 65	100
		39 to 48	130
No. 4 D	**.82 to .95	140 max	100
		70 max	130
No. 5 D	**.82 to .95	400 max	122
		165 max	160
Fuel Oils:			
No. 1	**.82 to .95	34 to 40	70
		32 to 35	100
No. 2	**.82 to .95	36 to 50	70
		33 to 40	100
No. 3	**.82 to .95	35 to 45	100
		32.8 to 39	130
No. 5A	**.82 to .95	50 to 125	100
		42 to 72	130
No. 5B	**.82 to .95	125 to	100
		400	122
		72 to 310	130
No. 6	**.82 to .95	450 to 3,000	122
		175 to 780	160
Fuel Oil—Navy Specification	**.99 max	110 to 225	122
		63 to 115	160
Fuel Oil—Navy II	1.0 max	1,500 max	122
		480 max	160
Gasoline	.68 to .74	30†	60
		29.9†	100
Gasoline (Natural)	.68	29.6†	68

*Unless otherwise noted.
**Depends on origin or percent and type of solvent.
†Data added from other sources.

TABLE 36. (Cont.)
KINEMATIC VISCOSITY OF COMMON LIQUIDS

Liquid	*Sg. at 60° F	VISCOSITY SSU	At ° F
Gas Oil	.89	73	70
		50	100
Insulating Oil:			
Transformer, switches and circuit breakers		115 max	70
		65 max	100
Kerosene	.78 to .82	35	68
		32.6	100
Machine Lubricating Oil (Average Pennsylvania Paraffin Base):			
Federal Specification No. 8	**.88 to .94	112 to 160	100
		70 to 90	130
Federal Specification No. 10	**.88 to .94	160 to 235	100
		90 to 120	130
Federal Specification No. 20	**.88 to .94	235 to 385	100
		120 to 185	130
Federal Specification No. 30	**.88 to .94	385 to 550	100
		185 to 255	130
Mineral Lard Cutting Oil:			
Federal Specification Grade 1		140 to 190	100
		86 to 110	130
Federal Specification Grade 2		190 to 220	100
		110 to 125	130
Petrolatum	.83	100	130
		77	160
Turbine Lubricating Oil:			
Federal Specification	.91 Average	400 to 440	100
(Penn Base)		185 to 205	130
VEGETABLE OILS:			
Castor Oil	.96 @ 68° F	1,200 to 1,500	100
		450 to 600	130
China Wood Oil	.94	1,425	69
		580	100
Cocoanut Oil	.93†	140 to 148	100
		76 to 80	130
Corn Oil	.92	135	130
		54	212
Cotton Seed Oil	.90†	176	100
		100	130
Creosote†	1.04 to 1.10	70	68
Linseed Oil, Raw	.94†	143	100
		93	130
Olive Oil	.92†	200	100
		115	130
Palm Oil	.92	221	100
		125	130
Peanut Oil	.92	195	100
		112	130
Rape Seed Oil	.92	250	100
		145	130
Rosin Oil	.98	1,500	100
		600	130
Rosin (Wood)	1.09 (Avg.)	500 to 20,000	200
		1,000 to 50,000	190
Sesame Oil	.92	184	100
		110	130
Soja Bean Oil (Soya)	.93 to .98	165	100
		96	130
Turpentine	.87	33	60
		32.6	100
SUGAR, SYRUPS, MOLASSES, ETC.			
Corn Syrups	1.5	5,000 to 500,000	100
		1,500 to 60,000	130
Glucose	1.4	35,000 to 100,000	100
		4, to 11,000	150
Honey (Raw)		340	100

*Unless otherwise noted.
**Depends on origin or percent and type of solvent.
†Data added from other sources.

TABLE 36. (Cont.)
KINEMATIC VISCOSITY OF COMMON LIQUIDS

Liquid	•Sg. at 60° F	VISCOSITY SSU	At ° F
Molasses "A" (First)	1.5	1,300 to 23,000 700 to 8,000	100 130
Molasses "B" (Second)	1.5	6,400 to 60,000 3,000 to 15,000	100 130
Molasses "C" (Blackstrap or final)	1.5	17,000 to 250,000 6,000 to 75,000	100 130
Sucrose Solutions (Sugar Syrups):			
60 Brix	1.29	230 92	70 100
62 Brix	1.30	310 111	70 100
64 Brix	1.31	440 148	70 100
66 Brix	1.33	650 195	70 100
68 Brix	1.34	1,000 275	.70 100
70 Brix	1.35	1,650 400	70 100
72 Brix	1.36	2,700 640	70 100
74 Brix	1.38	5,500 1,100	70 100
76 Brix	1.39	10,000 2,000	70 100
TARS:			
Tar-Coke Oven	1.12+	3,000 to 8,000 650 to 1,400	71 100
Tar-Gas House	1.16 to 1.30	15,000 to 300,000 2,000 to 20,000	70 100
Road Tar:			
Grade RT-2	1.07+	200 to 300 55 to 60	122 212
Grade RT-4	1.08+	400 to 700 65 to 75	122 212
Grade RT-6	1.09+	1,000 to 2,000 85 to 125	122 212
Grade RT-8	1.13+	3,000 to 8,000 150 to 225	122 212
Grade RT-10	1.14+	20,000 to 60,000 250 to 400	122 212
Grade RT-12	1.15+	114,000 to 456,000 500 to 800	122 212
Pine Tar	1.06	2,500 500	100 132
MISCELLANEOUS			
Corn Starch Solutions:			
22 °B	1.18	150 130	70 100
24	1.20	600 440	70 100
25	1.21	1,400 800	70 100
Ink—Printers	1.00 to 1.38	2,500 to 10,000 1,100 to 3,000	100 130
Tallow	.92 (Avg.)	56	212
Milk	1.02 to 1.05	.31.2†	68
Varnish—Spar	.9	1,425 650	68 100

•Unless otherwise noted.

†Data added from other sources.

KINEMATIC VISCOSITY CENTISTOKES

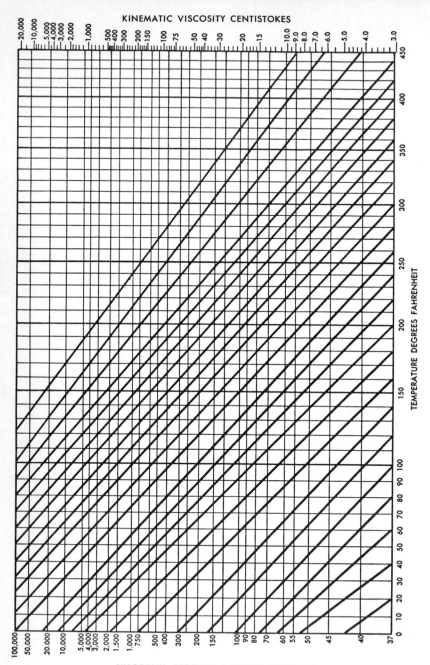

VISCOSITY, SECONDS SAYBOLT UNIVERSAL

FIG. 29. Viscosity—temperature chart.†

†*Courtesy Byron Jackson Co. See page 6.*

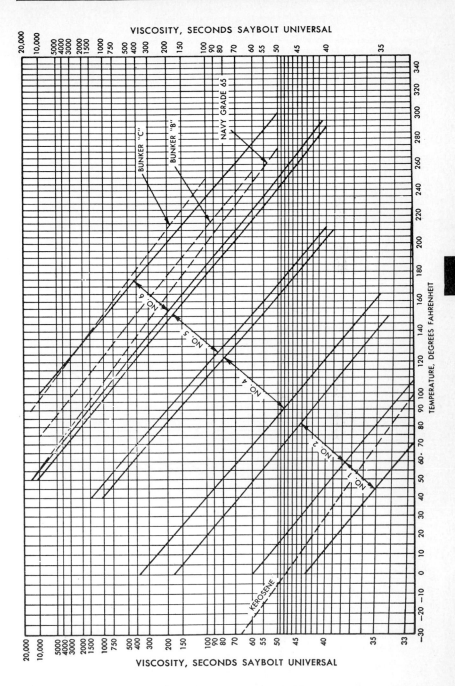

FIG. 30. Fuel oil viscosity limits. 1951 Navy grades.

USE OF VISCOSITY BLENDING CHART

Many liquids designated by such names as asphalt, molasses, oil, varnish, etc., are actually blends or cut-backs and have lower viscosities than the unblended liquids of the same name. On Figure 31, let oil, A, have the higher viscosity and oil, B, the lower viscosity. Mark the viscosity of A and B on the right and left hand scales, respectively, and draw a straight line connecting the two as shown. The viscosity of any blend of A and B will be shown by the intersection of the vertical line representing the percentage composition and the line described below.

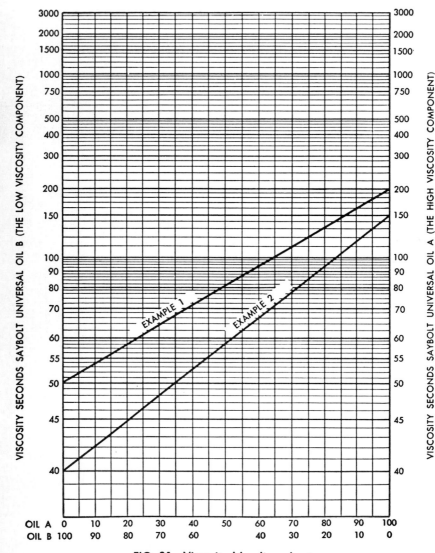

FIG. 31. Viscosity blending chart.

TABLE 36A.   VISCOSITY CONVERSION TABLE†

Seconds Saybolt Universal ssu	Kinematic Viscosity Centistokes *	Seconds Saybolt Furol ssf	Seconds Redwood 1 (Standard)	Seconds Redwood 2 (Admiralty)	Degrees Engler	Degrees Barbey	Seconds Parlin Cup #7	Seconds Parlin Cup #10	Seconds Parlin Cup #15	Seconds Parlin Cup #20	Seconds Ford Cup #3	Seconds Ford Cup #4	Approx. Seconds Mac Michael	Approx. Gardner Holt Bubble	Seconds Zahn Cup #1	Seconds Zahn Cup #2	Seconds Zahn Cup #3	Seconds Zahn Cup #4	Seconds Zahn Cup #5	Seconds Demmler #1	Seconds Demmler #10	Approx. Seconds Stormer 100 gm Load	Seconds Pratt and Lambert "F"
31	1.00	—	29	—	1.00	6200	—	—	—	—	—	—	—	—	—	—	—	—	—	—	—	—	—
35	2.56	—	32.1	—	1.16	2420	—	—	—	—	—	—	—	—	—	—	—	—	—	—	—	—	—
40	4.30	—	36.2	5.10	1.31	1440	—	—	—	—	—	—	—	—	—	—	—	—	—	—	—	—	—
50	7.40	—	44.3	5.83	1.58	838	—	—	—	—	—	—	—	—	—	—	—	—	—	—	—	2.6	—
60	10.3	—	52.3	6.77	1.88	618	—	—	—	—	—	—	—	—	—	—	—	—	—	—	—	3.6	—
70	13.1	12.95	60.9	7.60	2.17	483	—	—	—	—	—	—	—	—	—	—	—	—	—	—	—	4.6	—
80	15.7	13.70	69.2	8.44	2.45	404	—	—	—	—	—	—	—	—	—	—	—	—	—	—	—	5.5	—
90	18.2	14.44	77.6	9.30	2.73	348	—	—	—	—	—	—	—	—	—	—	—	—	—	—	—	6.4	—
100	20.6	15.24	85.6	10.12	3.02	307	—	15	—	—	—	—	125	—	38	18	—	—	—	6.5	—	7.3	—
150	32.1	19.30	128	14.48	4.48	195	40	21	—	—	—	—	145	A	47	20	—	—	—	10.0	1.0	11.3	—
200	43.2	23.5	170	18.90	5.92	144	46	25	—	—	—	—	165	A	54	23	—	—	—	13.5	1.4	15.2	—
250	54.0	28.0	212	23.45	7.35	114	—	30	—	—	—	—	198	—	62	26	—	—	—	16.9	1.7	19	—
300	65.0	32.5	254	28.0	8.79	95	52.5	35	6.0	3.0	30	20	225	B	73	29	—	—	—	20.4	2.0	23	—
400	87.60	41.9	338	37.1	11.70	70.8	66	39	7.2	3.2	42	28	270	C	90	37	—	—	—	27.4	2.7	31	7
500	110.0	51.6	423	46.2	14.60	56.4	79	41	7.8	3.4	50	34	320	D	—	46	—	—	—	34.5	3.5	39	8
600	132	61.4	508	54.4	17.50	47.0	92	43	8.5	3.6	58	40	370	F	—	55	—	—	—	41	4.1	46	9
700	154	71.1	592	64.6	20.45	40.3	106	65	9.0	3.9	67	45	420	G	—	63	22.5	—	—	48	4.8	54	9.5
800	176	81.0	677	73.8	23.35	35.2	120	86	9.8	4.1	74	50	470	H	—	72	24.5	18	—	55	5.5	62	10.8
900	198	91.0	762	83.0	26.30	31.3	135	108	10.7	4.3	82	57	515	H	—	80	27	20	—	62	6.2	70	11.9
1000	220	100.7	896	92.1	29.20	28.2	149	129	11.5	4.5	87	62	570	—	—	88	29	—	13	69	6.9	77	12.4
1500	330	150	1270	138.2	43.80	18.7	—	172	15.2	6.3	132	90	805	M	—	—	40	28	18	103	10.3	116	16.8
2000	440	200	1690	184.2	58.40	14.1	—	215	19.5	7.5	172	118	1070	Q	—	—	51	34	24	137	13.7	154	22
2500	550	250	2120	230	73.0	11.3	—	258	24	9	218	147	1325	T	—	—	63	41	29	172	17.2	193	27.6
3000	660	300	2540	276	87.60	9.4	—	300	28.5	11	258	172	1690	U	—	—	75	48	33	206	20.6	232	33.7
4000	880	400	3380	368	117.0	7.05	—	344	34	14	337	230	2110	V	—	—	—	63	43	275	27.5	308	45
5000	1100	500	4230	461	146	5.64	—	387	47	18	425	290	2635	W	—	—	—	77	50	344	34.4	385	55.8
6000	1320	600	5080	553	175	4.70	—	430	57	22	520	350	3145	X	—	—	—	—	65	413	41.3	462	65.5
7000	1540	700	5920	645	204.5	4.03	—	—	67	25	600	410	3670	—	—	—	—	—	75	481	48	540	77
8000	1760	800	6770	737	233.5	3.52	—	—	76	29	680	465	4170	Y	—	—	—	—	86	550	55	618	89
9000	1980	900	7620	829	263	3.13	—	—	86	32	765	520	4700	—	—	—	—	—	96	650	69	695	102
10000	2200	1000	8460	921	292	2.82	—	—	96	35	850	575	5220	Z	—	—	—	—	—	690	—	770	113
15000	3300	1500	12700	—	438	2.50	—	650	147	53	1280	860	7720	Z2	—	—	—	—	—	1030	—	1160	172
20000	4400	2000	18400	—	584	1.40	—	860	203	70	1715	1150	10500	Z3	—	—	—	—	—	1370	—	1540	234

* Kinematic Viscosity (in centistokes) = Absolute viscosity (in centipoises) / Density

Above 250 SSU use the following approximate conversion:

SSU = Centistokes × 4.62

Above the range of this table and within the range of the viscosimeter, multiply their rating by the following factors to convert to SSU:

Viscosimeter	Factor
Saybolt Fural	10.
Redwood Standard	1.095
Redwood Admiralty	10.87
Engler - Degrees	34.5

Viscosimeter	Factor
Parlin cup #15	98.2
Parlin cup #20	187.0
Ford cup #4	17.4

Viscosimeter	Factor
Mac Michael	1.92 (approx.)
Demmler #1	14.6
Demmler #10	13. (approx.)
Stormer	17.4

†Courtesy Hydraulic Institute See page 6.

V

PIPE LINE LOSSES

The loss of head in a pipe line may be computed by the Darcy-Weisbach formula for either viscous liquids or water, or may be read from tables which take into account the viscosity of the liquid being pumped.

To compute the loss by the formula various factors must first be selected or computed. They are: Relative Roughness, ϵ/D (Greek letter epsilon in inches divided by diameter in inches); Reynolds Number R; and friction factor, f.

RELATIVE ROUGHNESS ϵ/D.

Relative roughness is a ratio of the heights of protrusions inside the pipe to the average inside diameter of the pipe, both Epsilon (ϵ) and D are expressed in inches in the English system. From direct measurement and friction loss tests, it has been found a relation exists between relative roughness and the diameter of a pipe for a given material and method of fabrication. This is shown in Fig. 26.

REYNOLDS NUMBER, R.

Reynolds Number, R, is a dimensionless number or ratio of velocity in ft. per sec. times the internal diameter of the pipe in feet times the density in slugs per cu.ft. divided by the absolute viscosity in lb.sec. per sq.ft.

$$R = \frac{VD\rho}{\mu}$$

This is equivalent to $R = VD/v$ (VD divided by the kinematic viscosity). Reynolds Number is of great significance because it determines the type of flow, either laminar or turbulent, which will occur in any pipe line, the only exception being a critical zone roughly between an R of 2000 to 3500. Within this zone it is recommended that problems be solved by assuming that turbulent flow is likely to occur. Computation using this assumption gives the greatest value of friction loss and hence the result is on the safe side.

It is believed use of the charts shown herein will appeal to those solving problems involving viscous liquids. When discharge in gallons per minute are known or assumed, tables 1 and 2 give the velocity quickly. Hence by simple arithmetic and use of Fig. 32 the Reynolds Number is quickly obtained with adequate accuracy. For those who prefer the greater precision of an algebraic equation, Reynolds Number for a pipe line may also be computed from the following formula:

$$R = \frac{Q}{29.4 \; d \; v}$$

where Q is in Gpm, d is inside diameter of pipe in inches, and v (nu) is kinematic viscosity in ft.^{2}/sec.

HEAD LOSS IN PUMPING LIQUIDS

Fundamentals necessary to an understanding of movement of a liquid have been reviewed. It now remains for us to apply these fundamentals to field problems.

When Relative Roughness and Reynolds Number are selected and computed respectively, the friction factor f in the Darcy-Weisbach formula

$$h_f = f \frac{L}{D} \frac{V^2}{2g}$$

may be found in Fig. 33 for both the laminar and tubulent flow ranges remembering that relative roughness is significant only in the turbulent flow range. This selected value of f, when used in the above equation, together with the length (L) and diameter (D) in feet, and the velocity (V) in feet per second, the friction loss h_f is obtained and is expressed in feet of liquid flowing.

Explanation of Tables

Table 38 gives the loss in head expressed in feet of liquid flowing per 100 feet of new clean Schedule 40 steel pipe.

EXAMPLE: Find the friction loss of 50 Gpm of oil in 200 feet of 2 inch schedule 40 pipe. The oil has a viscosity of 440 centistokes and a specific gravity of 0.90. From Fig. 32 the viscosity in SSU is 2000. From Table 38 the loss in 100 feet of pipe is 78.5 feet of oil.

Use of Viscous Fluids Friction Tables

For LAMINAR FLOW, the pressure loss is directly proportional to the kinematic viscosity and the velocity of flow. Therefore, for intermediate values of kinematic viscosity and rate of flow (Gpm), the head loss can be obtained by direct interpolation of Table 38. For pipe sizes not shown, the pressure loss will vary inversely as the fourth power of the inside diameters for the same discharge rate. The values of head loss which will be found in the shaded area of Table 38 fall within the turbulent flow region rather than in the laminar or viscous flow region. For determination of rate of flow and pipe size in this region of turbulent flow, the method described above under heading "Head loss in pumping liquids" should be used.

FRICTION LOSS IN FITTINGS WITH VISCOUS FLOW†

When the piping system includes valves and fittings the following must be considered:

a) For TURBULENT flow the values of the equivalent lengths of straight pipe for valves and fittings as given in Table 4 should be used.

†*Courtesy Hydraulic Institute. See page 6.*

b) For LAMINAR flow the losses in valves and fittings can only be approximated. For fluids of relatively low viscosity, where the flow is adjacent to the turbulent region, the values of the equivalent straight pipe for valves and fittings, given in Table 4, can be used.

For viscosities above 500,000 SSU, the effect of the valve or fitting is small and it is probably necessary only to include its actual length as part of the pipe length. For the intermediate viscosities the approximate equivalent length can be estimated by interpolation using the following table as a guide:

TABLE 37.   FRICTION LOSS IN FITTINGS— LAMINAR FLOW.

	3-30 GPM	30-50 GPM	50-100 GPM	100-250 GPM	250-1000 GPM
Use full value from Table 4 when viscosity is:	100 SSU	200 SSU	300 SSU	400 SSU	500 SSU
Use ¾ value from Table 4 when viscosity is:	1000 SSU	2000 SSU	3000 SSU	4000 SSU	5000 SSU
Use ½ value from Table 4 when viscosity is:	10,000 SSU	20,000 SSU	30,000 SSU	40,000 SSU	50,000 SSU
Use ¼ value from Table 4 when viscosity is:	100,000 SSU	200,000 SSU	300,000 SSU	400,000 SSU	500,000 SSU
Use actual length of valve and fittings when the viscosity exceeds:	500,000 SSU	500,000 SSU	—	—	—

It must be noted that the above is only an approximation. Very little reliable test data on losses in valves and fittings for LAMINAR flow are available.

VALUES OF (VD") (V in $\frac{FT.}{SEC.}$ x D" in INCHES)

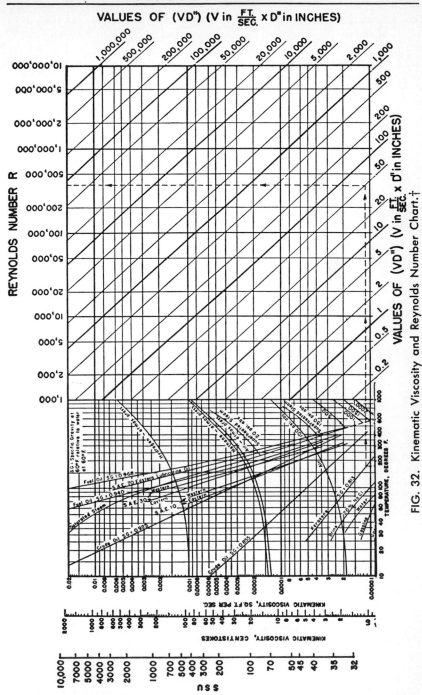

FIG. 32. Kinematic Viscosity and Reynolds Number Chart.†

†*Courtesy Hydraulic Institute. See page 6.*

TABLE 38. FRICTION LOSS IN HEAD FOR VISCOUS LIQUIDS†

Loss In Feet of Liquid Flowing in 100 Feet of New Schedule 40 Steel Pipe

Gpm	Pipe Size	KINEMATIC VISCOSITY - SECONDS SAYBOLT UNIVERSAL 100	200	300	400	500	1000	2000	3000	4000	5000	6000	8000	10,000	15,000
3	½	25.9	54.5	81.5	108.1	136.3	272.6	545.2	815.4	1088.0	1360.6	1630.9	2176.0	—	—
	¾	8.5	17.6	26.6	35.3	44.1	88.2	175.6	265.7	353.4	441.2	529.0	706.9	882.4	1323.6
	1	3.2	6.7	10.2	13.4	16.9	33.5	67.2	100.7	134.0	168.6	201.0	268.0	335.0	503.6
5	¾	14.1	29.3	44.1	58.9	73.7	147.8	293.4	441.2	589.1	736.9	882.4	1178.1	1471.5	2208.4
	1	5.3	11.3	16.9	22.4	28.0	55.9	112.0	168.6	224.1	279.5	335.0	448.1	559.0	838.5
	1¼	1.8	3.7	5.5	7.6	9.5	18.7	37.4	56.1	75.1	93.8	112.5	150.2	187.1	281.8
7	¾	19.6	41.3	61.9	82.5	103.0	205.6	411.2	619.1	824.7	1030.6	1235.9	1647.0	2060.5	—
	1	7.4	15.7	23.6	31.4	39.3	78.3	157.1	235.6	314.2	392.7	469.0	626.0	783.1	1175.8
	1¼	2.5	5.3	7.8	10.4	13.2	26.3	52.4	78.8	104.9	131.7	157.1	210.2	263.3	392.7
10	1	11.3	22.4	33.5	44.8	55.9	112.0	224.1	335.0	448.1	559.0	672.2	896.3	1120.4	1679.4
	1¼	3.7	7.6	11.3	15.0	18.7	37.4	75.1	112.5	150.2	187.1	224.1	300.3	374.2	561.3
	1½	1.9	4.2	6.0	8.1	10.2	20.3	40.4	60.8	80.9	101.2	122.4	161.7	203.3	302.6
15	1	25.4	33.5	50.4	67.2	83.9	168.6	335.0	503.6	672.2	838.5	1007.2	1342.1	1679.4	—
	1¼	6.5	11.3	16.9	22.4	28.2	56.1	112.5	168.6	224.1	281.8	337.3	450.5	561.3	843.2
	1½	3.0	6.0	9.0	12.2	15.2	30.3	60.8	91.0	122.4	152.5	182.5	242.6	302.6	455.1
20	1	41.6	41.6	67.2	89.6	112.0	224.1	448.1	672.2	896.3	1120.4	1342.1	1790.3	—	—
	1½	5.3	8.1	12.2	16.2	20.3	40.4	80.9	122.4	161.7	203.3	242.6	323.4	404.3	607.5
	2	1.5	3.0	4.4	6.0	7.4	14.8	29.8	44.6	59.4	74.2	88.9	117.8	147.8	221.8
25	1½	8.1	10.2	15.2	20.8	25.4	50.6	101.2	152.5	203.3	254.1	302.6	406.6	505.9	757.7
	2	2.3	3.7	5.5	7.4	9.2	18.5	37.2	55.7	74.2	92.9	111.3	147.8	184.8	279.5
	2½	0.92	1.8	2.8	3.7	4.6	9.2	18.2	27.3	36.5	45.5	54.7	73.0	91.2	136.3
30	1½	11.6	12.2	18.2	24.3	30.3	60.8	122.4	182.5	242.6	302.6	365.0	485.1	607.5	910.1
	2	3.2	4.4	6.7	9.0	11.1	22.2	44.6	66.8	89.0	111.3	134.0	177.9	221.8	335.0
	2½	1.4	2.2	3.2	4.4	5.5	10.9	22.0	32.8	43.9	54.7	65.6	87.5	109.5	164.0
40	1½	19.6	20.8	24.3	32.3	40.4	80.8	161.7	242.6	323.4	404.2	485.1	646.8	808.5	1215.1
	2	5.8	5.8	9.0	11.8	14.8	29.8	59.4	88.9	117.8	147.8	177.9	238.0	298.0	445.8
	2½	2.5	3.0	4.4	5.8	7.4	14.6	29.1	43.9	58.4	73.0	87.5	117.8	145.5	219.4
50	1½	28.9	32.3	32.3	40.4	50.6	101.2	203.3	302.6	404.3	505.9	607.5	808.5	1011.8	1517.7
	2	8.5	9.2	11.1	14.8	18.5	37.2	74.2	111.3	147.8	184.8	221.8	298.0	372.0	556.7
	2½	3.7	3.9	5.5	7.4	9.2	18.2	36.5	54.7	73.0	91.2	109.5	145.5	182.5	272.6
60	2	11.6	13.4	13.4	17.8	22.2	44.6	89.0	134.0	177.9	221.8	268.0	355.7	445.8	667.6
	2½	5.1	5.5	6.5	8.8	10.9	22.0	43.9	65.6	87.5	109.5	131.7	175.6	219.5	328.0
	3	1.8	1.8	2.8	3.7	4.6	9.2	18.5	27.5	36.7	46.0	55.2	73.5	92.0	138.6
70	2½	6.5	7.4	7.9	10.2	12.7	25.7	51.1	76.7	102.1	127.1	152.5	203.3	256.4	383.5
	3	2.3	2.5	3.2	4.4	5.3	10.7	21.5	32.1	43.0	53.6	64.2	85.7	107.2	161.7
	4	0.62	0.72	1.1	1.5	1.8	3.7	7.2	10.9	14.5	18.0	21.7	28.9	36.0	54.3
80	2½	8.3	9.7	9.7	11.8	14.6	29.1	58.4	87.5	117.8	145.5	175.6	233.3	291.1	439.0
	3	3.0	3.2	3.7	4.8	6.2	12.2	24.5	36.7	49.0	61.2	73.5	97.9	122.4	184.8
	4	0.83	0.83	1.2	1.7	2.1	4.2	8.3	12.5	16.6	20.6	24.7	33.0	41.3	61.9
100	2½	12.2	14.1	14.8	14.8	18.5	36.5	73.0	109.5	145.5	182.5	219.5	293.4	365.0	547.5
	3	4.4	5.1	5.1	6.2	7.6	15.2	30.7	46.0	61.2	76.5	91.9	122.4	152.5	228.7
	4	1.2	1.3	1.5	2.1	2.5	5.1	10.4	15.5	20.6	25.9	31.0	41.3	51.5	77.4

TURBULENT FLOW RANGE (shaded) — LAMINAR OR VISCOUS FLOW RANGE (unshaded)

†*Abridged and recalculated from Hydraulic Institute Tables.* *See page 6.*

TABLE 38. (Cont.) FRICTION LOSS IN HEAD FOR VISCOUS LIQUIDS
Loss In Feet of Liquid Flowing in 100 Feet of New Schedule 40 Steel Pipe

Gpm	Pipe Size	100	200	300	400	500	1000	1500	2000	4000	5000	6000	8000	10,000	15,000
							KINEMATIC VISCOSITY - SECONDS SAYBOLT UNIVERSAL								
120	3	6.2	7.2	7.4	7.4	9.2	18.5	27.5	36.7	73.5	91.9	110.2	147.8	184.8	274.9
	4	1.7	1.9	1.9	2.5	3.0	6.2	9.2	12.5	24.7	31.0	37.2	49.4	61.9	92.9
	6	0.23	0.25	0.37	0.49	0.60	1.2	1.8	2.3	4.8	6.0	7.2	9.7	12.0	18.0
140	3	7.9	9.2	9.9	9.9	10.6	21.5	32.9	43.0	85.7	107.2	129.4	170.9	214.8	321.1
	4	2.2	2.5	2.5	3.0	3.7	7.2	10.9	14.6	28.9	36.0	43.4	57.8	72.3	108.3
	6	0.30	0.35	0.42	0.55	0.69	1.4	2.1	2.8	5.5	6.9	8.3	11.3	14.1	21.0
160	3	10.2	11.6	13.2	13.2	13.2	24.5	36.7	49.0	97.9	122.4	147.8	196.4	244.9	367.3
	4	2.8	3.2	3.2	3.2	4.2	8.3	12.5	16.6	33.0	41.3	49.7	66.1	82.5	124.7
	6	0.39	0.42	0.48	0.65	0.81	1.6	2.3	3.2	6.5	8.1	9.7	12.7	15.9	24.0
180	3	12.2	14.6	16.2	16.2	16.2	27.5	41.3	55.2	110.2	138.6	166.3	219.5	274.9	413.5
	4	3.5	4.2	4.2	4.2	4.6	9.2	13.9	18.5	37.2	46.4	55.7	74.4	92.9	138.6
	6	0.46	0.55	0.55	0.72	0.90	1.8	2.8	3.7	7.2	9.0	10.8	14.3	18.0	27.0
200	3	15.0	17.8	20.3	20.3	20.3	30.7	46.0	61.2	122.4	152.5	184.8	244.9	307.2	459.7
	4	4.2	5.1	5.1	5.1	5.1	10.4	15.5	20.6	41.3	51.5	61.9	82.5	103.3	154.8
	6	0.58	0.69	0.69	0.81	0.99	2.0	3.0	3.9	8.1	9.9	12.0	15.9	20.1	30.0
250	4	6.0	7.4	8.1	8.1	8.1	12.9	19.4	25.9	51.5	64.4	77.4	103.3	129.4	194.0
	6	0.83	0.99	1.0	1.0	1.2	2.5	3.7	5.1	9.9	12.5	15.0	20.1	24.9	37.7
	8	0.21	0.28	0.28	0.35	0.42	0.83	1.2	1.7	3.5	4.2	5.1	6.7	8.3	12.5
300	4	8.5	9.9	11.6	11.6	11.6	15.5	23.3	31.0	61.9	77.4	92.9	124.7	154.8	233.3
	6	1.2	1.4	1.5	1.5	1.5	3.0	4.6	6.0	12.0	15.0	18.0	24.0	30.0	45.0
	8	0.30	0.39	0.39	0.42	0.51	0.99	1.5	2.0	3.9	5.1	6.0	8.1	9.9	15.0
400	6	1.9	2.3	2.5	2.8	2.8	3.9	6.0	8.1	15.9	20.1	24.0	32.1	40.0	60.1
	8	0.53	0.62	0.67	0.67	0.67	1.3	2.0	2.8	5.3	6.7	8.1	10.6	13.4	20.1
	10	0.18	0.21	0.23	0.23	0.28	0.53	0.81	1.1	2.1	2.8	3.2	4.4	5.3	8.1
500	6	2.8	3.5	3.7	4.2	4.2	5.1	7.4	9.9	20.1	24.9	30.0	40.0	50.1	75.1
	8	0.76	0.96	1.0	1.1	1.1	1.7	2.5	3.5	6.7	8.3	9.9	13.4	16.6	24.9
	10	0.25	0.32	0.35	0.35	0.35	0.67	1.0	1.3	2.8	3.5	4.2	5.3	6.7	10.2
600	6	4.2	5.1	5.3	5.5	6.0	6.2	9.0	12.0	24.0	30.0	37.0	48.0	60.0	90.1
	8	1.1	1.3	1.4	1.5	1.5	2.0	3.0	3.9	8.1	9.9	12.0	16.0	20.1	30.0
	10	0.37	0.42	0.46	0.51	0.51	0.81	1.2	1.6	3.2	4.2	4.9	6.5	8.1	12.0
700	6	5.3	6.2	6.9	7.4	8.1	8.3	10.6	14.1	28.0	35.1	42.5	56.1	70.0	105.1
	8	1.4	1.7	1.9	2.1	2.1	2.3	3.5	4.6	9.5	11.8	14.1	18.7	23.3	35.1
	10	0.46	0.58	0.62	0.69	0.69	0.95	1.4	1.9	3.7	4.6	5.5	7.6	9.5	14.1
800	6	6.5	8.1	8.5	9.2	9.7	11.1	12.0	16.0	32.1	40.0	48.0	64.0	80.2	120.1
	8	1.8	2.2	2.3	2.5	2.8	2.8	3.9	5.3	10.6	13.4	15.9	21.5	26.8	40.0
	10	0.60	0.69	0.78	0.88	0.92	1.1	1.6	2.1	4.4	5.3	6.5	8.5	10.9	16.2
900	6	8.1	9.9	10.6	11.6	12.0	13.9	13.9	18.0	36.0	45.0	54.1	72.1	90.1	135.1
	8	2.2	2.5	3.0	3.2	3.5	3.5	4.6	6.0	12.0	15.0	18.0	24.0	30.0	45.0
	10	0.74	0.85	0.99	1.1	1.2	1.2	1.8	2.5	4.8	6.0	7.2	9.7	12.0	18.2
1000	8	2.5	3.2	3.5	3.7	4.2	4.4	5.1	6.7	13.4	16.6	20.1	26.8	33.5	50.1
	10	0.89	1.0	1.2	1.3	1.4	1.4	2.0	2.8	5.3	6.7	8.1	10.9	13.4	20.1
	12	0.39	0.46	0.51	0.55	0.58	0.67	0.99	1.3	2.8	3.5	3.9	5.3	6.7	9.9

TURBULENT FLOW RANGE ▨   LAMINAR OR VISCOUS FLOW RANGE ☐

V

TABLE 38. (Cont.) FRICTION LOSS IN HEAD FOR VISCOUS LIQUIDS
Loss In Feet of Liquid Flowing in 100 Feet of New Schedule 40 Steel Pipe

Gpm	Pipe Size	20,000	30,000	40,000	50,000	60,000	80,000	100,000	150,000	200,000	500,000
					KINEMATIC VISCOSITY - SECONDS SAYBOLT UNIVERSAL						
3	2	46.2	69.3	92.4	116.0	139.0	185.0	231.0	347.0	462.0	1160.0
	2½	22.4	33.8	44.8	56.2	67.2	89.7	112.0	168.0	224.0	561.0
	3	9.25	13.9	18.5	23.1	27.7	37.0	46.1	69.3	92.5	231.0
5	2	76.5	116.0	153.0	192.0	230.0	307.0	384.0	575.0	768.0	1910.0
	2½	37.5	56.2	75.0	93.5	112.0	149.0	188.0	282.0	374.0	938.0
	3	15.7	23.6	31.4	39.3	47.2	63.0	78.5	118.0	157.0	393.0
7	2	106.0	162.0	212.0	266.0	319.0	425.0	532.0	798.0	1060.0	
	2½	47.0	70.5	93.8	117.0	141.0	188.0	236.0	352.0	470.0	1170.0
	3	21.9	33.0	44.0	55.1	65.8	87.8	110.0	164.0	219.0	549.0
10	2½	74.0	110.0	148.0	185.0	222.0	296.0	370.0	555.0	740.0	1850.0
	3	31.4	47.2	63.0	78.5	94.2	126.0	157.0	252.0	314.0	785.0
	4	10.4	16.2	21.2	26.6	31.8	42.5	53.1	79.8	106.0	266.0
15	2½	111.0	166.0	222.0	277.0	333.0	444.0	555.0	830.0	1110.0	
	3	46.2	69.3	92.4	116.0	139.0	185.0	231.0	347.0	462.0	1160.0
	4	15.5	24.2	31.6	39.2	47.1	63.0	78.5	118.0	157.0	393.0
20	3	62.3	93.5	125.0	156.0	187.0	249.0	312.0	467.0	623.0	1560.0
	4	20.8	32.3	42.3	53.1	63.8	85.0	106.0	159.0	213.0	531.0
	6	4.16	6.23	8.32	10.6	12.7	16.9	21.0	31.7	42.0	105.0
25	3	78.5	118.0	157.0	196.0	236.0	318.0	392.0	590.0	785.0	1960.0
	4	26.1	40.5	53.1	66.5	79.8	106.0	133.0	199.0	238.0	665.0
	6	5.08	7.60	10.2	12.7	15.3	20.3	25.3	38.1	50.9	129.0
30	3	92.3	139.0	185.0	231.0	277.0	369.0	462.0	693.0	924.0	
	4	31.2	47.5	64.8	78.2	95.5	128.0	159.0	238.0	318.0	955.0
	6	6.0	9.01	12.1	15.0	18.0	24.1	30.1	45.1	60.1	150.0
40	3	124.0	187.0	249.0	312.0	374.0	500.0	625.0	935.0	1250.0	
	4	41.5	64.8	85.5	106.0	128.0	170.0	212.0	318.0	425.0	1060.0
	6	8.02	12.2	16.2	20.3	24.2	32.3	40.5	60.5	81.0	202.0
50	4	52.0	80.9	106.0	133.0	159.0	212.0	266.0	400.0	531.0	1330.0
	6	10.2	15.2	20.3	25.3	30.5	40.6	50.8	76.3	102.0	254.0
	8	3.46	5.31	6.93	8.55	10.4	13.9	17.3	26.1	34.6	86.6
60	4	62.2	97.0	126.0	158.0	190.0	254.0	316.0	475.0	632.0	1580.0
	6	12.2	18.5	24.5	30.7	36.9	49.3	61.5	92.0	123.0	307.0
	8	4.16	6.47	8.32	10.4	12.7	17.1	21.2	31.9	42.5	106.0
70	4	73.8	113.0	138.0	185.0	221.0	295.0	369.0	555.0	740.0	1847.0
	6	14.1	21.4	28.6	35.8	43.0	57.2	71.5	108.0	143.0	358.0
	8	4.85	7.40	9.70	12.2	14.8	19.6	24.5	36.7	48.8	122.0
80	6	16.2	24.7	32.8	41.1	49.2	65.5	82.0	123.0	164.0	410.0
	8	5.55	8.30	11.1	12.8	16.6	22.2	27.8	41.5	55.5	139.0
	10	2.19	3.00	4.38	5.31	6.14	8.55	11.6	16.2	21.5	57.8
100	6	20.3	30.5	40.6	50.8	61.0	81.2	102.0	152.0	203.0	508.0
	8	6.93	10.4	13.6	17.3	20.8	27.7	34.7	52.0	69.2	173.0
	10	2.76	4.16	5.55	6.93	8.09	11.1	16.6	20.7	27.7	67.0

LAMINAR OR VISCOUS FLOW RANGE

TABLE 38. (Cont.) FRICTION LOSS IN HEAD FOR VISCOUS LIQUIDS
Loss In Feet of Liquid Flowing in 100 Feet of New Schedule 40 Steel Pipe

Gpm	Pipe Size	KINEMATIC VISCOSITY - SECONDS SAYBOLT UNIVERSAL									
		20,000	30,000	40,000	50,000	60,000	80,000	100,000	150,000	200,000	500,000
120	6	24.5	36.7	49.0	61.2	73.2	98.0	122.0	184.0	245.0	610.0
	8	8.30	12.4	16.6	20.7	24.9	33.3	41.6	62.3	83.1	207.0
	10	3.23	5.08	6.47	8.09	9.7	13.2	16.2	25.4	34.6	80.8
140	6	28.2	42.3	55.5	70.5	84.3	113.0	141.0	212.0	282.0	705.0
	8	9.70	14.5	19.4	24.2	29.1	38.8	48.5	72.5	97.0	243.0
	10	3.93	5.78	7.62	9.46	11.3	15.7	19.6	28.8	39.2	94.6
160	6	32.3	48.5	64.8	80.8	97.0	129.0	162.0	243.0	323.0	810.0
	8	11.1	16.6	22.2	27.7	33.2	44.5	55.5	83.0	111.0	277.0
	10	4.15	6.46	8.54	10.6	12.7	17.6	21.5	32.4	41.6	106.0
180	6	36.0	54.0	72.0	90.0	108.0	144.0	180.0	270.0	360.0	900.0
	8	12.4	18.5	24.9	31.2	37.4	50.0	62.2	93.7	125.0	312.0
	10	5.09	7.39	9.70	12.0	14.1	19.6	25.3	35.8	50.8	120.0
200	8	13.8	20.8	27.7	34.7	41.5	55.4	69.2	104.0	138.0	347.0
	10	5.31	8.08	10.9	13.6	15.9	22.4	27.7	41.6	53.1	136.0
	12	2.77	4.15	5.30	6.92	8.08	10.9	13.6	20.7	27.7	69.2
250	8	17.3	26.1	34.6	43.5	52.0	69.2	86.5	130.0	173.0	435.0
	10	6.70	9.94	13.4	16.6	19.9	27.7	34.7	52.0	69.3	166.0
	12	3.46	5.08	6.70	8.55	10.2	13.6	17.1	25.3	34.7	85.0
300	8	20.5	30.9	41.0	51.5	61.5	82.2	103.0	154.0	206.0	515.0
	10	8.09	12.0	16.2	20.6	25.4	33.7	42.3	63.4	80.9	206.0
	12	4.15	6.23	8.08	10.4	12.2	16.4	20.3	31.2	41.5	104.0
400	8	27.6	41.5	51.1	69.3	83.0	111.0	138.0	208.0	277.0	693.0
	10	11.0	15.9	21.2	28.4	34.0	45.3	53.1	80.9	109.0	284.0
	12	5.06	8.08	11.1	13.8	16.4	21.9	27.7	41.5	55.5	139.0
500	8	34.6	50.4	69.3	86.5	104.0	138.0	173.0	260.0	346.0	867.0
	10	13.4	20.1	28.2	35.0	42.3	56.0	67.0	102.0	134.0	351.0
	12	6.93	10.4	13.6	17.3	20.8	27.7	34.7	52.0	69.3	173.0
600	8	41.5	62.3	83.0	104.0	125.0	166.0	208.0	312.0	415.0	1040.0
	10	16.2	25.4	33.7	41.9	48.5	67.5	80.9	120.0	162.0	423.0
	12	8.10	12.4	16.4	20.8	24.9	33.3	41.5	62.2	83.0	208.0
700	8	49.0	73.3	98.0	122.0	147.0	196.0	245.0	367.0	490.0	1220.0
	10	18.9	29.8	39.7	49.6	55.5	79.5	94.6	139.0	199.0	496.0
	12	9.70	14.6	19.4	24.3	29.1	38.8	48.5	72.5	97.0	242.0
800	8	55.5	83.0	111.0	138.0	166.0	221.0	277.0	415.0	555.0	1382.0
	10	21.6	32.3	41.6	56.5	62.4	90.5	109.0	162.0	226.0	565.0
	12	11.1	16.6	22.2	27.7	33.2	44.2	55.5	83.0	115.0	277.0
900	8	62.9	94.2	125.0	157.0	188.0	252.0	314.0	470.0	628.0	1570.0
	10	25.4	38.1	50.9	63.5	71.6	102.0	120.0	183.0	254.0	635.0
	12	12.4	18.7	24.9	31.2	37.4	50.0	62.2	93.5	124.0	312.0
1000	8	70.0	105.0	140.0	175.0	211.0	282.0	351.0	528.0	702.0	1750.0
	10	28.6	43.0	57.3	67.0	80.9	114.0	136.0	204.0	287.0	670.0
	12	13.8	20.8	27.7	34.7	41.5	55.4	69.2	104.0	138.0	347.0

LAMINAR OR VISCOUS FLOW RANGE

V

Relative Roughness $\dfrac{\epsilon}{D}$ (Refer to Fig. 26)

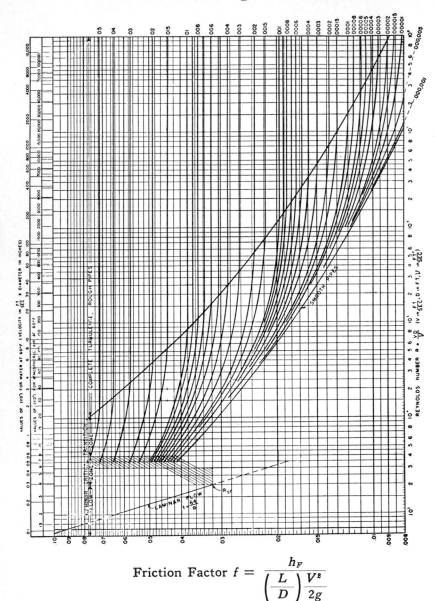

$$\text{Friction Factor } f = \frac{h_F}{\left(\dfrac{L}{D}\right)\dfrac{V^2}{2g}}$$

FIG. 33. Friction for any kind and size of pipe.†

†*Courtesy Hydraulic Institute. See page 6.*

CENTRIFUGAL PUMP PERFORMANCE WHEN HANDLING VISCOUS LIQUIDS†

It is recognized that the performance of centrifugal pumps is affected when handling viscous liquids. The effects are a marked increase in brake horsepower, a reduction in head, and some reduction in capacity at moderate and high viscosities.

It is the purpose of Fig. 34A and 34B, to provide a means of determining the performance of a conventional design of centrifugal pump handling a viscous liquid, when its performance on water is known. It is also intended to be used, by an approximate method, as an aid in selecting a pump for a given application. The corrections are based on tests of conventional single stage pumps of 2″ to 8″ size, handling petroleum oils. The correction curves are an average for several pumps and are, therefore, not exact for a particular pump. It is suggested that performance tests using the viscous liquids be conducted whenever facilities are available for an accurate test.

LIMITATIONS FOR USE

(a) Use only within the scales shown. DO NOT extrapolate.

(b) Use only for pumps of conventional hydraulic design, in the normal operating range with open or closed impellers. DO NOT use for mixed flow or axial flow pumps or for pumps of special hydraulic design for either viscous or non-uniform liquids.

(c) Use only where adequate NPSH is available in order to avoid the effect of cavitation.

(d) Use only on Newtonian (uniform) liquids. Gels and slurries, paper stock, and other non-uniform liquids may produce widely varying results, depending on the particular characteristics of the liquid.

INSTRUCTIONS FOR PRELIMINARY SELECTION OF A PUMP FOR GIVEN HEAD-CAPACITY-VISCOSITY CONDITION.

Given the desired capacity and head of the viscous liquid to be pumped and the viscosity and specific gravity at the pumping temperature, enter Fig. 34A & B at the bottom with the desired viscous capacity, (Q_{vis}) and proceed upward to the desired viscous head (H_{vis}) in feet of liquid. For multistage pumps, use head per stage. Proceed horizontally (either left or right) to the fluid viscosity, and then go upward to the correction curves. Divide the viscous capacity (Q_{vis}) by the capacity correction factor (C_Q) to get the approximate equivalent water capacity (Q_W approx.). Divide the viscous head (H_{vis}) by the head correction factor (C_H) from the curve marked "$1.0 \times Q_n$," to get the approximate equivalent water head (H_w approx.). Using this new equivalent water head-capacity point, select a pump in the usual manner.

†Courtesy Hydraulic Institute. See page 6.

The viscous efficiency and the viscous brake horsepower may then be calculated.

This procedure is approximate as the scales for capacity and head on the lower half of Fig. 34 A & B are based on the water performance. However, the procedure has sufficient accuracy for most pump selection purposes.

Example

Requirement: a pump to deliver 750 Gpm of oil at 100 feet total head of liquid having a viscosity of 1000 SSU and a specific gravity of 0.90 at the pumping temperature.

Enter Fig. 34B with 750 Gpm, go up to 100 feet head, over to 1000 SSU, and then up to the correction factors:

$$C_Q = 0.95 \qquad\qquad C_H = 0.92 \ (for \ 1.0 \ Q_n) \qquad\qquad C_E = 0.635$$

$$Q_W = \frac{750}{0.95} = 790 \ Gpm \qquad\qquad H_W = \frac{100}{0.92} = 108.8 \ \text{say 109 feet head}$$

Select a pump for a water capacity of 790 Gpm at 109 feet head. The selection should be at or close to the maximum efficiency point for water performance. If the pump selected has an efficiency on water of 81% at 790 Gpm, the efficiency for the viscous liquid will be as follows: $E_{vis} = 0.635 \times 81\% = 51.5\%$

The brake horsepower for pumping the viscous liquid is

$$bhp_{vis} = \frac{750 \times 100 \times 0.90}{3960 \times 0.515} = 33.1 \ hp$$

For performance curves of the pump selected, correct the water performance as shown in the following paragraphs.

INSTRUCTIONS FOR DETERMINING PUMP PERFORMANCE ON A VISCOUS LIQUID WHEN PERFORMANCE ON WATER IS KNOWN.

Given the complete performance characteristics of a pump handling water to determine the performance when pumping a liquid of a specified viscosity.

From the efficiency curve, locate the water capacity $(1.0 \ Q_n)$ at which maximum efficiency is obtained. From this capacity, determine the capacities $0.6 \times Q_n$, $0.8 \times Q_n$ and $1.2 \ Q_n$. Enter the chart at the bottom with the capacity at best efficiency $(1.0 \ Q_n)$, go upward to the head developed (in one stage) (H_w) at this capacity, then horizontally (either left or right) to the desired viscosity, and then proceed upward to the various correction curves. Read the values of C_E and C_Q, and of C_H for all four capacities. Multiply each capacity by C_Q to obtain the corrected capacities. Multiply each head by its corresponding head correction factor to obtain the corrected heads. Multiply each efficiency value by C_E to obtain the corrected efficiency values, which apply at the corresponding corrected capacities.

Plot corrected head and corrected efficiency against corrected capacity. Draw smooth curves through these points. The head at shut-off can be taken as approximately the same as that for water.

Calculate the viscous brake horsepower (bph_{vis}) from the formula given.

Plot these points and draw a smooth curve through them which should be similar to and approximately parallel to the bph curve for water.

Example†
Given the performance chart, Fig. 35 of a pump obtained by test on water, plot the performance of this pump when handling oil with a specific gravity of 0.90 and a viscosity of 1000 SSU at pumping temperature.

On the performance curve locate the best efficiency point which determines (Q_n), 750 Gpm. Tabulate capacity, head and efficiency for 0.6 × 750, 0.8 × 750 and 1.2 × 750 Gpm (see Table 39). Using 750 Gpm, 100 feet head and 1000 SSU, enter the chart and determine the correction factors. These are tabulated in Table 39. Multiply each value of head, capacity and efficiency by its correction factor to get the corrected values. Using the corrected values and the specific gravity, calculate brake horsepower. These calculations are shown in Table 39. Calculated points are plotted on Fig. 35 and corrected performance is represented by dashed curves.

TABLE 39.
SAMPLE CALCULATION VISCOUS PERFORMANCE†

	$0.6 \times Q_N$	$0.8 \times Q_N$	$1.0 \times Q_N$	$1.2 \times Q_N$
Water Capacity (Q_W) Gpm	450.0	600.0	750.0	900.0
Water head in feet (H_W)	114.0	108.0	100.0	86.0
Water efficiency (E_W)	72.5	80.0	82.0	79.5
Viscosity of liquid	1000 SSU			
C_Q—from chart	0.95	0.95	0.95	0.95
C_H—from chart	0.96	0.94	0.92	0.89
C_E—from chart	0.635	0.635	0.635	0.635
Viscous capacity—$Q_W \times C_Q$	427.0	570.0	712.0	855.0
Viscous head—$H_W \times C_H$	109.5	101.5	92.0	76.5
Viscous efficiency—$E_W \times C_E$	46.0	50.8	52.1	50.5
Specific gravity of liquid	0.90			
bhp viscous	23.1	25.9	28.6	29.4

$$bph \text{ viscous} = \frac{\text{viscous capacity} \times \text{viscous head} \times \text{specific gravity}}{3960 \times \text{viscous efficiency}}$$

†*Courtesy Hydraulic Institute. See page 6.*

VISCOSITY CORRECTIONS FOR SMALL PUMPS
between 10 to 100 GPM†

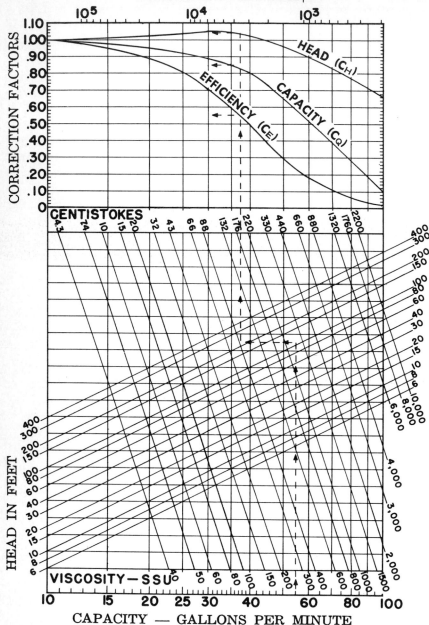

FIG. 34A. Correction factors—water performance to viscous performance for Centrifugal pumps.†

†*Courtesy Hydraulic Institute. See page 6.*

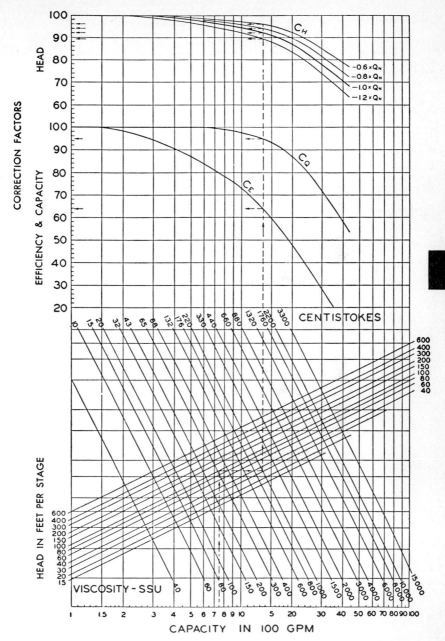

FIG. 34 B. Correction factors—water performance to viscous performance for Centrifugal pumps.†

†*Courtesy Hydraulic Institute. See page 6.*

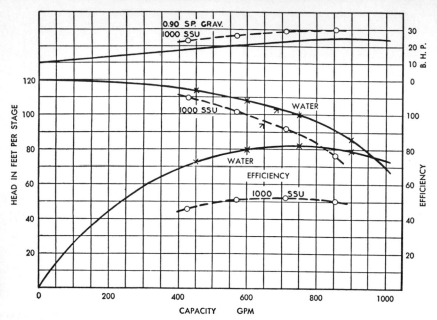

FIG. 35. Comparison of centrifugal pump performance when handling water and viscous material.†

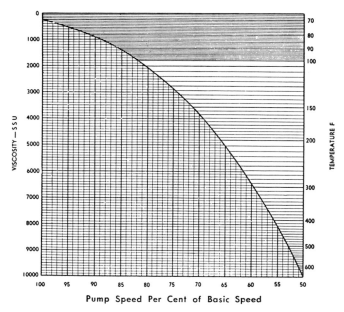

FIG. 36. Correction chart for viscosity and temperature, reciprocating pumps. †

†*Courtesy Hydraulic Institute. See page 6.*

SECTION VI—VOLATILE LIQUIDS

CONTENTS

VI

SECTION VI — PUMPING VOLATILE LIQUIDS

A volatile liquid is any liquid at a temperature near its boiling point. Thus any liquid is volatile at certain conditions for any liquid, if heated sufficiently, will vaporize. In thinking of volatile liquids, such liquids as gasoline and propane come to mind, but water at atmospheric pressure and near 212°F is just as truly a volatile liquid.

Any liquid at or near its boiling point, if the pressure remains constant, will vaporize if heat is added; or also if the temperature remains constant and the pressure is reduced the liquid will boil or vaporize. This is what happens in the suction line of a pump handling volatile liquids. The absolute pressure at the suction inlet of the pump is less than the absolute pressure in the suction vessel. If this were not true the liquid would not flow toward the pump.

The problem, therefore, in pumping volatile liquids, is to keep the absolute pressure at the suction inlet to the pump higher than the absolute vapor pressure at the pumping temperature, of the liquid being pumped. In other words, as explained in Section I of this Handbook, the available NPSH of the system must exceed the required NPSH of the pump if vaporization and vapor binding are to be avoided.

To make it possible to apply the method of analysis given in the discussion of NPSH in Section I tables showing the relationship between temperature, vapor pressure and specific gravity are included in this section for some of the commonly pumped volatile liquids. Tables giving this relationship for water will be found in Section IV.

Many volatile liquids, such as Propane, Butane, Ammonia, and Freon are stored in tanks at their vapor pressure. For example a tank of commercial propane located outdoors will be subject to atmospheric temperatures and the radiant heat of the sun. If such a tank on a hot summer day has a temperature of 110°F the pressure within the tank will be 213 psia. See Table 41. If the pump location is on the same level as the liquid in the tank, the pressure drop in the suction piping between the tank and pump will be sufficient to cause the propane to boil and vapor binding may result. To make pumping such volatile liquids possible and reliable one of the following suggested procedures may be used.

1. Set the tank and pump so that the vertical distance between the pump suction inlet and minimum liquid level in the tank is equal to or greater than the required NPSH of the pump plus all losses in the suction piping.

2. Add heat by means of steam coils in the storage tank so as to raise the temperature above that of the surrounding atmosphere. This will raise the vapor pressure in the tank. Cool the liquid in the suction line by direct radiation or by means of a heat exchanger so that the temperature where the liquid enters the pump is equal to atmospheric temperature.

3. Where heat cannot be added in the storage tank a heat exchanger located near the pump suction capable of reducing the temperature of the liquid sufficiently below atmospheric temperature may be used.

The purpose of all three methods is to supply the pump with liquid at a pressure above its vapor pressure at the suction inlet to the pump impeller.

REID VAPOR PRESSURE

The vapor pressure of gasolines is usually obtained by the Reid method. Because of the inadequacies of this test the true initial vapor pressure is not obtained. The relationship between the initial vapor pressure and the Reid vapor pressure and how they vary with temperature is given in Fig. 40.

NPSH FOR PUMPS HANDLING HYDROCARBON LIQUIDS†

The NPSH requirements of centrifugal pumps are normally determined on the basis of handling water. It is recognized that when pumping hydrocarbons, the NPSH to obtain satisfactory operation can be reduced for certain conditions. The permissible reduction in NPSH is a function of the vapor pressure and the specific gravity of the particular hydrocarbon being pumped.

It is the purpose of Fig. 37 to provide a means of estimating the NPSH required by a centrifugal pump when handling hydrocarbons of various gravities and vapor pressures in percentages of that required by the same pump when handling water. The correction curves are based on data obtained primarily from field experience. While these data had considerable variation, they have been correlated so that the curves are considered to be usable guides. The curves have the further purpose of providing a means of comparing future experience and stimulating the accumulation of additional information.

Limitations for use of net positive suction head correction chart for hydrocarbons. Fig. 37.

1. Use this chart for non-viscous hydrocarbons only.

2. Unusual operating conditions such as pumping hydrocarbons close to the cracking temperature may require additional NPSH.

INSTRUCTIONS FOR USING NPSH CORRECTION CHARTS FOR HYDROCARBONS

Enter Fig. 37 at bottom with the specific gravity at pumping temperature of the particular hydrocarbon to be handled and proceed upward to the sloping line corresponding to the absolute vapor pressure in psi at the pumping temperature. The left hand scale

†*Courtesy Hydraulic Institute. See page 6.*

of the chart will then show the percent of the water NPSH that will be required to pump the particular hydrocarbon satisfactorily.

Example—A pump that has been selected for a given capacity and head requires 6 feet NPSH to pump water. The pump is to handle commercial isobutane at 110°F which has a vapor pressure of 85.1 psi absolute and a specific gravity of 0.53. What NPSH is required?

Enter Fig. 37 at the specific gravity (at 110°F) of 0.53 and go upward to the point corresponding to a vapor pressure of 85.1 psi absolute at 110°F. This is found by interpolation between the lines labeled 50 psi and 100 psi of the fan shaped family of absolute vapor pressure lines in the chart. The left scale will then show the value of the correction factor to be applied to the water NPSH as 0.91.

Therefore, when pumping isobutane at 110°F the pump will require 0.91 × 6 or 5.5 feet NPSH.

If the isobutane is to be pumped at a temperature of 60°F, the vapor pressure will be 38.7 psi absolute and the specific gravity will be 0.56. In this case, the NPSH is the same as required for water, i.e., 6 ft.

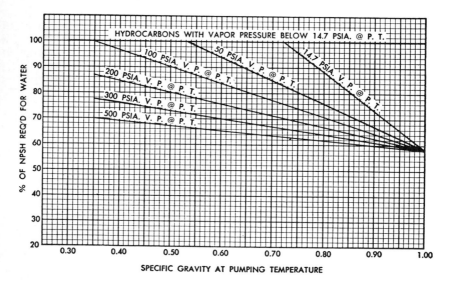

FIG. 37. NPSH correction chart for hydrocarbons. (Not to be used for other liquids.)

TABLE 41. VOLATILE LIQUIDS—VAPOR PRESSURE AND SPECIFIC GRAVITY

Temp °F	AMMONIA Vapor Press psia	Sg*	CARBON DIOXIDE Vapor Press psia	Sg*	FREON 12 Vapor Press psia	Sg*	BUTANE Vapor Press psia	Sg*	PROPANE Vapor Press psia	Sg*
—60	5.6	0.70								
—50	7.7	0.70								
—40	10.4	0.69			9.3	1.51			16.2	0.58
—30	13.9	0.68	220.6	1.03	12.0	1.50			20.3	0.57
—20	18.3	0.68	261.7	1.01	15.3	1.48			25.4	0.57
—10	23.7	0.67			19.2	1.47			31.4	0.56
0	30.4	0.66	308.6	0.99	23.9	1.45	7.3	0.62	38.2	0.55
10	38.5	0.66	361.8	0.97	29.4	1.43	9.2	0.61	46.0	0.55
20	48.2	0.65	422.0	0.95	35.8	1.42	11.6	0.61	55.5	0.54
30	59.7	0.64	489.7	0.92	43.2	1.40	14.4	0.60	66.3	0.53
40	73.3	0.63	565.0	0.89	51.7	1.38	17.7	0.60	78.0	0.52
50	89.2	0.63	650.1	0.85	61.4	1.36	21.6	0.59	91.8	0.52
60	107.6	0.62	744.3	0.81	72.4	1.34	26.3	0.59	107.1	0.51
70	128.8	0.61	848.8	0.76	84.8	1.32	31.6	0.58	124.0	0.50
80	153.0	0.60	964.4	0.68	98.8	1.30	37.6	0.57	142.8	0.49
90	180.6	0.59			114.3	1.28	44.5	0.56	164.0	0.48
100	211.9	0.58			131.6	1.26	52.2	0.56	187.0	0.47
110	247.0	0.57			150.7	1.24	60.8	0.55	213.0	0.46
120	286.4	0.56			171.8	1.22	70.8	0.54	240.0	0.45

* Water at 39.2°F = 1.00

VI

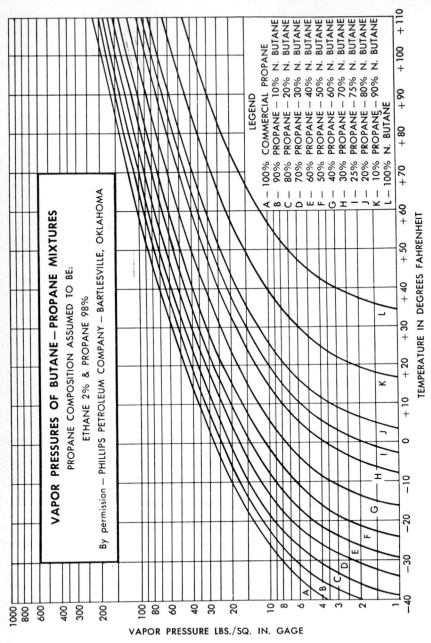

FIG. 38. Vapor pressures of Butane—Propane mixtures.

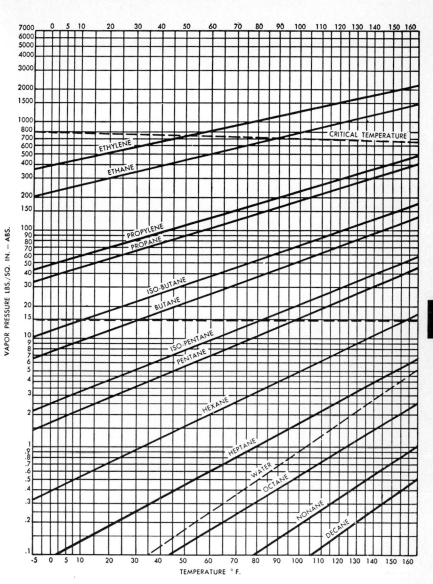

FIG. 39. Hydrocarbons—Temperature vs Vapor Pressure.

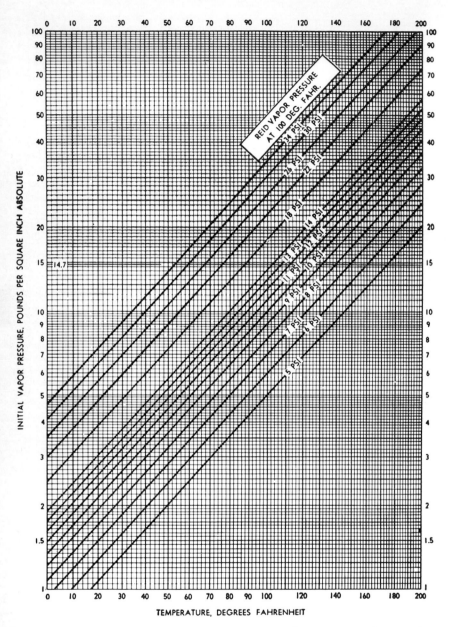

FIG. 40. Vapor pressures vs Temperatures for motor and natural gasolines.†

†*Courtesy Chicago Bridge & Iron Co. See page 6.*

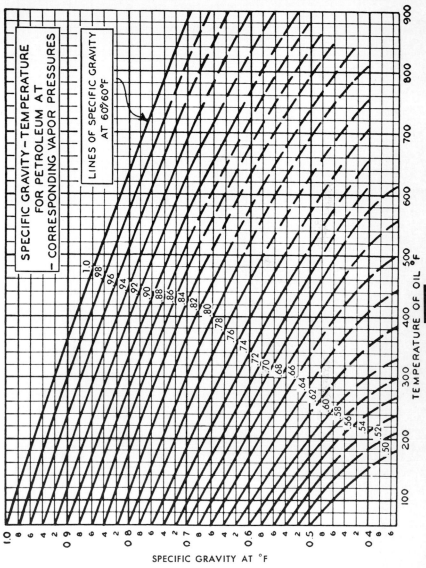

FIG. 41. Specific gravity and temperature relations of petroleum oils (approximate).†

†*Courtesy Hydraulic Institute. See page 6.*

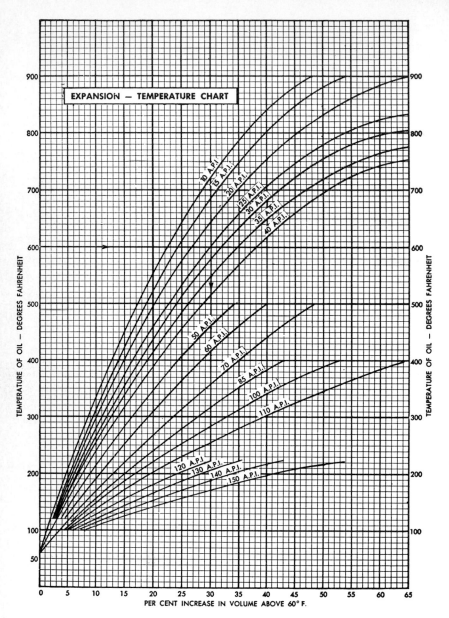

FIG. 42. Expansion—Temperature chart.†

†*Courtesy Hydraulic Institute. See page 6.*

SECTION VII—SOLIDS IN SUSPENSION

CONTENTS

VII

SECTION VII — PUMPING SOLIDS IN SUSPENSION
SEWAGE-SAND-SLURRIES-PAPER STOCK-FOODS

GENERAL PRINCIPLES

The pumping of a great variety of solid materials with liquid as the vehicle can be very successfully accomplished providing a few general principles are followed.

1. The pump should be located sufficiently below the liquid level in the suction bay so that the liquid reaches the suction eye of the impeller under a positive head.

2. All passages through the piping system, impeller, and volute should be large enough to pass the largest solid to be pumped.

3. Velocities through the pump and piping system should be such that the materials are held in suspension in the liquid. This results in less tendency to clog—less abrasion—less damage to the product pumped.

4. Velocity required in the pump varies with the pump characteristic and design.

5. Velocity required in the piping system depends upon the specific gravity, size, shape, consistency and friability of the material being pumped.

6. Pump materials and construction should be selected with due consideration of the substance pumped. Standard materials and design are suitable for the majority of applications but special metals, rubber linings, special stuffing box construction, or other features should be used in many instances.

SEWAGE AND TRASH PUMPS

The pumping of sewage is a special problem for sewage may contain a great variety of solids in suspension. It is likely to contain anything that can be flushed down a toilet including towels, diapers, etc.; anything that can fall or be thrown into a manhole; anything that can flush into a catch basin on a city street including leaves, branches, etc.; or any type of industrial waste.

The principal consideration in pumping sewage is the passing of solids. Hydraulic performance and efficiency is secondary although also important. A consideration of how pumps clog will be useful in arriving at a plant design and a pump selection that will avoid this difficulty. Clogging can generally be attributed to one of the following causes:

1. Material that is too big or too long to flow through the suction piping, and around the elbows to the pump. This clogging generally occurs at an elbow. This type of clogging may be eliminated by screening to prevent large objects reaching the piping system or macerating equipment to reduce the solids in size.

2. Rags and flexible trash that wrap over the entering edge of the impeller blades. A gradual accumulation at this point will eventually cause a complete stoppage in the impeller. The solution to this problem is in the pump design. Sharp entering edges on the impeller blades are to be avoided. While they do improve the hydraulic efficiency of the pump they do so only at a sacrifice in non-clog ability. A generously rounded entering edge so that rags will have a tendency to slide off the blade reduces clogging. Since it is wrapping around the blade that causes clogging at this point, if the pump had no blades the cause would be removed. Such a "Bladeless" pump, remarkably free from clogging, has been available for several years.

Clogging has been a major problem in low capacity pumps. As the capacity and, therefore, the pump size increases the problem lessens. Large sewage and storm water pumps with relatively sharp blades have an excellent record of non-clog ability. Any pump with stationary guide or diffusor vanes is not suitable for pumping sewage.

SLUDGE, SAND & SLURRIES

Sludges, sands, and slurries, as encountered in pumping practice, are mixtures of abrasive materials and, except in the less abrasive sludges (where reciprocating pumps may be used), centifugal pumps meet most requirements by having the casing, impeller, shaft and bearings constructed in suitable materials.

In pumping practice generally the lowest velocity that will keep the material in suspension and propel it in the center of the stream flow and away from the wall of the pipe will be the most economical, for this will result in the minimum pressure drop due to friction, the least abrasion of the pipe walls and the least damage to friable products. The range of velocities required is indicated in Table 42, which gives the particle sizes of natural abrasives together with the minimum hydraulic subsiding values or fall velocities that must prevail in pipes to keep the solids in suspension, and in Fig. 43, which shows the friction losses measured in pipe lines from dredges where high velocities must be maintained.

In the pumping of sand, test data shows that the minimum velocity is not affected much by pipe size. Experiments indicate that pipe-line pressure loss in feet of liquid is equal to the loss by the carrier (water) multiplied by the measured specific gravity of the liquid mixture. In the turbulent flow range, the velocity components continually fluctuate and cause dispersion of the solids in the pipe and assist in keeping them in suspension. A number of authors conclude that the results of flow tests in a small pipe diameter are only qualitative when used to estimate pipe-friction in a larger line.

Pump design and construction will vary considerably depending upon the abrasiveness of the material being handled. For mixtures with low abrasive qualities conventional materials and design may be satisfactory; or it may be found advisable to modify a conventional design by using special wearing rings and stuffing boxes with flushing connections. Clear flushing liquid at a pressure above the casing pressure in the pump is piped to these parts to keep them flushed free of the abrasive material. For very abrasive conditions, special materials and completely special design are required.

DIGESTED SLUDGE

As velocities below 5 ft. per second and often 3 ft. per second are not unusual in sludge mains, the formulae used for water can be used only as a base. Field experience using data as shown in Fig. 44 indicates that the calculation of pumping heads is in reasonable agreement with head discharge curves on pumps tested in the production laboratory (based on volumetric liquid field measurements with accuracy of about 5%). Some engineers have used higher friction loss values which results in the centrifugal pump operating to the right of the selected condition point on the head-capacity curve. Installations exist where pumps are discharging a sludge at a capacity much larger than that at which they were tested in the laboratory.

M. R. Vincent Daviss, Assoc. M. Inst. C.E. in test at Saltley Works, Birmingham, England, of estimated 92% sludge at 80 cu. ft. per min. in 12-inch nominal diameter pipe, 20,000 ft. long, showed friction loss 2.6 times that of actual test made only with water in the same line. He concluded the old pipe effective diameter was 10.25 inches, which gives a velocity of about 2.3 fps. Were it a 12-inch pipe, the velocity would have been 1.7 fps. which gives a test result that correlates with Fig. 44. It is recognized that it has been quite customary to allow from 2 to 4 times the water friction loss in pumping sludges of 98% or less. L. F. Mountfort, discusser of Daviss' paper, points out that 98% sludge is in some respect easier to deal with than water. Recognizing full well the ramifications of the sludge pumping problem, it is indicated that Fig. 44 can be used safely as a guide in estimating pipe friction losses caused by flow of sludges.

SLURRIES

A slurry is a liquid, usually water, in which foreign material is suspended in varying quantities. There are many types of slurries such as coal, salt and the like in many different industries. The application of pumping equipment for such service depends largely on the type and quantity of foreign matter present in the mixture and the properties of the liquid carrier. No definite rules of application can be set down in this Handbook, but the following has been found essentially correct:

1. Flotation tailings from the milling of iron ores can be transported at a velocity of 5 to 7 fps in non-acid water. Pipe does not endure for 15 years but scouring action keeps pipe clean and reasonably free from pitting. The use of 15 year pipe-friction modifying factor appears to be too liberal and causes oversizing and overpowering.

2. Material such as iron-pyrites ground to the fineness required for flotation when thickened to a pulp can be pumped through pipes at reasonable velocities.

3. The head per stage should be kept as low as practical so as to hold vane-tip velocity to a minimum and to reduce erosion at the wearing rings.

4. In a series of tests on a powdered glass-sand-plaster of paris mixture hardened iron impellers have proven more durable than rubber lined pumps although rubber lined pumps have their field of application.

5. In pumping coal, the maximum quantity of fines (100 mesh) appears to act as a lubricant in the mixture. Coal-water slurries up to 35% by weight can be pumped with a viscosity comparable to water at 5 fps velocity. The critical velocity for 2 to 3 inch top-size solids is 7 to 9 fps but a safe velocity is 10-12 fps in 8 inch pipe, and 11-13 fps in 10 inch pipe.

6. Clay slurries up to 50% solids by weight can be pumped through a 4 inch pipe. SSU viscosity tests are unreliable for these slurries. The apparent viscosity varies from 25 to 85 times that for water as shown on Fig. 32.

7. Bentonite slurries are stiff even when they contain only 25% solids by weight.

8. Thirty (30) percent solids by weight of some clays are too viscous to pump in a centrifugal pump.

9. It is possible to lift 60% solids by weight of iron and coke dusts or flue dirt.

10. It is notable that mining operations run solids as high as 70% by weight

This information indicates the great diversity of pumping applications and the necessity for careful analysis of the probable field conditions before the final selection of pumping equipment.

TABLE 42. FALL VELOCITIES VARIOUS ABRASIVES

Diameter Millimeters	Mesh Size U.S. Fine	Fall Velocity Ft./Sec.	SOIL GRAIN SIZE IDENTIFICATION			
			A.S.T.M.	U.S. Bur. Soils U.S.D.A.	M.I.T.	International
.0002		.000000098			Med. Clay	Fine Clay
.0006		.00000092	Clay	Clay	Coarse Clay	Coarse Clay
.001		.0000023				
^02		.0000092			Fine Silt	Fine Silt
.005		.000056				
.006		.000082	Silt	Silt	Med. Silt	Coarse Silt
.02		.00092			Coarse Silt	Fine Mo.
.05	270	.0056		V. F. Sand		Coarse Mo.
.06	230	.0082	Fine Sand		Fine Sand	
.10	150	.024		Fine Sand		Fine Sand
.20	70	.069				
.25	60	.085		Sand	Med. Sand	Med. Sand
.30		.105				
.50	35	.173	Coarse Sand	Coarse Sand		Coarse Sand
.60	30	.206				
1.00	18	.327		Fine Gravel	Coarse Sand	V. C. Sand
2.00	10	.556				

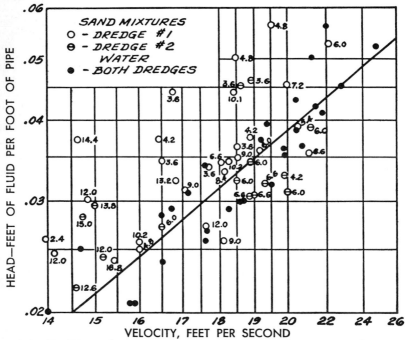

FIG. 43. Friction losses in 24″ I.D. Dredge pipes when water and water sand mixtures are being pumped.

FRICTION LOSS OF DIGESTED SLUDGE
IN 6, 8, AND 10 INCH DIAMETER PIPE

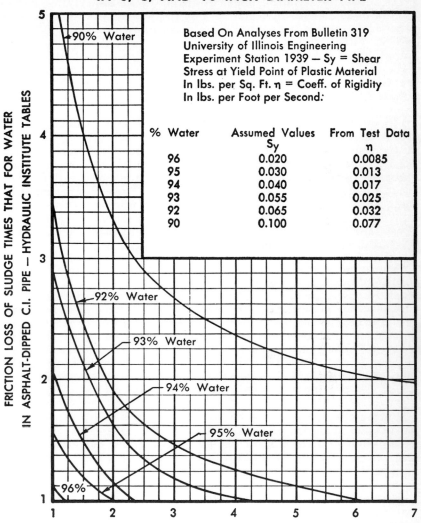

Based On Analyses From Bulletin 319 University of Illinois Engineering Experiment Station 1939 — S_y = Shear Stress at Yield Point of Plastic Material In lbs. per Sq. Ft. η = Coeff. of Rigidity In lbs. per Foot per Second:

% Water	Assumed Values S_y	From Test Data η
96	0.020	0.0085
95	0.030	0.013
94	0.040	0.017
93	0.055	0.025
92	0.065	0.032
90	0.100	0.077

FRICTION LOSS OF SLUDGE TIMES THAT FOR WATER IN ASPHALT-DIPPED C.I. PIPE — HYDRAULIC INSTITUTE TABLES

VELOCITY IN FEET PER SECOND

FIG. 44. Friction loss of digested sludge in 6, 8 and 10 in. diameter pipe.

PAPER STOCK

In the manufacture of paper of all kinds the underlying principle is to reduce all material to a pulp and, by adding necessary chemicals, obtain a homogeneous mass known as pulp or paper stock. This involves large volumes of water in the process work, all of which must be removed before the finished product is made. The types of stock encountered in connection with pumping are: reclaimed paper, ground wood stock, sulphite and soda stock, sulphate and kraft stock, and chemical pulp (cooked stock).

In most process work from the chippers and grinders to the stock chests the maximum consistency bone dry by weight is 3%. Experience has shown that where water is plentiful stock is more easily handled in lower percentages. Capacities or flow rates are usually given in terms of the number of tons of air dry stock per 24-hour day, at an average percentage. These figures must be reduced to a workable basis of gallons per minute. Table 44 for making such conversions is found in this Section. Pipe Friction Loss tables for various stock percentages and pipe sizes are also included and must be used when figuring total head.

The actual selection of a pump for this type of service requires additional data and experience in handling paper stock, together with a knowledge of the performance of a centrifugal pump. For instance, the pumping of dirty stock with fibrous and stringy material is best accomplished by use of a closed impeller stock pump with good solid handling ability. On the other hand, the handling of clean, homogeneous stock of a very heavy percentage requires a pump with a specially designed open impeller to keep down the entrance velocity and prevent the pump from "dewatering" the stock and causing it to pile up in the suction piping.

Rating charts are published on the basis of handling water, and curves are included in this section (Figs. 45 and 46 to enable calculation of reduction in design capacity and design head for a given percentage of stock for both closed and open impeller pumps.

Example: Given the characteristic and efficiency curves for a pump handling water, correct these curves for a closed impeller pump when pumping 3.15% ground wood paper stock.

Table 43 shows that 3.15% ground wood is equal to 3.0% sulfate stock. The characteristic curve is corrected by using Fig. 45 applying the head correction factors corresponding to various percentages of design capacity.

The efficiency curve is corrected by using Fig. 46 which shows that the efficiency at design point is reduced 28 points at a reduced capacity which is 67% of design capacity. The *efficiency correction applies only to the design point.*

TABLE 43. REQUIRED PERCENTAGE OF PAPER STOCKS
TO EQUAL PERFORMANCE OF PUMP LIFTING
KRAFT-SULPHATE

Kraft-Sulfate	Reclaimed Paper	Jute	Ground Wood	Sulfite-Soda
1.0	1.95	1.65	1.50	1.25
1.2	2.20	1.85	1.70	1.40
1.5	2.55	2.15	2.00	1.70
1.7	2.75	2.35	2.15	1.85
2.0	3.05	2.60	2.40	2.15
2.5	3.55	3.05	2.80	2.60
3.0	4.05	3.45	3.15	3.00
3.5	4.45	3.90	3.50	
4.0	4.90	4.30		
4.5	5.25	4.75		
5.0	5.65	5.15		

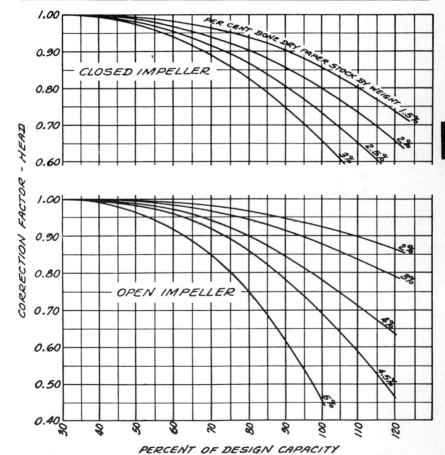

FIG. 45. Effect of Sulfate stock on centrifugal pump characteristic.

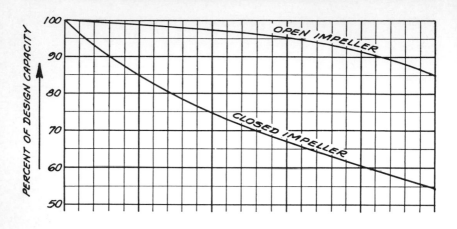

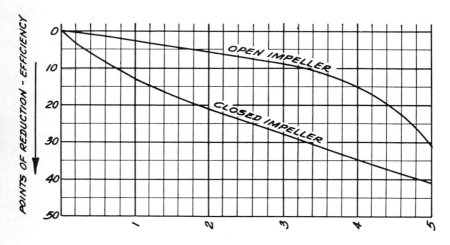

FIG. 46. Effect of Sulfate paper stock on centrifugal pump capacity and efficiency.

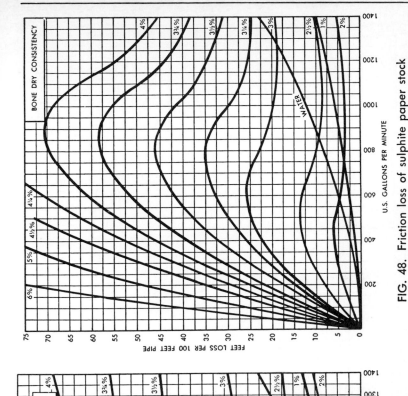

FIG. 48. Friction loss of sulphite paper stock through 6 inch cast iron pipe.

FIG. 47. Friction loss of groundwood paper stock through 6 inch cast iron pipe.†

†*Courtesy Hydraulic Institute. See page 6.*

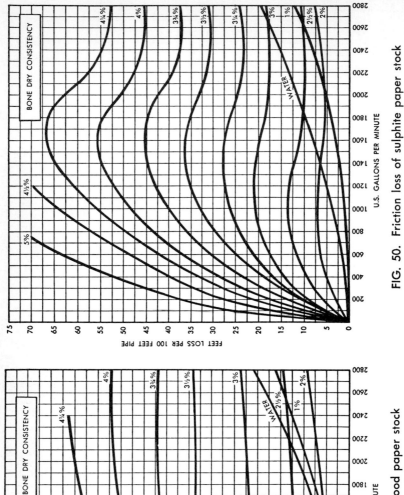

FIG. 50. Friction loss of sulphite paper stock through 8 inch cast iron pipe.

FIG. 49. Friction loss of groundwood paper stock through 8 inch cast iron pipe.

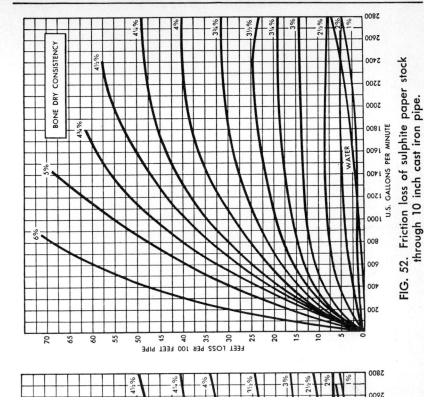

FIG. 52. Friction loss of sulphite paper stock through 10 inch cast iron pipe.

FIG. 51. Friction loss of groundwood paper stock through 10 inch cast iron pipe.

VII

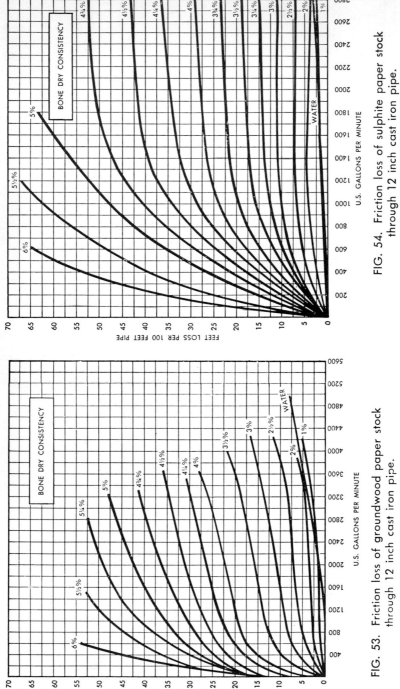

FIG. 54. Friction loss of sulphite paper stock through 12 inch cast iron pipe.

FIG. 53. Friction loss of groundwood paper stock through 12 inch cast iron pipe.

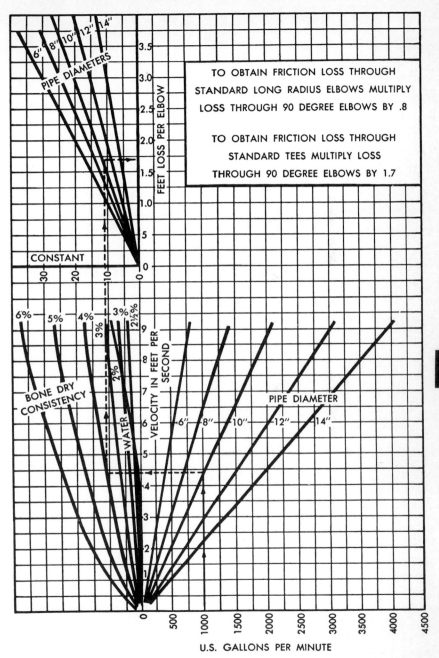

FIG. 55. Estimated friction loss for standard short radius 90 deg. elbows.

TABLE 44. WEIGHTS, VOLUMES, ETC., OF LIQUID PULP STOCK CARRYING VARIOUS PERCENTAGES OF AIR DRY STOCK.†

% Dry stock in 100 lbs. of Liquid "K"	Lbs. dry stock in 1 cu. ft. of liquid $0.625X"K"$	No. of Cu. ft. containing 1 Lb. of Stock $\frac{1.6}{"K"}$	Lbs. of dry stock in 1 gal. of Liquid $\frac{"K"\cdot8.34}{100}$	No. of gal. containing 1 Lb. of Stock $\frac{11.97}{"K"}$	Cu. ft. of Liq. per Min. per ton of dry stock per 24 hrs. $\frac{2.22}{"K"}$	Gals. of liquid per Min. per ton of Dry stock per 24 hrs. $\frac{16.62}{"K"}$	Lbs. liquid per ton of Dry Stock per 24 hrs. $\frac{138.88}{"K"}$	Lbs. of water per lb. of stock $\frac{100}{"K"}-1$	Gallons water per lb. of stock $\left[\frac{100}{K}-1\right]\frac{1}{8.35}$	Gallons water per ton of stock $\left[\frac{100}{K}-1\right]240$	Gallons water per min. per ton of dry stock per 24 hrs. $\left[\frac{100}{K}-1\right]\frac{1}{6.02}$
.10	.0625	16.	.008	119.55	22.22	166.20	1,388.88	999.00	119.36	238,710	165.78
.20	.1250	8.	.017	59.77	11.11	83.10	694.44	499.00	59.76	119,996	82.89
.25	.1562	6.40	.021	47.87	8.88	66.49	555.55	399.00	47.75	95,511	66.32
.30	.1875	5.33	.025	39.90	7.41	55.41	462.96	332.33	39.78	79,555	55.24
.33	.2063	4.80	.028	36.27	6.72	50.32	420.84	302.10	36.17	72,487	50.17
.35	.2187	4.57	.029	34.20	6.35	47.50	396.83	284.71	34.08	68,154	47.33
.40	.2500	4.00	.033	29.92	5.55	41.56	347.20	249.00	29.80	59,605	41.39
.45	.2812	3.56	.038	26.60	4.94	36.94	308.64	221.22	26.48	53,093	36.77
.50	.3125	3.20	.042	23.92	4.44	33.25	277.77	199.00	23.82	47,760	33.08
.55	.3437	2.91	.046	21.76	4.04	30.22	252.52	180.82	21.64	43,490	30.05
.60	.3750	2.66	.050	19.95	3.70	27.71	231.48	165.66	19.83	39,758	27.54
.65	.4062	2.46	.054	18.41	3.42	25.57	213.68	152.85	18.29	36,681	25.40
.70	.4375	2.28	.058	17.10	3.17	23.75	198.42	141.86	17.00	34,284	23.58
.75	.4687	2.13	.063	15.96	2.96	22.16	185.18	132.33	15.84	31,678	21.99
.80	.5000	2.00	.067	14.96	2.78	20.78	173.61	124.00	14.84	29,683	20.61
.85	.5312	1.88	.071	14.06	2.61	19.56	163.40	116.65	13.98	28,024	19.39
.90	.5624	1.78	.075	13.30	2.47	18.47	154.32	110.11	13.18	26,426	18.30
.95	.5937	1.68	.079	12.61	2.34	17.50	146.19	104.26	12.48	25,022	17.33

†*Courtesy Paper & Pulp Mill Catalog.*   Note: For conversion—1% Bone Dry Stock=1.1% Air Dry Stock.

TABLE 44. (Cont.) WEIGHTS, VOLUME, ETC. OF LIQUID PULP STOCK CARRYING VARIOUS PERCENTAGES OF AIR DRY STOCK

% Dry stock in 100 lbs. of Liquid "K"	Lbs. dry stock in 1 cu. ft. of liquid $0.625 \times$"K"	No. of Cu. ft. containing 1 Lb. of Stock $\frac{1.6}{\text{"K"}}$	Lbs. of dry stock in 1 gal. of Liquid $\frac{\text{"K"} \cdot 8.34}{100}$	No. of gal. containing 1 Lb. of Stock $\frac{11.97}{\text{"K"}}$	Cu. ft. of liquid per Min. per ton of dry stock per 24 hrs. $\frac{2.22}{\text{"K"}}$	Gals. of liquid per Min. per ton of dry stock per 24 hrs. $\frac{16.62}{\text{"K"}}$	Lbs. liquid per Min. per ton of Dry Stock per 24 hrs. $\frac{138.8}{\text{"K"}}$	Lbs. of water per lb. of stock $\frac{100}{\text{"K"}}-1$	Gallons water per lb. of stock $\left[\frac{100}{\text{K}}-1\right]\frac{1}{8.35}$	Gallons water per ton of stock $\left[\frac{100}{\text{K}}-1\right]240$	Gallons water per min. per ton of dry stock per 24 hrs. $\left[\frac{100}{\text{K}}-1\right]\frac{1}{6.02}$
1.00	.6250	1.60	.084	11.97	2.22	16.62	138.88	99.00	11.85	23,698	16.49
1.25	.7812	1.28	.104	9.57	1.78	13.30	111.11	79.00	9.45	18,911	13.13
1.50	.9375	1.07	.125	7.98	1.48	11.08	92.59	65.66	7.86	15,712	10.91
1.75	1.0937	.91	.146	6.84	1.27	9.50	79.37	56.14	6.72	13,439	9.33
2.00	1.2500	.80	.167	5.97	1.11	8.31	69.44	49.00	5.86	11,760	8.15
2.25	1.4062	.71	.188	5.32	.99	7.39	61.73	43.44	5.20	10,437	7.23
2.50	1.5625	.64	.209	4.79	.89	6.65	55.55	39.00	4.67	9,360	6.48
2.75	1.7187	.58	.230	4.35	.81	6.04	50.50	35.36	4.23	8,465	5.88
3.00	1.8750	.53	.251	3.99	.74	5.54	46.29	32.33	3.87	7,759	5.37
3.50	2.1875	.46	.292	3.42	.63	4.75	39.68	27.57	3.30	6,616	4.58
4.00	2.5000	.40	.334	2.99	.55	4.15	34.72	24.00	2.87	5,750	3.99
4.50	2.8125	.36	.376	2.74	.49	3.69	30.86	21.22	2.54	5,100	3.53
5.00	3.1250	.32	.418	2.39	.44	3.32	27.77	19.00	2.27	4,560	3.16
5.50	3.4375	.29	.459	2.18	.40	3.02	25.25	17.18	2.06	4,115	2.85
6.00	3.7500	.27	.501	1.99	.37	2.77	23.15	15.66	1.87	3,750	2.61
6.50	4.0625	.25	.542	1.84	.34	2.56	21.36	14.38	1.72	3,450	2.37
7.00	4.3750	.23	.584	1.71	.32	2.38	19.84	13.29	1.59	3,180	2.21
7.50	4.6875	.21	.626	1.60	.29	2.22	18.51	12.33	1.48	2,960	2.04
8.00	5.0000	.20	.667	1.50	.28	2.08	17.36	11.50	1.38	2,760	1.91

VII

FOOD HANDLING PUMPS

Commercial canners have long desired to convey foods hydraulically for this method represents a much less expensive means than mechanical conveyors. The problem is, of course, to handle the foods without clogging the pump or piping system and without damaging the foods. This is a manifold problem that involves not only the pump but also a satisfactory means of mixing the food with the liquid vehicle and finally separating the food and the liquid without damage to the product.

Hydraulic elevators that could handle such products as peas and cut beans have been on the market for many years, but new equipment is on the market that will handle the food so gently that the following foods have been successfully conveyed: apples, apricots, artichokes, cut asparagus, beans (green, lima, shelled, string, sprouts, dried or soaked), beets (peeled, diced, sugar), blueberries, brussel sprouts, carrots, cauliflower rosettes, cherries (maraschino), chili-sauce, collard, corn (kernel), cranberries, dressings, boiled eggs, egg yolks, liquid eggs, grapes (crushed as pumped to pressing room), grits, mash, mushrooms, olives (green and ripe), onions, oranges, peas (black-eyed, field and sweet), peppers, pickles, pimientos, pineapple pulp from cores and fruit meat, white potatoes, rice (prior to soaking), soy beans (with oil extracted while pumping), soups, strawberries (except Marshall variety), sugar (raw cane juice, cachaza, syrups, molasses), tomato catsup, tomato juice, sea foods, such as fingerlings with only 2% loss, oysters, shrimp.

Fig. 56 shows a sketch of a typical installation using pump, rod reel washer and scavenger reel with water supply tank. This installation provides for vortexing of food in the hopper to the pump. This vortex is very important for it causes very light foods that normally float on top of the liquid to sink and be drawn uniformly into the pump suction. It also causes long foods like string beans to enter the stream with their length parallel to the stream flow. The forced vortex is limited so air is not drawn into the pump.

There are only six parts of a pump in contact with foods, namely; the housing or volute, back-head, removable drive shaft, packing, impeller and front-head. The interior of a pump for food handling service should be smoothly finished with no sharp corners, holes, pits, crevices, cracks or threads. Contact surfaces should be either ground to form a tight seal or to accommodate a rubber or single-service gasket.

Pump construction can be made to resist attack by foods, soaps, detergents and the germicidal agents used in cleaning. Stainless steel is satisfactory except for salt brines. Monel metal can be used for brines but not for corn, lima beans or peas where copper may produce darkening. Aluminum is corroded by alkalis and certain acids. Bronze is fairly corrosion resistant, but is not good for *conveying brines in which foods are canned* because of possible discoloration of the end product. Experience shows that for most applications the iron fitted pump with stainless steel sleeves has been doing a creditable job. Contamination by lubricants is impossible with well designed pumps.

The following suggestions, based on field experience, are offered as a guide in pump selection and application.

1. The solids should be mixed with the liquid at a uniform rate and vortexed into the pump suction. The vortex should be limited so that air is not drawn into the pump.

2. Although the pump capacity required will depend upon the tonnage to be handled, the pump preferably should be selected so that it will operate at its point of peak efficiency or slightly to the right of this point on the characteristic curve.

3. The speed of the pump should be selected to meet the head requirements of the system. Heads up to 110 ft. have been successful with some foods. The system should be designed to keep the head as low as possible.

4. The ratio of water to food solids should be as great as is practicable or economical. For peas one gallon per pound and for string beans 3 gallons per pound has been found practical.

5. With most foods a pump with a bladed impeller will damage the food. A pump with a "Bladeless" impeller is recommended.

6. Food solids should be carefully separated from the liquid as this is a common point of product damage.

For new uses it is recommended that the first pumping unit be installed with a provision for variable speed operation and observation of condition of the product after passing through the pump be made at the top of a riser prior to a bend. There is evidence that short radius ells, rough pipe joints or beads inside of welded pipe can cause more damage to foods than the pump itself. A velocity in the pipe of 5 fps should be tried first as this velocity appears to be above the critical for movement of food suspensions without clogging.

When pumping foods with hot water, write to the manufacturer for the required minimum suction head to obtain performance comparable with cold water. (See fundamentals concerning NPSH in Section I of this Handbook).

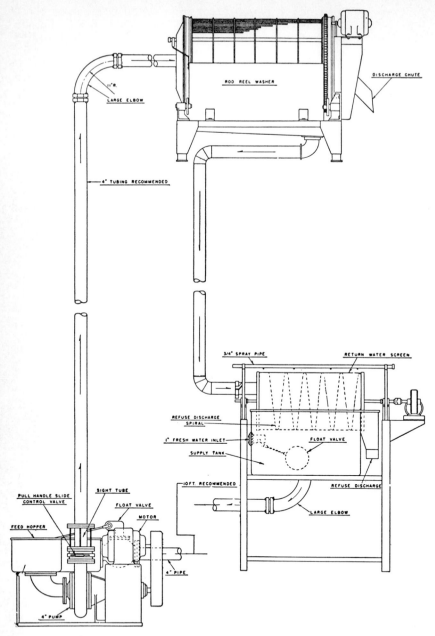

FIG. 56. Line drawing of typical installation including pump, rod reel washer and scavenger reel with supply tank.†

Chisholm Ryder Corp. See page 6.

SECTION VIII—CHEMICAL LIQUIDS

CONTENTS

SECTION VIII—CHEMICAL LIQUIDS

MATERIALS OF CONSTRUCTION FOR PUMPING VARIOUS LIQUIDS†

Although pumps produced by various manufacturers will differ in design and performance detail, they follow the same general pattern in the utilization of materials for handling specific liquids. This is natural since the manufacturer has little control over the corrosive reaction between the materials and the liquids handled and, hence, must use those types which experience has indicated as being most satisfactory for the particular application under consideration.

Because of the many variables which influence the rate at which corrosion may occur, it is not possible to make positive predictions which will cover every application. However, for the guidance of both pump manufacturers and users, the Materials Specifications Committee of the Hydraulic Institute has compiled a list of the liquids more commonly encountered in industry, along with the materials generally associated with their use. This data is shown in Table 46.

DATA ON VARIOUS LIQUIDS

The liquids are assumed to be of commercial quality and of the degree of purity usually encountered. However, one must recognize that the presence of a foreign substance, even in small percentages, may, and frequently does, have a profound effect upon the corrosiveness of the solution and, hence, upon the choice of materials. For instance, the presence of a small percentage of soluble chloride or other halide in many of the liquids included in the table may greatly intensify their corrosive properties. Conversely, certain substances, such as the chromates and dichromates, may inhibit the corrosive action of many solutions on ferrous metals. Further, some liquids, noticeably the vegetable oils, while relatively inactive when fresh, may, upon exposure to heat and/or the atmosphere, turn rancid and become quite corrosive. While cast iron might be used safely with such oils when sweet, it would not necessarily be satisfactory after they had soured. In the latter case, other, more resistant materials would probably be required.

In some cases the satisfactory use of a particular material is restricted to a definite temperature and/or concentration range, and where this is known to occur, the limitations are so noted in the tabulation. As the corrosion rate usually increases with tem-

†Abridged from Standards of Hydraulic Institute. See page 6.

perature, the latter becomes an important factor in making a material selection. Where the space is left blank in the appropriate column, it is assumed the materials listed are suitable over the ranges of concentration and temperature normally encountered.

PUMP CONSTRUCTION MATERIALS

The materials listed are those most commonly used in the principal parts of the pump, such as casings, impellers, cylinders, and, hence, are primarily castings. Wrought materials, such as shafts, should, where practical, be of similar composition to the castings used, and, in the case of ferrous materials, would carry the designation of the American Iron and Steel Institute. Cross-reference is made to such materials in the listings.

Since it is not possible in any generalization to say with certainty that any one material will best withstand the corrosive attack of a given liquid, more than one type is usually included. However, the order of listing does not necessarily indicate relative superiority, as certain factors predominating in one instance may be sufficiently overshadowed in others to reverse the arrangement.

When the liquid to be handled is an electrolyte, combinations of dissimilar metals which may promote galvanic reactions should, where practical, be avoided. The rate of corrosion, where metals widely separated in the galvanic series are used, will depend upon such things as the nature of the electrolyte, temperature, velocity, and particularly, the relative cathode-anode surface area. Although bronze fittings in an iron pump handling sea water may initially accelerate the corrosion of the surface of the iron, the overall rate is sometimes sufficiently low to make the use of large pumps, so fitted, economically sound.

VIII

SELECTION OF MATERIALS

The pump construction and materials selected as suitable for each application are tabulated opposite the corresponding liquids in Table 46. To simplify identification, each construction and materials selection is designated by descriptive letters or a number as follows:

(1) Iron or Bronze Fitted....SF   (3) All Bronze ....AB
(2) All Iron............................AI   (4) Types 8, 9, 10, 11............SS

To simplify recording, the symbol SS is used in those cases where types 8, 9, 10, 11 would normally be listed. This does not necessarily mean, however, that all are equally effective in all environments. It merely means that each type has been satisfactorily applied in handling that liquid under some, possibly all, conditions.

Other materials, including corrosion resisting steels, are listed by number in accordance with Table 45.

TABLE 45 MATERIAL SELECTION CHART†

Institute Selection	Corresponding Society Designation			REMARKS					
	ASTM	ACI	AISI						

A48 Class

	ASTM	ACI	AISI	Class	Tensile Strength	Transverse Loading—Pounds		
						.875″ Diam.	1.20″ Diam.	2.00″ Diam.
1	20	..	..	20	20,000	900	1,800	6,000
	25	..	..	25	25,000	1,025	2,000	6,800
	30	..	..	30	30,000	1,150	2,200	7,600
	35	..	..	35	35,000	....	....	....
	40	..	..	40	40,000	....	....	....
	50	..	..	50	50,000	....	....	....

Inst.	ASTM	ACI	AISI	Grade	Cu.	Sn.	Pb.	Zn.	P.	Tensile	Elong.%
2	....	..	..	CB1	89.00	11.00	....	...	0.20	35,000	10
	B143, 1B	..	..	CB2	88.00	8.00	....	4.00	...	40,000	20
	B143, 2A	..	..	CB3	88.00	6.00	....	4.50	...	34,000	22
	B145, 4A	..	..	CB4	85.00	5.00	1.50	5.00	...	30,000	20
		..	..	CB5	88.00	10.00	2.00	...	...	35,000	10
	B144, 3A	..	..	CB6	80.00	10.00	10.00	...	...	25,000	8

Inst.	ASTM	ACI	AISI	C.	Mn.	Si.	Ni.	Cr.	Mo.	Tensile	Yield	Elong.%
3	A216, WCB	..	1030	0.35	0.70	0.60	...	...	...	70,000	36,000	22
4	A217, C5-8	..	501	0.20	...	...	...	5.00	0.50	90,000	60,000	18
5	A296, CA15	CA15	410	0.15	...	...	...	13.00	...	90,000	65,000	18
6	A296, CB30	CB30	..	0.30	...	...	1.00	20.00	...	65,000	30,000	..
7	A296, CC50	CC50	446	0.50	...	...	2.00	28.00	...	55,000	.....	..

Inst.	ASTM	ACI	AISI	C.	Mn.	P.	S.	Si.	Ni.	Cr.	Mo.	Cu.	Elong.%
8	A296, CF-8	CF-8	304	0.08	1.50	0.05	0.05	2.00	8.00 11.00	18.00 21.00	...	...	35

Tensile Strength 70,000—Yield 28,000

Inst.	ASTM	ACI	AISI	C.	Mn.	P.	S.	Si.	Ni.	Cr.	Mo.	Cu.	Elong.%
9	A296, CF-8M	CF-8M	316	0.08	1.50	0.05	0.05	2.00	9.00 12.00	18.00 21.00	2.00 3.00	...	30

Tensile Strength 70,000—Yield 30,000

Inst.	ASTM	ACI	AISI	C.	Mn.	P.	S.	Si.	Ni.	Cr.	Mo.	Cu.	Elong.%
10	....	CN-7M	..	0.07	1.50	0.04	0.04	4.00	20.00 30.00	18.00 22.00	3.50	4.50	30

Tensile Strength 65,000—Yield 30,000

Inst.	ASTM	ACI	AISI	REMARKS
11	....	..	..	A series of proprietary, nickel-base alloys containing chromium, molybdenum, and other elements, with less than 20% iron.
12	....	..	..	A special 14.25% silicon cast iron, which is not effected by most corrodents. It is hard and extremely brittle.

Inst.	ASTM	ACI	AISI	Ni-Resist	C.	Si.	Mn.	Ni.	Cu.	Cr.
13	....	..	..	Type I	3.00	1.00	1.00-1.50	17.50	7.50	1.75-2.50
				Type II	3.00	2.80	.80-1.50	22.00	.50	1.75-2.50

Tensile Strength 25,000

Inst.	ASTM	ACI	AISI		Ni.	Fe.	Mn.	Si.	Cu.	Elong.%
14	....	..	..	Monel Metal	60.00	3.50	3.50	1.00 2.00	23.00	22

Tensile Strength 65,000—Yield 30,000

Inst.	ASTM	ACI	AISI	REMARKS
15	....	..	..	Commercial nickel castings for handling strong, hot alkalies, where pure white product is desired.

ASTM—American Society for Testing Materials   Cu = Copper   C = Carbon   Mo = Molybdenum
    ACI—Alloy Casting Institute   Sn = Tin   Mn = Manganese   S = Sulphur
    AISI—American Iron & Steel Institute   Pb = Lead   Si = Silicon   Cr = Chromium
                                Zn = Zinc   Ni = Nickel   Fe = Iron

†*Courtesy Hydraulic Institute See Page 6.*

TABLE 46. MATERIALS OF CONSTRUCTION & PACKING SUGGESTED WHEN PUMPING VARIOUS MATERIALS.†

Liquid and Condition	Sg. at 60°F	Material Recommended[1]	Packing Recommended By:‡		
			Durametallic[2]	Crane	Anchor[4]
Acetaldehyde	0.78	Al	D-110 & 777-NMT	C-06	317-3687
Acetate Solvents		SF, Al, AB, SS	D-110 & 777-NMT	C-06	851 TT AB 808 A
Acetone	0.79	SF, Al	D-110 & 777-NMT	C-06	808 A
Acetic Anhydride	1.08	SS, 12	D-110 & 777-NMT	C-06	811 XX
Acids:					
Acetic (Cold Conc.)	1.05	SS, 12	D-110	111M-SS5	811 XX
Acetic (Cold Dil.)		AB, SS, 12	D-110	111M-SS5	AB-808 A-811 XX
Acetic (Boiling Conc.)		9, 10, 11, 12	999-NM	111M-SS5	811 XX
Acetic (Boiling Dil.)		9, 10, 11, 12	999-NM	111M-SS5	811 XX
Arsenic (Ortho)	2.0-2.5	SS, 12	999-NM	C-06	851 TT
Benzoic	1.27	SS	110-D-222	C-06	851 TT
Boric (Aqueous)		AB, SS, 12	110-B-777	C-06	820 NJ
Butyric (Conc.)	0.96	SS	D-110	C-06	851 TT
Carbolic (Conc.)	1.07	Al, SS	D-110	C-98	851 TT
Carbolic (Aqueous)		SF, SS	D-110	C-98	SP-820 NJ-SS-851 TT
Carbonic (Aqueous)		AB	777-NMT	C-06	820 NJ
Chromic (Aqueous)		SS, 12	110 BLA-B-999	C-98	820 NJ
Citric (Aqueous)		AB, SS, 12	777 NM & D-110	C-06	AB-820 NJ-811 XX
Fatty (Oleic, Palmitic, etc.)		AB, SS	D-110 & D-220	C-06	AB-820 NJ-811 XX
Formic	1.22	9, 10, 11	999 NMT	C-98	851 TT
Fruit		AB, SS, 14	777 NM & D-110	C-06	AB-820 NJ-851 TT
Hydrochloric (Coml. Conc.)	1.16‡	11, 12	666-F[5]	C-98	842
Hydrochloric (10% Cold)	1.05‡	10, 11, 12, 14, 15	666-F[5]	C-98	842
Hydrochloric (10% Hot)	1.05‡	11, 12	666-F[5]	C-98	842
Hydrocyanic	0.70	Al, SS	777 NM	C-98	842
Hydroflouric (Anhydrous with Hydrocarbon)		3, 14	666-F[5]	C-1045	888
Hydroflouric (Aqueous)		AB, 14	666-F[5]	C-1045	888
Hydrofluosilicic	1.30	AB, 14	B-999	C-1045	888
Lactic	1.25	AB, SS, 12	777-NM	C-06	909
Mine Water		AB, SS	777-NM	111M-SS1	386
Mixed (Sulfuric & Nitric)		Al, 3, SS, 12		C-1045	317
Muriatic (See Acid, Hydrochloric)					
Naphenic		Al, 5, SS		C-06	909
Nitric (Conc. Boiling)	1.4‡	6, 7, 10, 12	666-F[5]	C-98	842
Nitric (Dil.)		5, 6, 7, 8, 9, 10, 12	666-F[5]	C-98	842
Oxalic (Cold)	1.65	SS, 12	777-NM	C-06	851 TT
Oxalic (Hot)		10, 11, 12	999-NM	C-06	Anklon
Ortho-Phosphoric	1.36-1.4‡	9, 10, 11	B-110 BLA & B-999	C-98	850
Picric	1.76	SS, 12		C-98	851 TT
Pyrogallic	1.45	SS		C-98	851 TT
Pyroligneous	1.02-1.03‡	AB, SS		C-98	AB-820 NJ-811 XX
Sulphuric (>77% Cold)	1.69-1.84	Al, 10, 11, 12	B-110 BLA & B-999	C-98	842
Sulphuric (65/93% > 175 deg. F.)	1.60-1.84‡	11, 12	B-110 BLA & B-999	C-98	842

See footnotes at end of table.

VIII

TABLE 46. (Cont.)

Liquid and Condition	Sg. at 60°F	Material Recommended[1]	Packing Recommended By:[‡] Durametallic[2]	Crane	Anchor[4]
Acids (Continued)					
Sulphuric (65/93% <175 deg. F.)	1.60-1.84[‡]	10, 11, 12	B-110 BLA & B-999	C-98	842
Sulphuric (10-65%)	1.07-1.56[‡]	10, 11, 12	B-110 BLA & B-999	C-98	842
Sulphuric (<10%)	1.00-1.07[‡]	AB, 10, 11, 12, 14	B-110 BLA & B-999	C-98	842
Sulphuric (Fuming)	1.92-1.94	3, 10, 11	B-110 BLA	C-98	842
Sulphurous		AB, SS	B-110 BLA	C-98	842
Tannic		AB, SS, 14	777-NM	C-98	842
Tartaric (Aqueous)		AB, SS, 14	110-B-777	C-06	888
Alcohols		AB, SF	710-B-777	C-06	820 NJ
Alum (See Aluminum Sulphate and Potash Alum)					
Aluminum Sulphate (Aqueous)		10, 11, 12, 14	B-110 BLA & B-999	C-06	842
Ammonia, Aqua		Al	B-110 & B777	111M-SS6	850-858
Ammonium Bicarbonate (Aqueous)		Al	B-110 & B777	111M-SS6	850-858
Ammonium Chloride (Aqueous)		9, 10, 11, 12, 14	B-110 BLA & B-999	C-06	851 TT
Ammonium Nitrate (Aqueous)		Al, SS, 14	999-NM	C-06	851 TT
Ammonium Phosphate (Aqueous)		Al, SS, 14	B-110 BLA & B-999	C-06	851 TT
Ammonium Sulphate (Aqueous)		Al, SS	B-110 BLA & B-999	C-06	850-858
Ammonium Sulphate (with H_2SO_4)		AB, 9, 10, 11, 12	B-110 BLA & B-999	C-98	227
Aniline	1.02	SF, Al	710-B-777	111M-SS3	804
Aniline Hydrochl. (Aqueous)		11, 12	710-B-777	C-06	850
Asphalts: (See Sect. V)					
Blended or Virgin	0.98-1.4	Al, 5	D-110	805MD	199
Barium Chloride (Aqueous)		Al, SS	999-NMT	C-06	888
Barium Nitrate (Aqueous)		Al, SS	999-NMT	C-06	888
Beer	1.01[‡]	AB, 8	777-NM & D-110	C-06	909
Beer Wort		AB, 8	777-NM & D-110	C-06	909
Beet Juice		AB, 8	777-NM & D-110	C-06	909
Beet Pulp		AB, SF, SS	777-NM & D-110	C-06	909
Benzene (See Benzol)					
Benzine (See Petroleum Ether)					
Benzol	0.88	SF, Al	710-B-777	111M-SS3	905
Black Liquor (See Liquors, Pulp Mill)					
Blood		AB, SF	D-110	C-06	Anklon
Brines:					
Calcium Chloride (pH>8)		Al	999-NMT	811-SS1	851 TT
Calcium Chloride (pH<8)		AB, 10, 11, 13, 14	999-NMT	811-SS1	820 NJ
Calcium-Magnesium Chlorides (Aqueous)		AB, 10, 11, 13, 14	999-NMT	811-SS1	820 NJ
Calcium-Sodium Chloride (Aqueous)		AB, 10, 11, 13, 14	999-NMT	811-SS1	820 NJ
Sodium Chloride (<3%, Cold)	1.02	AB, Al, 13	110-B-777	811-SS1	820 NJ
Sodium Chloride (>3%, Cold)	1.02-1.20	AB, SS, 13, 14	110-B-777	811-SS1	820 NJ
Sodium Chloride (>3%, Hot)		9, 10, 11, 12, 14	110-B-777	811-SS1	851 TT

See footnotes at end of table.

TABLE 46. (Cont.)

Liquid and Condition	Sg. at 60°F	Material Recommended[1]	Packing Recommended By:[‡] Durametallic[2]	Crane	Anchor[4]
Brines: (Continued)					
Sea Water	1.03	AB, SF, Al	110-B-777	811-SS1	387 F
Butane	0.59[‡]	SF, Al, 3	710-B-777	111M-SS3	905
Calcium Bisulfite (Paper Mill)	1.06	9, 10, 11	B-110 BLA & B-999	C-06	811 XX
Calcium Chlorate (Aqueous)		10, 11, 12	999-NMT	C-06	820 NJ
Calcium Hypochlorite		Al, 10, 11, 12	999-NMT	C-06	820 NJ
Calcium-Magnesium Chloride (See Brines)					
Cane Juice		AB, SF, 13	110-D-222	C-06	909
Carbon Bisulfide	1.26	Al	D-110	C-06	851 TT
Carbonate of Soda (See Soda Ash)			110-B-777	C-06	
Carbon Tetrachloride (Anhydrous)	1.50	SF, Al	710-B-777	C-06	820 NJ
Carbon Tetrachloride (Plus Water)		AB, 8	710-B-777	C-06	820 NJ
Catsup		AB, SS	D-110	C-06	909
Caustic Potash (See Potassium Hydroxide)					
Caustic Soda (See Sodium Hydroxide)					
Cellulose Acetate		9, 10, 11	D-110 & 777-NMT	C-06	851 TT
Chlorate of Lime (See Calcium Chlorate)					
Chloride of Lime (See Calcium Hypochlorite)					
Chlorine Water (Depends on Concentration)		9, 10, 11, 12	999-NMT	111M-SS1	851 TT
Chlorobenzene	1.1	AB, SF, 8	710-B-777	C-06	820 NJ
Chloroform	1.5	AB, SS, 14	710-B-777	C-06	804
Chrome Alum (Aqueous)		10, 11, 12	999-NM	C-98	808 A
Condensate (See Water, Distilled)					
Copperas, Green (See Ferrous Sulfate)					
Copper Ammonium Acetate (Aqueous)		Al, SS	B-999	C-98	842
Copper Chloride (Cupric) (Aqueous)		11, 12	B-999	C-98	842
Copper Nitrate		SS	666-F[5]	C-98	842
Copper Sulfate (Blue Vitriol) (Aqueous)		SS, 12	B-999	C-98	842
Creosote (See Oil, Creosote)			D-110	805MD	
Cresol, Meta	1.03	Al, 5	D-110	805MD	820 NJ
Cyanide (See Sodium or Potassium Cyanide)					
Cyanogen (in water)		Al	999-NM	C-98	804
Diphenyl	0.99	Al, 3	110-D-222	111M-SS2	820 NJ
Enamel		Al	D-110 & 777-NM	C-06	Teflon
Ethanol (See Alcohols)					
Ethane[‡]	0.37[‡]	SF, Al, 3[‡]	710-B-777	111M-SS2	
Ethylene Chloride (Cold)	1.28	AB, SS, 14	710-B-777	C-06	317-3687
Ferric Chloride (Aqueous)		11, 12	666-F[5]	C-06	820 NJ
Ferric Sulphate (Aqueous)		SS, 12	666-F[5]	C-06	820 NJ
Ferrous Chloride (Cold-Aqueous)		11, 12	666-F[5]	C-06	820 NJ
Ferrous Sulphate (Aqueous)		9, 10, 11, 12, 14	666-F[5]	C-06	820 NJ
Formaldehyde	1.08	AB, SS	777-NMT	C-06	804
Fruit Juices		AB, SS, 14	110-D-222	C-06	909
Furfural	1.16	AB, Al, SS	D-110 & B-777	C-06	820 NJ

VIII

See footnotes at end of table.

TABLE 46. (Cont.)

Liquid and Condition	Sg. at 60°F	Material Recommended[1]	Packing Recommended By:[‡] Durametallic[2]	Crane	Anchor[4]
Gasolines:					
Pentane	0.63‡	AI, SF	710-B-777	111M-SS3	317-3687
Hexane	0.66‡	AI, SF	710-B-777	111M-SS3	317-3687
Heptane	0.69‡	AI, SF	710-B-777	111M-SS3	317-3687
Octane	0.71‡	AI, SF	710-B-777	111M-SS3	317-3687
Nonane	0.72‡	AI, SF	710-B-777	111M-SS3	317-3687
Decane	0.73‡	AI, SF	710-B-777	111M-SS3	317-3687
Undecane	0.74‡	AI, SF	710-B-777	111M-SS3	317-3687
Dodecane	0.75‡	AI, SF	710-B-777	111M-SS3	317-3687
Glaubers Salt (See Sodium Sulfate)					
Glucose	1.35-1.44‡	AB, SF	777-NM	C-06	1108
Glue (Hot)	1.20-1.25‡	SF, AI	110-D-222	810W	317 W
Glue Sizing		AB	110-D-222	810W	317 W
Glycerol (Glycerin)	1.26	AB, SF, AI	777-NMT	C-06	820 NJ
Green Liquor (See Liquors, Pulp Mill)					
Heptane (See Gasolines)		SF, AI			
Hydrogen Peroxide (Aqueous)		SS	666-F[5]	C-1045	820 NJ
Hydrogen Sulfide (Aqueous)		SS	110-D-222	C-98	820 NJ
Kaolin Slip (In Water)		AI, 3	B-777	111M-SS1	851 TT
Kaolin Slip (In Acid)		10, 11, 12	B-999	C-98	851 TT
Kerosene (See Oil, Kerosene)			710-B-777	111M-SS3	
Lard (Hot)		SF, AI	D-110	C-06	909
Lead Acetate (Aqueous) (Sugar of Lead)		9, 10, 11, 14	110-D-222	C-98	842
Lead (Molten)		AI, 3		C-98	842
Lime Water (Milk of Lime)		AI	777-NMT	SS6J	820 NJ
Liquors, Pulp Mill:					
Black		AI, 3, 9, 10, 11, 12, 14	666-F[5]	C-06	811 XX
Green		AI, 3, 9, 10, 11, 12, 14	666-F[5]	C-06	811 XX
White		AI, 3, 9, 10, 11, 12, 14	666-F[5]	C-06	811 XX
Pink		AI, 3, 9, 10, 11, 12, 14	666-F[5]	C-06	811 XX
Sulfite		9, 10, 11	B-110-BLA	C-06	811 XX
Lithium Chloride (Aqueous)		AI	110-B-777	111M-SS1	811 XX
Lye, Caustic (See Potassium & Sodium Hydroxide)					
Magnesium Chloride (Aqueous)		10, 11, 12	999-NM	C-06	851 TT
Magnesium Sulfate (Aqueous) (Epsom Salts)		AI, SS	999-NM	C-06	851 TT
Manganese Chloride (Aqueous)		AI, SS, 12	999-NM	C-06	820 NJ
Manganous Sulfate (Aqueous)		AB, AI, SS	999-NM	C-06	820 NJ
Mash		AB, SF, 8	110-D-222	C-06	909
Mercuric Chloride (Very dil. Aqueous)		9, 10, 11, 12	999-NM	C-06	851 TT
Mercuric Chloride (Coml. Conc. Aqueous)		11, 12	999-NM	C-06	851 TT
Mercuric Sulfate (in H_2SO_4)		10, 11, 12	999-NM	C-98	820 NJ
Mercurous Sulfate (in H_2SO_4)		10, 11, 12	999-NM	C-98	820 NJ
Methyl Chloride	0.92‡	AI	710-B-777	C-06	856
Methylene Chloride	1.34	AI, 8	710-B-777	C-06	856
Milk	1.03-1.04	8	D-110 or 777-NM	C-06	909

See footnotes at end of table.

TABLE 46. (Cont.)

Liquid and Condition	Sg. at 60°F	Material Recommended[1]	Packing Recommended By:[‡]		
			Durametallic[2]	Crane	Anchor[4]
Mine Water (See Acid, Mine Water)					
Miscella (20% Soyabean Oil and Solvent	.075	Al	110-D-222	111M-SS1	851 TT
Molasses		AB, SF	110-D-222	C-06	909
Mustard		AB, SS, 12	110-D-222	C-06	909
Naphtha	0.78-0.88	SF, Al	710-B-777	111M-SS3	820 NJ
Naphtha (Crude)	0.92-0.95	SF, Al	710-B-777	111M-SS3	820 NJ
Nicotine Sulfate		10, 11, 12, 14	B-110 BLA & B-999	896	851 TT
Nitre (See Potassium Nitrate)					
Nitre Cake (See Sodium Bisulfate)					
Nitro Ethane	1.04	SF, Al	710-B-777	896	804
Nitro Methane	1.14	SF, Al	710-B-777	896	804
Oils:					
Coal Tar		SF, Al, SS	D-110	101AL	820 NJ
Coconut	0.91	AB, SF, SS, Al, 14	110-D-222	C-06	820 NJ
Creosote	1.04-1.10	SF, Al	D-110	805MD	317
Crude (Cold)		SF, Al	710-B-777	111M-SS2	317
Crude (Hot)		3	D-110	101AL	811
Essential		AB, SF, Al	110-D-222	101AL	317
Fuel	0.82-1.00[‡]	SF, Al	710-B-777	111M-SS2	317
Kerosene	0.78-0.82[‡]	SF, Al	710-B-777	111M-SS2	317-3687
Linseed	0.94	AB, SF, Al, SS, 14	710-B-777	111M-SS2	317
Lubricating	0.88-0.94[‡]	SF, Al	710-B-777	111M-SS2	317
Mineral	0.88-0.94[‡]	SF, Al	710-B-777	111M-SS2	317
Olive	0 90	SF, Al	710-B-777	111M-SS2	317
Palm	0.90	AB, SF, Al, SS, 14	710-B-777	111M-SS2	317
Quenching	0.91	SF, Al	710-B-777	111M-SS2	317
Rapeseed	0.92	AB, SS, 14	710-B-777	111M-SS2	317
Soya Bean	0.93-0.98[‡]	AB, SF, Al, SS, 14	710-B-777	111M-SS2	820
Turpentine	0.87	SF, Al	710-B-777	111M-SS2	820 NJ
Paraffin (Hot)	0.90[‡]	SF, Al	110-D-222	C-06	317-3687
Perhydrol (See Hydrogen Peroxide)					
Petroleum Ether		SF, Al	710-B-777	111M-SS2	804
Phenol (See Acid, Carbolic)					
Photographic Developers		SS	110-B-777	111M-SS2	888
Potash (Plant Liquor)		AB, SS, 13, 14	110-B-777	111M-SS2	888
Potash Alum (Aqueous)		AB, 9, 10, 11, 12, 13, 14	B-110 BLA & B-999	111M-SS5	386
Potassium Bichromate (Aqueous)		Al	666-F[5]	C-98	851 TT
Potassium Carbonate (Aqueous)		Al	110-B-777	111M-SS1	851 TT
Potassium Chlorate (Aqueous)		SS, 12	666-F[5]	C-98	851 TT
Potassium Chloride (Aqueous)		AB, SS, 14	110-B-777	111M-SS1	820
Potassium Cyanide (Aqueous)		Al	777-NM	C-06	851 TT
Potassium Hydroxide (Aqueous)		Al, 5, SS, 13, 14, 15	666-F[5]	SS6J	853
Potassium Nitrate (Aqueous)		Al, 5, SS	B-110-BLA	SS6J	851 TT
Potassium Sulfate (Aqueous)		AB, SS	110-B-777	111M-SS1	820
Propane (C[3]H[8])	0.51[‡]	SF, Al, 3	710-B-777	111M-SS3	317-3687
Pyridine	0.98	Al	710-B-777	111M-SS3	851 TT
Pyridine Sulphate		10, 12	B-110 BLA & B-999	111M-SS5	851 TT

VIII

See footnotes at end of table.

TABLE 46. (Cont.)

Liquid and Condition	Sg. at 60°F	Material Recommended[1]	Packing Recommended By:‡		
			Durametallic[2]	Crane	Anchor[4]
Rhidolene		SF	710-B-777	810	317-3687
Rosin (Colophony) (Paper Mill)		Al	110-D-222	100AL	851 TT
Sal Ammoniac (See Ammonium Chloride)					
Salt Lake (Aqueous)		AB, SS, 12	110-B-777	111M-SS1	808 A
Salt Water (See Brines)					
Sea Water (See Brines)					
Sewage		AB, SF, Al	110-B-777	111M-SS1	386
Shellac		AB	110-B-777	111M-SS1	842
Silver Nitrate (Aqueous)		SS, 12	666-F⁵	C-06	811 XX
Slop, Brewery		AB, SF, Al	110-D-222	810(MICA)	317
Slop, Distillers	1.05	AB, SS	110-D-222	810(MICA)	317
Soap Liquor		Al	110-B-777	SS6J	851 TT
Soda Ash (Cold Aqueous)		Al	110-B-777	SS6J	851 TT
Soda Ash (Hot Aqueous)		SS, 13, 14	110-B-777	SS6J	888
Sodium Bicarbonate (Aqueous)		Al, SS, 13	110-B-777	SS6J	851 TT
Sodium Bisulfate (Aqueous)		10, 11, 12	110-B-777	SS6J	851 TT
Sodium Carbonate (See Soda Ash)					
Sodium Chlorate (Aqueous)		SS, 12	666-F⁵	SS6J	851 TT
Sodium Chloride (See Brines)					
Sodium Cyanide (Aqueous)		Al	777-NM	SS6J	851 TT
Sodium Hydroxide (Aqueous)		Al, 5, SS, 13, 14, 15	666-F⁵	SS6J	851 TT
Sodium Hydrosulfite (Aqueous)		SS	B-110-BLA	SS6J	851 Tl
Sodium Hypochlorite		10, 11, 12	666-F⁵	SS6J	851 TT
Sodium Hyposulfite (See Sodium Thiosulfate)					
Sodium Meta Silicate		Al	777-NM	SS6J	851 TT
Sodium Nitrate (Aqueous)		Al, 5, SS	B-110 BLA	SS6J	851 TT
Sodium Phosphate:					
Monobasic (Aqueous)		AB, SS	999-NM	810S	386
Dibasic (Aqueous)		AB, Al, SS	777-NM	810S	386
Tribasic (Aqueous)		Al	110-B-777	111M-SS1	851 TT
Meta (Aqueous)		AB, SS	110-B-777	111M-SS1	386
Hexameta (Aqueous)		SS	110-B-777	111M-SS1	851 TT
Sodium Plumbite (Aqueous)		Al	666-F⁵	810S	851 TT
Sodium Silicate (Aqueous)‡	1.38‡	Al‡	777-NM	810S	
	1.41‡		999-NM		
Sodium Sulfate (Aqueous)		AB, SS	110-B-777	111M-SS1	820
Sodium Sulfide (Aqueous)		Al, SS	110-B-777	111M-SS1	851 TT
Sodium Sulfite (Aqueous)		AB, SS	110-B-777	111M-SS1	820
Sodium Thiosulfate (Aqueous)		SS	110-B-777	111M-SS1	851 TT
Stannic Chloride (Aqueous)		11, 12	666-F⁵	SS6J	851 TT
Stannous Chloride (Aqueous)		11, 12	666-F⁵	SS6J	851 TT
Starch		AB, SF	B-777	810(MICA)	909
Strontium Nitrate (Aqueous)		Al, 8	999-NM	SS5	853
Sugar (Aqueous)		AB, SS, 13	110-D-222	C-06	909
Sulfite Liquors (See Liquors, Pulp Mill)					
Sulfur (In Water)		AB, Al, SS	110-D-222	C-06	842
Sulfur (Molten)		Al	110-D-222	101AL-SS2	851 TT

See footnotes at end of table.

TABLE 46. (Cont.)

Liquid and Condition	Sg. at 60°F	Material Recommended[1]	Packing Recommended By:[‡]		
			Durametallic[2]	Crane	Anchor[4]
Sulfur Chloride (Cold)		Al	110 BLA-B-999	896	851 TT
Syrup (See Sugar)					
Tallow (Hot)	0.90	Al	110-D-222	810	862
Tanning Liquors		AB, SS, 12, 14	777-NM	SS6J	842
Tar (Hot)		Al, 3	B-110	805MD	842
Tar & Ammonia (In Water)		Al	B-110	805MD	856
Tetrachloride of Tin (See Stannic Chloride)					
Tetraethyl Lead	1.66	SF, Al	710-B-777	810S(11)	317-3687
Toluene (Toluol)	0.87	SF, Al	710-B-777	810S(11)	905
Trichloroethylene	1.47	AB, SF, Al, 8	710-B-777	810S(11)	905
Urine		AB, SS	110-B-777	810	317
Varnish		AB, SF, Al, 8, 14	710-B-777	810S(11)	820 NJ
Vegetable Juices		AB, SS,14	110-D-222	C-06	820
Vinegar		AB, SS, 12	110-D-222	C-06	820 NJ
Vitriol, Blue (See Copper Sulfate)					
Vitriol, Green (See Ferrous Sulfate)					
Vitriol, Oil of (See Acid Sulfuric)					
Vitriol, White (See Zinc Sulfate)					
Water, Boiler Feed:					
Not Evaporated pH>8.5	1.0	Al	110-B-777	111M-SS1	808A
High Makeup pH>8.5	1.0	SF	110-B-777	111M-SS1	808A
Low Makeup Evaporated, any pH	1.0	4, 5, 8, 14	110-B-777	111M-SS1	808A
Water Distilled:			110-B-777		
High Purity	1.0	AB, 8	110-B-777	C-06	808A
Condensate	1.0	AB, SF	110-B-777	111M-SS1	386
Water, Fresh	1.0	SF	110-B-777	111M-SS1	386
Water, Mine (See Acid, Mine Water)					
Water, Salt & Sea (See Brines)					
Whiskey		AB, 8	110-D-222	C-06	909
White Liquor (See Liquors, Pulp Mill)					
White Water (Paper Mill)		AB, SF, Al	110-B-777	C-64	909
Wine		AB, 8	110-D-222	C-06	909
Wood Pulp (Stock)		AB, SF, Al	110-B-777	C-64	808 A
Wood Vinegar (See Acid, Pyroligneous)					
Wort (See Beer Wort)					
Xylol (Xylene)	0.87	SF, Al, SS	710-B-777	C-06	804
Yeast		AB, SF	110-D-222	C-06	909
Zinc Chloride (Aqueous)		9, 10, 11, 12	100-BLA & B-999	810	842
Zinc Sulfate (Aqueous)		AB, 9, 10,1L	999-NM	SS5	842

† Data from Standards of Hydraulic Institute 10th Edition except as noted:

‡ Data added from other sources.

[1] For meaning of symbols see Table 45 and preceding text.

[2] Symbol number of packing recommended by Durametallic Corp., Kalamazoo, Mich.

[3] Symbol number of packing recommended by Crane Packing Co., Morton Grove, Ill.

[4] Symbol number of packing recommended by Anchor Packing Co., 401 N. Broad St., Philadelphia, Pa.

[5] In non-oxidizing applications use A-666-S.

MECHANICAL SEALS

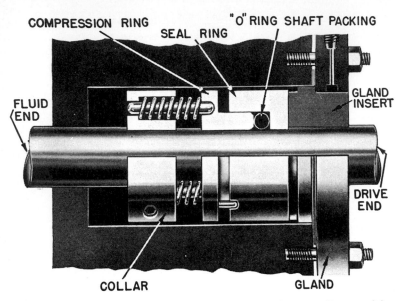

FIG. 57. Typical mechanical seal. Single inside type illustrated.†

When stuffing box packing is used some of the liquid being pumped or a separate sealing fluid must be permitted to drip from the packing box. This drip is the only means of lubricating and cooling the packing box. To meet the needs of industry for a dripless box, mechanical seals were developed and are especially applicable when sealing a pump handling corrosive, costly, volatile, toxic or gritty fluids. Their use results in lowered maintenance costs, fewer shut-downs, greater safety and more economical operation. They are particularly suitable for use in pumps handling light hydrocarbons, corrosive crude stocks, caustics, acids, solvents and other fluids difficult to seal with conventional packing.

To prevent leakage two essential anti-frictional mating rings lapped together are used. The rotating ring is sealed against leakage to and rotates with the shaft. The stationary member is generally fixed in the stuffing box or gland and leakage prevented by sealing with "O" rings or gaskets. In Fig. 57 gaskets are illustrated. The two mating rings are held together by spring and hydraulic pressure.

Mechanical seals can be built for a wide range of pressures and temperatures using in their construction any machineable material including steel or its alloys, carbon, ceramics or fibre.

†Courtesy Durametallic Corp. See page 6.

pH VALUES

The acidity or alkalinity of a solution is expressed by its pH value. A neutral solution such as water has a pH value of 7.0. Decreasing pH values from 7.0 to 0.0 indicate increasing acidity and increasing pH values from 7.0 to 14.0 indicate increasing alkalinity. Since the pH value denotes the acidity or alkalinity of a liquid it gives some indication of the materials required in constructing a pump to handle the liquid. The pH value alone, however, is not conclusive. Many other factors must be considered. However, as an approximate guide, Table 47a may be found helpful.

TABLE 47a. MATERIALS OF CONSTRUCTION INDICATED BY pH VALUE.

pH Value	Material of Construction
0 to 4	Corrosion Resistant Alloy Steels.
4 to 6	All Bronze.
6 to 8	Bronze Fitted or Standard Fitted.
8 to 10	All Iron.
10 to 14	Corrosion Resistant Alloys.

The following tables give approximately pH values. From "modern pH and Chlorine Control", W. A. Taylor & Co., by permission.

TABLE 47. APPROXIMATE pH VALUES.

ACIDS

Hydrochloric, N	0.1	Formic, 0.1N	2.3
Hydrochloric, 0.1N	1.1	Lactic, 0.1N	2.4
Hydrochloric, 0.01N	2.0	Acetic, N	2.4
Sulfuric, N	0.3	Acetic, 0.1N	2.9
Sulfuric, 0.1N	1.2	Acetic, 0.01N	3.4
Sulfuric, 0.01N	2.1	Benzoic, 0.01N	3.1
Orthophosphoric, 0.1N	1.5	Alum, 0.1N	3.2
Sulfurous, 0.1N	1.5	Carbonic (saturated)	3.8
Oxalic, 0.1N	1.6	Hydrogen sulfide, 0.1N	4.1
Tartaric, 0.1N	2.2	Arsenious (saturated)	5.0
Malic, 0.1N	2.2	Hydrocyanic, 0.1N	5.1
Citric, 0.1N	2.2	Boric, 0.1N	5.2

TABLE 47. (Cont.) APPROXIMATE pH VALUES.

BASES

Sodium hydroxide, N	14.0	Ammonia, N	11.6
Sodium hydroxide, 0.1N	13.0	Ammonia, 0.1N	11.1
Sodium hydroxide, 0.01N	12.0	Ammonia, 0.01N	10.6
Potassium hydroxide, N	14.0	Potassium cyanide, 0.1N	11.0
Potassium hydroxide, 0.1N	13.0	Magnesia (saturated)	10.5
Potassium hydroxide, 0.01N	12.0	Sodium sesquicarbonate, 0.1N	10.1
Sodium metasilicate, 0.1N	12.6	Ferrous hydroxide (saturated)	9.5
Lime (saturated)	12.4	Calcium carbonate (saturated)	9.4
Trisodium phosphate, 0.1N	12.0	Borax, 0.1N	9.2
Sodium carbonate, 0.1N	11.6	Sodium bicarbonate, 0.1N	8.4

BIOLOGIC MATERIALS

Blood, plasma, human	7.3-7.5	Duodenal contents, human	4.8-8.2
Spinal fluid, human	7.3-7.5	Feces, human	4.6-8.4
Blood, whole, dog	6.9-7.2	Urine, human	4.8-8.4
Saliva, human	6.5-7.5	Milk, human	6.6-7.6
Gastric contents, human	1.0-3.0	Bile, human	6.8-7.0

FOODS

Apples	2.9-3.3	Milk, cows	6.3-6.6
Apricots	3.6-4.0	Olives	3.6-3.8
Asparagus	5.4-5.8	Oranges	3.0-4.0
Bananas	4.5-4.7	Oysters	6.1-6.6
Beans	5.0-6.0	Peaches	3.4-3.6
Beers	4.0-5.0	Pears	3.6-4.0
Blackberries	4.9-5.5	Peas	5.8-6.4
Bread, white	5.0-6.0	Pickles, sour	3.0-3.4
Beets	4.9-5.5	Pickles, dill	3.2-3.6
Butter	6.1-6.4	Pimento	4.6-5.2
Cabbage	5.2-5.4	Plums	2.8-3.0
Carrots	4.9-5.3	Potatoes	5.6-6.0
Cheese	4.8-6.4	Pumpkin	4.8-5.2
Cherries	3.2-4.0	Raspberries	3.2-3.6
Cider	2.9-3.3	Rhubarb	3.1-3.2
Corn	6.0-6.5	Salmon	6.1-6.3
Crackers	6.5-8.5	Sauerkraut	3.4-3.6
Dates	6.5-8.5	Shrimp	6.8-7.0
Eggs, fresh white	7.6-8.0	Soft drinks	2.0-4.0
Flour, wheat	5.5-6.5	Spinach	5.1-5.7
Gooseberries	2.8-3.0	Squash	5.0-5.4
Grapefruit	3.0-3.3	Strawberries	3.0-3.5
Grapes	3.5-4.5	Sweet potatoes	5.3-5.6
Hominy (lye)	6.8-8.0	Tomatoes	4.0-4.4
Jams, fruit	3.5-4.0	Tuna	5.9-6.1
Jellies, fruit	2.8-3.4	Turnips	5.2-5.6
Lemons	2.2-2.4	Vinegar	2.4-3.4
Limes	1.8-2.0	Water, drinking	6.5-8.0
Maple syrup	6.5-7.0	Wines	2.8-3.8

TABLE 48. PHYSICAL PROPERTIES OF CALCIUM CHLORIDE AND SODIUM CHLORIDE†

CALCIUM CHLORIDE

Degrees Baume 60°F	Specific gravity 60°/60°F	Degrees Salometer 60°F	% CaCl₂ by weight	Lb. CaCl₂ per gallon of solution (approx.)	Freezing Point °F
0	1.000	0	0	0	32.
1.	1.007	4	1	....	31.1
2.1	1.015	8	2	....	30.4
3.4	1.024	12	3	½	29.5
4.5	1.032	16	4	....	28.6
5.7	1.041	22	5	....	27.7
6.8	1.049	26	6	1	26.6
8.	1.058	32	7	....	25.5
9.1	1.067	36	8	....	24.3
10.2	1.076	40	9	1½	22.8
11.4	1.085	44	10	....	21.3
12.5	1.094	48	11	....	19.7
13.5	1.103	52	12	2	18.1
14.6	1.112	58	13	....	16.3
15.6	1.121	62	14	....	14.3
16.8	1.131	68	15	2½	12.2
17.8	1.140	72	16	....	10.
19.	1.151	76	17	....	7.5
20.	1.160	80	18	3	4.6
21.	1.169	84	19	....	1.7
22.	1.179	88	20	3½	—1.4
23.	1.188	92	21	....	—4.9
24.	1.198	96	22	....	—8.6
25.	1.208	100	23	....	—11.6
26.	1.218	104	24	4	—17.1
27.	1.229	108	25	....	—21.8
28.	1.239	112	26	....	—27.
29.	1.250	116	27	4½	—32.6
30.	1.261	120	28	....	—39.2
31.	1.272	124	29	....	—46.2
32.	1.283	128	30	5	—54.4

SODIUM CHLORIDE

Specific gravity 60°/60°F	Degrees Baume 60°F	Degrees Salometer 60°F	% NaCl by weight	Lb. NaCl per gallon solution	Freezing point °F
1.000	0	0	0	0	32.0
1.007	1.04	3.8	1	0.084	30.5
1.015	2.07	7.6	2	0.169	29.3
1.022	3.08	11.4	3	0.256	27.8
*1.029	4.08	15.2	4	0.344	26.6
1.036	5.07	18.9	5	0.433	25.2
1.044	6.07	22.7	6	0.523	23.9
1.051	7.06	26.5	7	0.617	22.5
1.059	8.01	30.3	8	0.708	21.2
1.066	8.97	33.9	9	0.802	19.9
1.073	9.90	37.5	10	0.897	18.7
1.081	10.86	41.3	11	0.994	17.4
1.089	11.80	45.2	12	1.092	16.0
1.096	12.73	49.2	13	1.190	14.7
1.104	13.64	53.0	14	1.289	13.
1.111	14.54	56.8	15	1.389	12.2
1.119	15.46	60.6	16	1.495	11.0
1.127	16.37	64.4	17	1.602	9.8
1.135	17.27	68.2	18	1.710	8.5
1.143	18.16	71.9	19	1.819	7.3
1.151	19.03	75.5	20	1.928	6.1
1.159	19.92	79.1	21	2.037	5.0
1.168	20.80	83.0	22	2.147	3.9
1.176	21.68	86.9	23	2.266	2.8
1.184	22.54	90.9	24	2.376	1.7
1.192	23.39	94.7	25	2.488	+0.5
1.201	24.27	98.5	26	2.610	—1.1
1.204	24.60	100.	26.395	2.661	—1.6

Temperature correction 1° Salometer for every 7½° F added to reading for temperatures above 60°F; subtracted below.

*Specific gravity of sea water.

CaCl₂ is the most commonly used brine.
†Courtesy Ingersoll-Rand Co. See page 6.

VII

TABLE 49. SPECIFIC GRAVITY OF CAUSTIC SODA SOLUTIONS 15°C (59°F) BY LUNGE.†

Specific gravity	Degrees Baume	Degrees Twaddell	Per cent NaOH	Per cent Na²O	One gallon contains pounds NaOH	pounds Na²O
1.007	1.0	1.4	0.61	0.47	0.051	0.039
1.014	2.0	2.8	1.20	0.93	0.101	0.079
1.022	3.1	4.4	2.00	1.55	0.170	0.132
1.029	4.1	5.8	2.70	2.10	0.232	0.180
1.036	5.1	7.2	3.35	2.60	0.289	0.225
1.045	6.2	9.0	4.00	3.10	0.345	0.268
1.052	7.2	10.4	4.64	3.60	0.407	0.316
1.060	8.2	12.0	5.29	4.10	0.467	0.362
1.067	9.1	13.4	5.87	4.55	0.522	0.405
1.075	10.1	15.0	6.55	5.08	0.587	0.455
1.083	11.1	16.6	7.31	5.67	0.660	0.512
1.091	12.1	18.2	8.00	6.20	0.728	0.564
1.100	13.2	20.0	8.68	6.73	0.796	0.617
1.108	14.1	21.6	9.42	7.30	0.870	0.674
1.116	15.1	23.2	10.06	7.80	0.936	0.726
1.125	16.1	25.0	10.97	8.50	1.029	0.797
1.134	17.1	26.8	11.84	9.18	1.119	0.868
1.142	18.0	28.4	12.64	9.80	1.203	0.933
1.152	19.1	30.4	13.55	10.50	1.301	1.008
1.162	20.2	32.4	14.37	11.14	1.392	1.079
1.171	21.2	34.2	15.13	11.73	1.477	1.145
1.180	22.1	36.0	15.91	12.33	1.565	1.213
1.190	23.1	38.0	16.77	13.00	1.664	1.290
1.200	24.2	40.0	17.67	13.70	1.768	1.371
1.210	25.2	42.0	18.58	14.40	1.874	1.453
1.220	26.1	44.0	19.58	15.18	1.992	1.554
1.231	27.2	46.2	20.59	15.96	2.113	1.638
1.241	28.2	48.2	21.42	16.76	2.216	1.734
1.252	29.2	50.4	22.64	17.55	2.363	1.832
1.263	30.2	52.6	23.67	18.35	2.492	1.932
1.274	31.2	54.8	24.81	19.23	2.635	2.042
1.285	32.2	57.0	25.80	20.00	2.764	2.143
1.297	33.2	59.4	26.83	20.80	2.901	2.249
1.308	34.1	61.6	27.80	21.55	3.032	2.350
1.320	35.2	64.0	28.83	22.35	3.173	2.460
1.332	36.1	66.4	29.93	23.20	3.324	2.576
1.345	37.2	69.0	31.22	24.20	3.501	2.714
1.357	38.1	71.4	32.47	25.17	3.673	2.848
1.370	39.2	74.0	33.69	26.12	3.848	2.983
1.383	40.2	76.6	34.96	27.10	4.031	3.125
1.397	41.2	79.4	36.25	28.10	4.222	3.273
1.410	42.2	82.0	37.47	29.05	4.405	3.415
1.424	43.2	84.8	38.80	30.08	4.606	3.571
1.438	44.2	87.6	39.99	31.00	4.794	3.716
1.453	45.2	90.6	41.41	32.10	5.016	3.888
1.468	46.2	93.6	42.83	33.20	5.242	4.063
1.483	47.2	96.6	44.38	34.40	5.487	4.253
1.498	48.2	99.6	46.15	35.70	5.764	4.459
1.514	49.2	102.8	47.60	36.90	6.008	4.658
1.530	50.2	106.0	49.02	38.00	6.253	4.847

†*Courtesy Ingersoll-Rand Co. See page 6.*

SECTION IX—MECHANICAL DATA

CONTENTS

IX

TABLE 50. CAST IRON PIPE DIMENSIONS.†

Nominal Diameter	CLASS A 100 Foot Head 43 Pounds Pressure			CLASS B 200 Foot Head 86 Pounds Pressure			CLASS C 300 Foot Head 130 Pounds Pressure			CLASS D 400 Foot Head 173 Pounds Pressure		
	Outside Dia-meter	Wall Thick-ness	Inside Dia-meter	Outside Dia-meter	Wall Thick-ness	Inside Dia-meter	Outside Dia-meter	Wall Thick-ness	Inside Dia-meter	Outside Dia-meter	Wall Thick-ness	Inside Dia-meter
Inches	Inches	Inches	Inches	Inches	Inches	Inches	Inches	Inches	Inches	Inches	Inches	Inches
3	3.80	0.39	3.02	3.96	0.42	3.12	3.96	0.45	3.06	3.96	0.48	3.00
4	4.80	0.42	3.96	5.00	0.45	4.10	5.00	0.48	4.04	5.00	0.52	3.96
6	6.90	0.44	6.02	7.10	0.48	6.14	7.10	0.51	6.08	7.10	0.55	6.00
8	9.05	0.46	8.13	9.05	0.51	8.03	9.30	0.56	8.18	9.30	0.60	8.10
10	11.10	0.50	10.10	11.10	0.57	9.96	11.40	0.62	10.16	11.40	0.68	10.04
12	13.20	0.54	12.12	13.20	0.62	11.96	13.50	0.68	12.14	13.50	0.75	12.00
14	15.30	0.57	14.16	15.30	0.66	13.98	15.65	0.74	14.17	15.65	0.82	14.01
16	17.40	0.60	16.20	17.40	0.70	16.00	17.80	0.80	16.20	17.80	0.89	16.02
18	19.50	0.64	18.22	19.50	0.75	18.00	19.92	0.87	18.18	19.92	0.96	18.00
20	21.60	0.67	20.26	21.60	0.80	20.00	22.06	0.92	20.22	22.06	1.03	20.00
24	25.80	0.76	24.28	25.80	0.89	24.02	26.32	1.04	24.22	26.32	1.16	24.00
30	31.74	0.88	29.98	32.00	1.03	29.94	32.40	1.20	30.00	32.74	1.37	30.00
36	37.96	0.99	35.98	38.30	1.15	36.00	38.70	1.36	39.98	39.16	1.58	36.00
42	44.20	1.10	42.00	44.50	1.28	41.94	45.10	1.54	42.02	45.58	1.78	42.02
48	50.50	1.26	47.98	50.80	1.42	47.96	51.40	1.71	47.98	51.98	1.96	48.06
54	56.66	1.35	53.96	57.10	1.55	54.00	57.80	1.90	54.00	58.40	2.23	53.94
60	62.80	1.39	60.02	63.40	1.67	60.06	64.20	2.00	60.20	64.82	2.38	60.06
72	75.34	1.62	72.10	76.00	1.95	72.10	76.88	2.39	72.10			
84	87.54	1.72	84.10	88.54	2.22	84.10						

Nominal Diameter	CLASS E 500 Foot Head 217 Pounds Pressure			CLASS F 600 Foot Head 260 Pounds Pressure			CLASS G 700 Foot Head 304 Pounds Pressure			CLASS H 800 Foot Head 347 Pounds Pressure		
	Outside Dia-meter	Wall Thick-ness	Inside Dia-meter	Outside Dia-meter	Wall Thick-ness	Inside Dia-meter	Outside Dia-meter	Wall Thick-ness	Inside Dia-meter	Outside Dia-meter	Wall Thick-ness	Inside Dia-meter
Inches	Inches	Inches	Inches	Inches	Inches	Inches	Inches	Inches	Inches	Inches	Inches	Inches
6	7.22	0.58	6.06	7.22	0.61	6.00	7.38	0.65	6.08	7.38	0.69	6.00
8	9.42	0.66	8.10	9.42	0.71	8.00	9.60	0.75	8.10	9.60	0.80	8.00
10	11.60	0.74	10.12	11.60	0.80	10.00	11.84	0.86	10.12	11.84	0.92	10.00
12	13.78	0.82	12.14	13.78	0.89	12.00	14.08	0.97	12.14	14.08	1.04	12.00
14	15.98	0.90	14.18	15.98	0.99	14.00	16.32	1.07	14.18	16.32	1.16	14.00
16	18.16	0.98	16.20	18.16	1.08	16.00	18.54	1.18	16.18	18.54	1.27	16.00
18	20.34	1.07	18.20	20.34	1.17	18.00	20.78	1.28	18.22	20.78	1.39	18.00
20	22.54	1.15	20.24	22.54	1.27	20.00	23.02	1.39	20.24	23.02	1.51	20.00
24	26.90	1.31	24.28	26.90	1.45	24.00	27.76	1.75	24.26	27.76	1.88	24.00
30	33.10	1.55	30.00	33.46	1.73	30.00						
36	39.60	1.80	36.00	40.04	2.02	36.00						

The A.W.W.A. Standard Specifications, Section 3 states: "For pipes whose standard thickness is less than 1 inch, the thickness of metal in the body of the pipe shall not be more than 0.08 of an inch less than the standard thickness, and for pipes whose standard thickness is 1 inch or more, the variation shall not exceed 0.10 of an inch, except that for spaces not exceeding 8 inches in length in any direction, variations from the standard thickness of 0.02 of an inch in excess of the allowance above given shall be permitted."

Courtesy Cast Iron Pipe Research Association. See page 6.

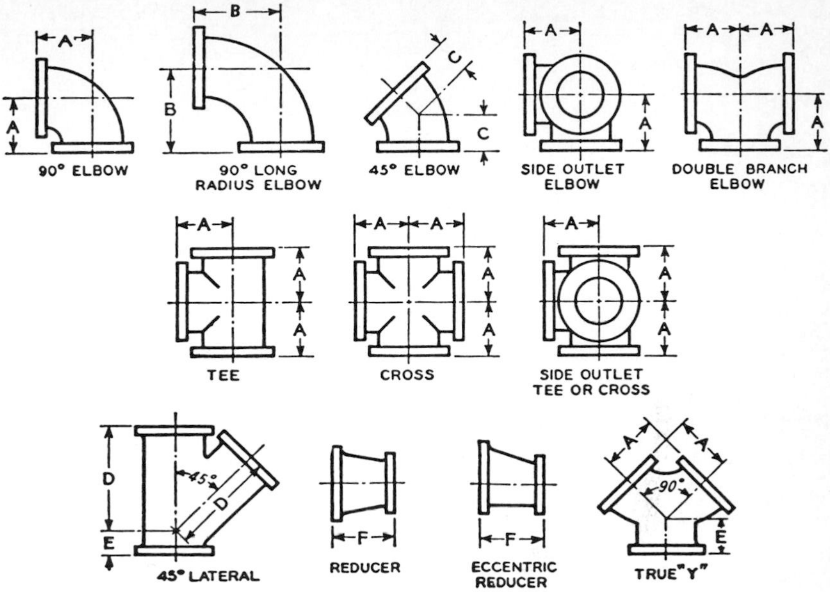
90° ELBOW
90° LONG RADIUS ELBOW
45° ELBOW
SIDE OUTLET ELBOW
DOUBLE BRANCH ELBOW
TEE
CROSS
SIDE OUTLET TEE OR CROSS
45° LATERAL
REDUCER
ECCENTRIC REDUCER
TRUE "Y"
A
B
C
D
E
F
45°
90°

TABLE 51. CLASS 125 CAST IRON FLANGES AND FITTINGS.†

		A	B	C	D	E	F			
Nominal Pipe Size	Inside Diam. of Fittings	Center to Face 90 Deg. Elbow Tees, Crosses True "Y" and Double Branch Elbow	Center to Face 90 Deg. Long Radius Elbow	Center to Face 45 Deg. Elbow	Center to Face Lateral	Short Center to Face True "Y" and Lateral	Face to Face Reducer	Diam. of Flange	Thick-ness of Flange	Wall Thick-ness
1	1	3½	5	1¾	5¾	1¾	....	4¼	7/16	5/16
1¼	1¼	3¾	5½	2	6¼	1¾	....	4⅝	½	5/16
1½	1½	4	6	2¼	7	2	....	5	9/16	5/16
2	2	4½	6½	2½	8	2½	5	6	⅝	5/16
2½	2½	5	7	3	9½	2½	5½	7	11/16	5/16
3	3	5½	7¾	3	10	3	6	7½	¾	⅜
3½	3½	6	8½	3½	11½	3	6½	8½	13/16	7/16
4	4	6½	9	4	12	3	7	9	15/16	½
5	5	7½	10¼	4½	13½	3½	8	10	15/16	½
6	6	8	11½	5	14½	3½	9	11	1	9/16
8	8	9	14	5½	17½	4½	11	13½	1⅛	⅝
10	10	11	16½	6½	20½	5	12	16	1 3/16	¾
12	12	12	19	7½	24½	5½	14	19	1¼	13/16
14 OD	14	14	21½	7½	27	6	16	21	1⅜	⅞
16 OD	16	15	24	8	30	6½	18	23½	1 7/16	1
18 OD	18	16½	26½	8½	32	7	19	25	1 9/16	1 1/16
20 OD	20	18	29	9½	35	8	20	27½	1 11/16	1⅛
24 OD	24	22	34	11	40½	9	24	32	1⅞	1¼
30 OD	30	25	41½	15	49	10	30	38¾	2⅛	1 7/16
36 OD	36	28*	49	18	....	....	36	46	2⅜	1⅝
42 OD	42	31*	56½	21	....	....	42	53	2⅝	1 13/16
48 OD	48	34*	64	24	....	....	48	59½	2¾	2

All dimensions given in inches.

*Does not apply to true Y's or double branch elbows.

†*Courtesy American Society of Mechanical Engineers. See page 6.*

TABLE 52. AMERICAN STANDARD C.I. PIPE FLANGES.†††

Nominal Pipe Size Inches	Dia. of Flange	Dia. of Bolt Circle	No. of Bolts	*25 lb. Standard Flange Thickness	*25 lb. Standard Size Bolts	*25 lb. Standard Lgth. Bolts	*125 lb. Standard Flange Thickness	*125 lb. Standard Size Bolts	*125 lb. Standard Lgth. Bolts
1	4¼	3⅛	4				7/16	½	1¾
1¼	4⅝	3½	4				½	½	2
1½	5	3⅞	4				9/16	½	2
2	6	4¾	4				⅝	⅝	2¼
2½	7	5½	4				11/16	⅝	2½
3	7½	6	4				¾	⅝	2½
3½	8½	7	8				13/16	⅝	2¾
4	9	7½	8	¾	⅝	2¼	15/16	⅝	3
5	10	8½	8	¾	⅝	2¼	15/16	¾	3
6	11	9½	8	¾	⅝	2¼	1	¾	3¼
8	13½	11¾	8	¾	⅝	2¼	1⅛	¾	3½
10	16	14¼	12	⅞	⅝	2½	13/16	⅞	3¾
12	19	17	12	1	⅝	2¾	1¼	⅞	3¾
14 OD	21	18¾	12	1⅛	¾	3¼	1⅜	1	4¼
16 OD	23½	21¼	16	1⅛	¾	3¼	17/16	1	4½
18 OD	25	22¾	16	1¼	¾	3½	19/16	1⅛	4¾
20 OD	27½	25	20	1¼	¾	3½	111/16	1⅛	5
24 OD	32	29½	20	1⅜	¾	3¾	1⅞	1¼	5½
30 OD	38¾	36	28	1½	⅞	4¼	2⅛	1¼	6¼
36 OD	46	42¾	32	1⅝	⅞	5	2⅜	1½	7
42 OD	53	49½	36	1¾	1	5¼	2⅝	1½	7½
48 OD	59½	56	44	2	1	5½	2¾	1½	7¾
54 OD	66¼	62¾	44	2¼	1	5¾	3	1¾	8½
60 OD	73	69¼	52	2¼	1⅛	6	3⅛	1¾	8¾
72 OD	86½	82½	60	2½	1⅛	6¼	3½	1¾	9½
84 OD	99¾	95½	64	2¾	1¼	7¼	3⅞	2	10½
96 OD	113¼	108½	68	3	1¼	7¾	4¼	2¼	11½

These flanges are all with plain face.

†250 lb. std. flanges have 1/16 in. raised face. This is included in flange thickness.

††800 lb. std. flanges are of two types; raised face and male-female. Raised face and male side of male-female have 1/4 in. raised face which is not included in flange thickness. Female side is faced 3/16 in. deep within a raised face not included in flange thickness.

Nominal pipe size	*250 lb. Standard Flange dia.	*250 lb. Standard Flange thickness†	*250 lb. Standard Bolt circle dia.	*250 lb. Standard Bolt No.	*250 lb. Standard Bolt size	*800 lb. Standard Flange dia.	*800 lb. Standard Flange thickness††	*800 lb. Standard Bolt circle dia.	*800 lb. Standard Bolts No.	*800 lb. Standard Bolts size
1	4⅞	11/16	3½	4	⅝					
1¼	5¼	¾	3⅞	4	⅝					
1½	6⅛	13/16	4½	4	¾					
2	6½	⅞	5	8	⅝	6½	1¼	5	8	⅝
2½	7½	1	5⅞	8	¾	7½	1⅜	5⅞	8	¾
3	8¼	1⅛	6⅝	8	¾	8¼	1½	6⅝	8	¾
3½	9	13/16	7¼	8	¾	9	1⅝	7¼	8	⅞
4	10	1¼	7⅞	8	¾	10¾	1⅞	8½	8	⅞
5	11	1⅜	9¼	8	¾	13	2⅛	10½	8	1
6	12½	17/16	10⅝	12	¾	14	2¼	11½	12	1
8	15	1⅝	13	12	⅞	16½	2½	13¾	12	1⅛
10	17½	1⅞	15¼	16	1	20	2⅞	17	16	1¼
12	20½	2	17¾	16	1⅛	22	3	19¼	20	1¼
14 OD	23	2⅛	20¼	20	1⅛					
16 OD	25½	2¼	22½	20	1¼					
18 OD	28	2⅜	24¾	24	1¼					
20 OD	30½	2½	27	24	1¼					
24 OD	36	2¾	32	24	1½					
30 OD	43	3	39¼	28	1¾					
36 OD	50	3⅜	46	32	2					
42 OD	57	311/16	52¾	36	2					
48 OD	65	4	60¾	40	2					

*Pressure ratings at ordinary room temperatures

Standard, lb.	Size, in.	Max. rating, psi
25	4-36	43
25	42-96	25
125	1-12	175
125	14-48	150
125	54-96	No established rating
250	1-12	400
250	14-48	300
800	2-12	800

Authority: ASA B16 b2—1931 (25 lb) ASA B16b—1944 (250 lb)
ASA B16.1—1948 (125 lb) ASA B16b1—1931 (800 lb)

†††*Courtesy American Society Mechanical Engineers. See page 6.*

TABLE 53. PROPERTIES OF STEEL AND WROUGHT IRON PIPE.†

Nominal Diameter	Schedule	Outside Diameter	Wall Thickness	Internal Diameter	Internal Area	ϵ/D $\epsilon = 0.00015$ ft.
Inches		Inches	Inches	Inches	Sq. Inches	
⅛	40 (S)	0.405	0.068	0.269	0.0568	0.00669
	80 (X)		0.095	0.215	0.0363	0.00837
¼	40 (S)	0.540	0.088	0.364	0.1041	0.00495
	80 (X)		0.119	0.302	0.0716	0.00596
⅜	40 (S)	0.675	0.091	0.493	0.1909	0.00365
	80 (X)		0.126	0.423	0.1405	0.00426
½	40 (S)	0.840	0.109	0.622	0.3039	0.00289
	80 (X)		0.147	0.546	0.2341	0.00330
	160		0.187	0.466	0.1706	0.00386
	(XX)		0.294	0.252	0.0499	0.00714
¾	40 (S)	1.050	0.113	0.824	0.5333	0.00218
	80 (X)		0.154	0.742	0.4324	0.00243
	160		0.218	0.614	0.2961	0.00293
	(XX)		0.308	0.434	0.1479	0.00415
1	40 (S)	1.315	0.133	1.049	0.8643	0.00172
	80 (X)		0.179	0.957	0.7193	0.00188
	160		0.250	0.815	0.5217	0.00221
	(XX)		0.358	0.599	0.2818	0.00301
1¼	40 (S)	1.660	0.140	1.380	1.496	0.00130
	80 (X)		0.191	1.278	1.283	0.00141
	160		0.250	1.160	1.057	0.00155
	(XX)		0.382	0.896	0.6305	0.00201
1½	40 (S)	1.900	0.145	1.610	2.036	0.00112
	80 (X)		0.200	1.500	1.767	0.00120
	160		0.281	1.338	1.406	0.00135
	(XX)		0.400	1.100	0.9503	0.00164
2	40 (S)	2.375	0.154	2.067	3.356	0.00087
	80 (X)		0.218	1.939	2.953	0.00093
	160		0.343	1.689	2.241	0.00107
	(XX)		0.436	1.503	1.774	0.00120
2½	40 (S)	2.875	0.203	2.469	4.788	0.000729
	80 (X)		0.276	2.323	4.238	0.000775
	160		0.375	2.125	3.547	0.000847
	(XX)		0.552	1.771	2.464	0.00102
3	40 (S)	3.500	0.216	3.068	7.393	0.000587
	80 (X)		0.300	2.900	6.605	0.000621
	160		0.437	2.626	5.416	0.000685
	(XX)		0.600	2.300	4.155	0.000783
3½	40 (S)	4.000	0.226	3.548	9.887	0.000507
	80 (X)		0.318	3.364	8.888	0.000535
	(XX)		0.636	2.728	5.845	0.000660
4	40 (S)	4.500	0.237	4.026	12.73	0.000447
	80 (X)		0.337	3.826	11.50	0.000470
	120		0.437	3.626	10.33	0.000496
	160		0.531	3.438	9.283	0.000524
	(XX)		0.674	3.152	7.803	0.000571

S = Wall thickness formerly designated "standard weight".   X = Wall thickness formerly designated "extra heavy."
XX = Wall thickness formerly designated "double extra heavy".

†*Courtesy Hydraulic Institute. See page 6.*

TABLE 53. (Cont.) PROPERTIES OF STEEL AND WROUGHT IRON PIPE.

Nominal Diameter	Schedule	Outside Diameter	Wall Thickness	Internal Diameter	Internal Area	ϵ/D $\epsilon = 0.00015$ ft.
Inches		Inches	Inches	Inches	Sq. Inches	
5	40 (S)	5.563	0.258	5.047	20.01	0.000357
	80 (X)		0.375	4.813	18.19	0.000374
	120		0.500	4.563	16.35	0.000394
	160		0.625	4.313	14.61	0.000417
	(XX)		0.750	4.063	12.97	0.000443
6	40 (S)	6.625	0.280	6.065	28.89	0.000293
	80 (X)		0.432	5.761	26.07	0.000312
	120		0.562	5.501	23.77	0.000327
	160		0.718	5.189	21.15	0.000347
	(XX)		0.864	4.897	18.83	0.000368
8	20	8.625	0.250	8.125	51.85	0.000222
	30 (S)		0.277	8.071	51.16	0.000223
	40 (S)		0.322	7.981	50.03	0.000226
	60		0.406	7.813	47.94	0.000230
	80 (X)		0.500	7.625	45.66	0.000236
	100		0.593	7.439	43.46	0.000242
	120		0.718	7.189	40.59	0.000250
	140		0.812	7.001	38.50	0.000257
	(XX)		0.875	6.875	37.12	0.000262
	160		0.906	6.813	36.46	0.000264
10	20	10.75	0.250	10.250	82.52	0.000176
	(S)		0.279	10.192	81.58	0.000177
	30 (S)		0.307	10.136	80.69	0.000178
	40 (S)		0.365	10.020	78.85	0.000180
	60 (X)		0.500	9.750	74.66	0.000185
	80		0.593	9.564	71.84	0.000188
	100		0.718	9.314	68.13	0.000193
	120		0.843	9.064	64.53	0.000199
	140		1.000	8.750	60.13	0.000206
	160		1.125	8.500	56.75	0.000212
12	20	12.75	0.250	12.250	117.86	0.000147
	30		0.330	12.090	114.80	0.000149
	(S)		0.375	12.000	113.10	0.000150
	40		0.406	11.938	111.93	0.000151
	(X)		0.500	11.750	108.43	0.000153
	60		0.562	11.626	106.16	0.000155
	80		0.687	11.376	101.64	0.000158
	100		0.843	11.064	96.14	0.000163
	120		1.000	10.750	90.76	0.000167
	140		1.125	10.500	86.59	0.000171
	160		1.312	10.126	80.53	0.000178
14 OD	10	14.00	0.250	13.500	143.14	0.000133
	20		0.312	13.376	140.52	0.000135
	30		0.375	13.250	137.89	0.000136
	40		0.437	13.126	135.32	0.000137
	60		0.593	12.814	128.96	0.000140
	80		0.750	12.500	122.72	0.000144
	100		0.937	12.126	115.49	0.000148
	120		1.062	11.876	110.77	0.000152
	140		1.250	11.500	103.87	0.000157
	160		1.406	11.188	98.31	0.000161

S=Wall thickness formerly designated "standard weight".   X=Wall thickness formerly designated "extra heavy"
XX=Wall thickness formerly designated "double extra heavy".

TABLE 53. (Cont.) PROPERTIES OF STEEL AND WROUGHT IRON PIPE.

Nominal Diameter	Schedule	Outside Diameter	Wall Thickness	Internal Diameter	Internal Area	ϵ/D $\epsilon = 0.00015$ ft.
Inches		Inches	Inches	Inches	Sq. Inches	
16 OD	10	16.00	0.250	15.500	188.69	0.000116
	20		0.312	15.376	185.69	0.000117
	30		0.375	15.250	182.65	0.000118
	40		0.500	15.000	176.72	0.000120
	60		0.656	14.688	169.44	0.000121
	80		0.843	14.314	160.92	0.000126
	100		1.031	13.938	152.58	0.000129
	120		1.218	13.564	144.50	0.000133
	140		1.437	13.126	135.32	0.000137
	160		1.562	12.876	130.21	0.000140
18 OD	10	18.00	0.250	17.500	240.53	0.000103
	20		0.312	17.376	237.13	0.000104
	(S)		0.375	17.250	233.71	0.000104
	30		0.437	17.126	230.36	0.000105
	(X)		0.500	17.000	226.98	0.000106
	40		0.562	16.876	223.68	0.000107
	60		0.718	16.564	215.49	0.000109
	80		0.937	16.126	204.24	0.000112
	100		1.156	15.688	193.30	0.000115
	120		1.343	15.314	184.19	0.000118
	140		1.562	14.876	173.81	0.000121
	160		1.750	14.500	165.13	0.000124
20 OD	10	20.00	0.250	19.500	298.65	0.0000923
	20		0.375	19.252	291.04	0.0000935
	30		0.500	19.000	283.53	0.0000947
	40		0.593	18.814	278.01	0.0000957
	60		0.812	18.376	265.21	0.0000980
	80		1.031	17.938	252.72	0.000100
	100		1.250	17.500	240.53	0.000103
	120		1.500	17.000	226.98	0.000106
	140		1.750	16.500	213.83	0.000109
	160		1.937	16.126	204.24	0.000112
24 OD	10	24.00	0.250	23.500	433.74	0.0000766
	20		0.375	23.250	424.56	0.0000774
	(S)		0.500	23.000	415.48	0.0000783
	30		0.562	22.876	411.01	0.0000787
	40		0.687	22.626	402.07	0.0000796
	60		0.937	22.126	384.50	0.0000814
	80		1.218	21.564	365.22	0.0000835
	100		1.500	21.000	346.36	0.0000857
	120		1.750	20.500	330.06	0.0000878
	140		2.062	19.876	310.28	0.0000906
	160		2.312	19.376	294.86	0.0000929
30 OD	10	30.00	0.312	29.376	677.76	0.0000613
	20		0.500	29.000	660.52	0.0000621
	30		0.625	28.750	649.18	0.0000626

S = Wall thickness formerly designated "standard weight."   X = Wall thickness formerly designated "extra heavy."
XX = Wall thickness formerly designated "double extra heavy".

IX

TABLE 54. WEIGHTS AND DIMENSIONS OF COPPER AND BRASS PIPE AND TUBES.†

Nominal Size Inches	Outside Diameter Inches	Type K		Type L		Type M		Copper and Brass Pipe—Regular Wt.		Weight per Ft.—Lb.		
		Inside Diameter Inches	Weight per Ft. Lb.	Inside Diameter Inches	Weight per Ft. Lb.	Inside Diameter Inches	Weight per Ft. Lb.	Outside Diameter Inches	Inside Diameter Inches	67% Copper	85% Copper	100% Copper
⅛	.250	.186	.085	.200	.068	.20	.068	.405	.281	.246	.253	.259
¼	.375	.311	.134	.315	.126	.325	.106	.540	.375	.437	.450	.460
⅜	.500	.402	.269	.430	.198	.450	.144	.675	.494	.612	.630	.643
½	.625	.527	.344	.545	.284	.569	.203	.840	.625	.911	.938	.957
⅝	.750	.652	.418	.666	.362	.690	.263					
¾	.875	.745	.641	.785	.454	.811	.328	1.050	.822	1.24	1.27	1.30
1	1.125	.995	.839	1.025	.653	1.055	.464	1.315	1.062	1.74	1.79	1.83
1¼	1.375	1.245	1.04	1.265	.882	1.291	.681	1.660	1.368	2.56	2.63	2.69
1½	1.625	1.481	1.36	1.505	1.14	1.571	.940	1.900	1.600	3.04	3.13	3.20
2	2.125	1.959	2.06	1.985	1.75	2.009	1.46	2.375	2.062	4.02	4.14	4.23
2½	2.625	2.435	2.92	2.465	2.48	2.495	2.03	2.875	2.500	5.83	6.00	6.14
3	3.125	2.907	4.00	2.945	3.33	2.981	2.68	3.500	3.062	8.31	8.56	8.75
3½	3.625	3.385	5.12	3.425	4.29	3.459	3.58	4.000	3.500	10.85	11.17	11.41
4	4.125	3.857	6.51	3.905	5.38	3.935	4.66	4.500	4.000	12.29	12.66	12.94
4½								5.000	4.500	13.74	14.15	14.46
5	5.125	4.805	9.67	4.875	7.61	4.907	6.66	5.563	5.063	15.40	15.85	16.21
6	6.125	5.741	13.87	5.845	10.20	5.881	8.91	6.625	6.125	18.44	18.99	19.41
7								7.625	7.062	23.92	24.63	25.17
8	8.125	7.583	25.90	7.725	19.29	7.785	16.46	8.625	8.000	30.05	30.95	31.63

The National Bureau of Standards has recommended the elimination of the 3½" and 4½" pipe sizes.

†Courtesy Ingersoll-Rand Company. See page 6.

TABLE 55. CYLINDRICAL TANKS SET VERTICALLY.
CAPACITY IN U. S. GALLONS PER FOOT OF DEPTH.

Dia. of Tank	Cap. U.S. Gals.	Dia. of Tank	Cap. U.S. Gals.	Dia. of Tank	Cap. U.S. Gals.	Dia. of Tank	Cap. U.S. Gals.	Dia. of Tank	Cap. U.S. Gals.	Dia. of Tank	Cap. U.S. Gals.	Dia. of Tank	Cap. U.S. Gals.	Dia. of Tank	Cap. U.S. Gals.	Dia. of Tank	Cap. U.S. Gals.	Dia. of Tank	Cap. U.S. Gals.
1' 0"	5.87	2' 3"	29.74	3' 6"	71.97	4' 9"	132.56	6' 0"	211.51	9' 6"	530.24	13' 0"	992.91	16' 6"	1599.5	20' 0"	2350.1	23' 6"	3244.6
1' 1"	6.89	2' 4"	31.99	3' 7"	75.44	4' 10"	137.25	6' 3"	229.50	9' 9"	558.51	13' 3"	1031.5	16' 9"	1648.4	20' 3"	2409.2	23' 9"	3314
1' 2"	8.00	2' 5"	34.31	3' 8"	78.99	4' 11"	142.02	6' 6"	248.23	10' 0"	587.52	13' 6"	1070.8	17' 0"	1697.9	20' 6"	2469.1	24' 0"	3384.1
1' 3"	9.18	2' 6"	36.72	3' 9"	82.62	5' 0"	146.88	6' 9"	267.69	10' 3"	617.26	13' 9"	1110.8	17' 3"	1748.2	20' 9"	2529.6	24' 3"	3455
1' 4"	10.44	2' 7"	39.21	3' 10"	86.33	5' 1"	151.82	7' 0"	287.88	10' 6"	640.74	14' 0"	1151.5	17' 6"	1799.3	21' 0"	2591	24' 6"	3526.6
1' 5"	11.79	2' 8"	41.78	3' 11"	90.13	5' 2"	156.83	7' 3"	308.81	10' 9"	678.95	14' 3"	1193.0	17' 9"	1851.1	21' 3"	2653	24' 9"	3598.9
1' 6"	13.22	2' 9"	44.43	4' 0"	94.00	5' 3"	161.93	7' 6"	330.48	11' 0"	710.90	14' 6"	1235.3	18' 0"	1903.6	21' 6"	2715.8	25' 0"	3672
1' 7"	14.73	2' 10"	47.16	4' 1"	97.96	5' 4"	167.12	7' 9"	352.88	11' 3"	743.58	14' 9"	1278.2	18' 3"	1956.8	21' 9"	2779.3	25' 3"	3745.8
1' 8"	16.32	2' 11"	49.98	4' 2"	102.12	5' 5"	172.38	8' 0"	376.01	11' 6"	776.99	15' 0"	1321.9	18' 6"	2010.8	22' 0"	2843.6	25' 6"	3820.3
1' 9"	17.99	3' 0"	52.88	4' 3"	106.12	5' 6"	177.72	8' 3"	399.88	11' 9"	811.14	15' 3"	1366.4	18' 9"	2065.5	22' 3"	2908.6	25' 9"	3895.6
1' 10"	19.75	3' 1"	55.86	4' 4"	110.32	5' 7"	183.15	8' 6"	424.48	12' 0"	846.03	15' 6"	1411.5	19' 0"	2120.9	22' 6"	2974.3	26' 0"	3971.6
1' 11"	21.58	3' 2"	58.92	4' 5"	114.61	5' 8"	188.66	8' 9"	449.82	12' 3"	881.65	15' 9"	1457.4	19' 3"	2177.1	22' 9"	3040.8	26' 3"	4048.4
2' 0"	23.50	3' 3"	62.06	4' 6"	118.97	5' 9"	194.25	9' 0"	475.89	12' 6"	918.00	16' 0"	1504.1	19' 6"	2234.0	23' 0"	3108	26' 6"	4125.9
2' 1"	25.50	3' 4"	65.28	4' 7"	123.42	5' 10"	199.92	9' 3"	502.70	12' 9"	955.09	16' 3"	1551.4	19' 9"	2291.7	23' 3"	3175.9	26' 9"	4204.1
2' 2"	27.58	3' 5"	68.58	4' 8"	127.95	5' 11"	205.67										

To find the capacity of tanks of larger diameter than shown in the table select a tank of ½ the desired size and multiply the capacity given in the table by 4, or one of 1/3 size and multiply by 9, etc.

The capacity of a square tank where the length of one side equals the diameter of a round tank is equal to the capacity of the round tank divided by 0.7854.

TABLE 56. CYLINDRICAL TANKS SET HORIZONTALLY AND PARTIALLY FILLED.

DIAMETER	GALLONS PER FOOT OF LENGTH WHEN TANK IS FILLED								
	1/10	1/5	3/10	2/5	1/2	3/5	7/10	4/5	9/10
1 ft	.3	.8	1.4	2.1	2.9	3.6	4.3	4.9	5.5
2 ft	1.2	3.3	5.9	8.8	11.7	14.7	17.5	20.6	22.2
3 ft	2.7	7.5	13.6	19.8	26.4	33.0	39.4	45.2	50.1
4 ft	4.9	13.4	23.8	35.0	47.0	59.0	70.2	80.5	89.0
5 ft	7.6	20.0	37.0	55.0	73.0	92.0	110.0	126.0	139.0
6 ft	11.0	30.0	53.0	78.0	106.0	133.0	158.0	182.0	201.0
7 ft	15.0	41.0	73.0	107.0	144.0	181.0	215.0	247.0	272.0
8 ft	19.0	52.0	96.0	140.0	188.0	235.0	281.0	322.0	356.0
9 ft	25.0	67.0	112.0	178.0	238.0	298.0	352.0	408.0	450.0
10 ft	30.0	83.0	149.0	219.0	294.0	368.0	440.0	504.0	556.0
11 ft	37.0	101.0	179.0	265.0	356.0	445.0	531.0	610.0	672.0
12 ft	44.0	120.0	214.0	315.0	423.0	530.0	632.0	741.0	800.0
13 ft	51.0	141.0	250.0	370.0	496.0	621.0	740.0	850.0	940.0
14 ft	60.0	164.0	291.0	430.0	576.0	722.0	862.0	989.0	1084.0
15 ft	68.0	188.0	334.0	494.0	661.0	829.0	988.0	1134.0	1253.0

IX

TABLE 57. V-BELT DRIVES.†

RECOMMENDED V-BELT CROSS-SECTIONS FOR VARIOUS HP. AND SPEEDS

Horsepower	MOTOR SPEED—RPM						
	1750	1160	870	690	575	490	435
½	A	A	A				
¾	A	A	A				
1	A	A	A				
1½	A	A	A				
2	A	A	A				
3	A	A	B (or A)				
5	B (or A)	B (or A)	B				
7½	B	B	B				
10	B	B	B or C				
15	B	B or C	C (or B)				
20	B or C	C (or B)	C	D	D		
25	C (or B)	C	C	D	D		
30	C	C	C	D	D		
40	C	C or D	C or D	D	D		
50	C	C or D	C or D	D	D		
60	C	C or D	D (or C)	D	D	E	E
75	C	D (or C)	D	D	D (or E)	E	E
100	C	D	D	D or E	E (or D)	E	E
125	....	D	D	D or E	E (or D)	E	E
150	....	D	D	E (or D)	E	E	E
200	....	D	D	E	E	E	E
250	....	D	D	E	E	E	E
300 and above	....	D	D	E	E	E	E

HP. TRANSMITTED BY V-BELTS BASED ON 180° ARC OF CONTACT

Velocity in Feet Per Minute	Cross-Section A	Cross-Section B	Cross-Section C	Cross-Section D	Cross-Section E	Velocity in Feet Per Minute	Cross-Section A	Cross-Section B	Cross-Section C	Cross-Section D	Cross-Section E
	width ½" thick ⅜"	width ²¹⁄₃₂" thick ½"	width ⅞" thick ⅝"	width 1¼" thick ¾"	width 1½" thick 1"		width ½" thick ⅜"	width ²¹⁄₃₂" thick ½"	width ⅞" thick ⅝"	width 1¼" thick ¾"	width 1½" thick 1"
1000	.9	1.2	3.0	5.5	7.5	2600	2.2	2.8	6.7	12.9	17.5
1100	1.0	1.3	3.2	6.0	8.2	2700	2.2	2.9	6.9	13.3	18.0
1200	1.0	1.4	3.4	6.5	8.9	2800	2.3	3.0	7.1	13.7	18.5
1300	1.1	1.5	3.6	7.0	9.6	2900	2.3	3.1	7.3	14.1	19.3
1400	1.2	1.6	3.8	7.5	10.3	3000	2.4	3.2	7.5	14.5	19.8
1500	1.3	1.7	4.0	8.0	11.0						
1600						3100	2.5	3.3	7.7	14.8	20.0
1700	1.4	1.8	4.3	8.4	11.6	3200	2.5	3.4	7.9	15.1	20.5
1800	1.5	1.9	4.6	8.8	12.2	3300	2.5	3.5	8.1	15.4	21.0
1900	1.6	2.1	4.9	9.2	12.8	3400	2.6	3.6	8.3	15.7	21.3
2000	1.6	2.2	5.2	9.6	13.4	3500	2.6	3.7	8.5	16.0	21.8
	1.7	2.3	5.5	10.0	14.0						
2100						3600	2.7	3.8	8.6	16.3	22.0
2200	1.8	2.4	5.7	10.5	14.8	3700	2.7	3.9	8.7	16.6	22.8
2300	1.9	2.5	5.9	11.0	15.2	3800	2.8	4.0	8.8	16.9	23.0
2400	1.9	2.6	6.1	11.5	15.8	3900	2.8	4.1	8.9	17.2	23.3
2500	2.0	2.7	6.3	12.0	16.4	4000	2.8	4.2	9.0	17.5	23.5
	2.1	2.8	6.5	12.5	17.0	5000	2.8	4.2	9.0	17.5	23.5

$$\text{No. of belts required} = \frac{\text{hp of drive}}{(\text{hp per belt}) \left(1 - \dfrac{.175\,(D-d)}{C}\right)}$$

D = pitch diam. of large pulley, inches.
d = pitch diam. of small pulley, inches.
C = center distance ,inches.
For pump, compressor and blower drives 40% more belting than shown by above formula should be used.

†*Courtesy Dayton Rubber Manufacturing Co. See page 6.*

TABLE 58. FUNCTIONS OF NUMBERS.

No.	Square	Cube	Sq. Rt.	Cu. Rt.	Reciprocal	Circum.	Area
1	1	1	1.0000	1.0000	1.000000000	3.1416	0.7854
2	4	8	1.4142	1.2599	.500000000	6.2832	3.1416
3	9	27	1.7321	1.4423	.333333333	9.4248	7.0686
4	16	64	2.0000	1.5874	.250000000	12.5664	12.5664
5	25	125	2.2361	1.7100	.200000000	15.7080	19.635
6	36	216	2.4495	1.8171	.166666667	18.850	28.274
7	49	343	2.6458	1.9129	.142857143	21.991	38.485
8	64	512	2.8284	2.0000	.125000000	25.133	50.266
9	81	729	3.0000	2.0801	.111111111	28.274	63.617
10	100	1,000	3.1623	2.1544	.100000000	31.416	78.540
11	121	1,331	3.3166	2.2240	.090909091	34.558	95.033
12	144	1,728	3.4641	2.2894	.083333333	37.699	113.10
13	169	2,197	3.6056	2.3513	.076923077	40.841	132.73
14	196	2,744	3.7417	2.4101	.071428571	43.982	153.94
15	225	3,375	3.8730	2.4662	.066666667	47.124	176.71
16	256	4,096	4.0000	2.5198	.062500000	50.265	201.06
17	289	4,913	4.1231	2.5713	.058823529	53.407	226.98
18	324	5,832	4.2426	2.6207	.055555556	56.549	254.47
19	361	6,859	4.3589	2.6684	.052631579	59.690	283.53
20	400	8,000	4.4721	2.7144	.050000000	62.832	314.16
21	441	9,261	4.5826	2.7589	.047619048	65.973	346.36
22	484	10,648	4.6904	2.8020	.045454545	69.115	380.13
23	529	12,167	4.7958	2.8439	.043478261	72.257	415.48
24	576	13,824	4.8990	2.8845	.041666667	75.398	452.39
25	625	15,625	5.0000	2.9240	.040000000	78.540	490.87
26	676	17,576	5.0990	2.9625	.038461538	81.681	530.93
27	729	19,683	5.1962	3.0000	.037037037	84.823	572.56
28	784	21,952	5.2915	3.0366	.035714286	87.965	615.75
29	841	24,389	5.3852	3.0723	.034482759	91.106	660.52
30	900	27,000	5.4772	3.1072	.033333333	94.248	706.86
31	961	29,791	5.5678	3.1414	.032258065	97.389	754.77
32	1,024	32,768	5.6569	3.1748	.031250000	100.53	804.25
33	1,089	35,937	5.7446	3.2075	.030303030	103.67	855.30
34	1,156	39,304	5.8310	3.2396	.029411765	106.81	907.92
35	1,225	42,875	5.9161	3.2711	.028571429	109.96	962.11
36	1,296	46,656	6.0000	3.3019	.027777778	113.10	1,017.88
37	1,369	50,653	6.0828	3.3322	.027027027	116.24	1,075.21
38	1,444	54,872	6.1644	3.3620	.026315789	119.38	1,134.11
39	1,521	59,319	6.2450	3.3912	.025641026	122.52	1,194.59
40	1,600	64,000	6.3246	3.4200	.025000000	125.66	1,256.64
41	1,681	68,921	6.4031	3.4482	.024390244	128.81	1,320.25
42	1,764	74,088	6.4807	3.4760	.023809524	131.95	1,385.44
43	1,849	79,507	6.5574	3.5034	.023255814	135.09	1,452.20
44	1,936	85,184	6.6332	3.5304	.022727273	138.23	1,520.53
45	2,025	91,125	6.7082	3.5569	.022222222	141.37	1,590.43
46	2,116	97,336	6.7823	3.5830	.021739130	144.51	1,661.90
47	2,209	103,823	6.8557	3.6088	.021276600	147.65	1,734.94
48	2,304	110,592	6.9282	3.6342	.020833333	150.80	1,809.56
49	2,401	117,649	7.0000	3.6593	.020408163	153.94	1,885.74
50	2,500	125,000	7.0711	3.6840	.020000000	157.08	1,963.50

IX

TABLE 58. (Cont.) FUNCTIONS OF NUMBERS.

No.	Square	Cube	Sq. Rt.	Cu. Rt.	Reciprocal	Circum.	Area
51	2,601	132,651	7.1414	3.7084	.019607843	160.22	2,042.82
52	2,704	140,608	7.2111	3.7325	.019230769	163.36	2,123.72
53	2,809	148,877	7.2801	3.7563	.018867925	166.50	2,206.18
54	2,916	157,464	7.3485	3.7798	.018518519	169.65	2,290.22
55	3,025	166,375	7.4162	3.8030	.018181818	172.79	2,375.83
56	3,136	175,616	7.4833	3.8259	.017857143	175.93	2,463.01
57	3,249	185,193	7.5498	3.8485	.017543860	179.07	2,551.76
58	3,364	195,112	7.6158	3.8709	.017241379	182.21	2,642.08
59	3,481	205,379	7.6811	3.8930	.016949153	185.35	2,733.97
60	3,600	216,000	7.7460	3.9149	.016666667	188.50	2,827.43
61	3,721	226,981	7.8102	3.9365	.016393443	191.64	2,922.47
62	3,844	238,328	7.8740	3.9579	.016129032	194.78	3,019.07
63	3,969	250,047	7.9373	3.9791	.015873016	197.92	3,117.25
64	4,096	262,144	8.0000	4.0000	.015625000	201.06	3,216.99
65	4,225	274,625	8.0623	4.0207	.015384615	204.20	3,318.31
66	4,356	287,496	8.1240	4.0412	.015151515	207.34	3,421.19
67	4,489	300,763	8.1854	4.0616	.014925373	210.49	3,525.65
68	4,624	314,432	8.2462	4.0817	.014705882	213.63	3,631.68
69	4,761	328,509	8.3066	4.1016	.014492754	216.77	3,739.28
70	4,900	343,000	8.3666	4.1213	.014285714	219.91	3,848.45
71	5,041	357,911	8.4261	4.1408	.014084517	223.05	3,959.19
72	5,184	373,248	8.4853	4.1602	.013888889	226.19	4,071.50
73	5,329	389,017	8.5440	4.1793	.013698630	229.34	4,185.39
74	5,476	405,224	8.6023	4.1983	.013513514	232.48	4,300.84
75	5,625	421,875	8.6603	4.2172	.013333333	235.62	4,417.86
76	5,776	438,976	8.7178	4.2358	.013157895	238.76	4,536.46
77	5,929	456,533	8.7750	4.2543	.012987013	241.90	4,656.63
78	6,084	474,552	8.8318	4.2727	.012820513	245.04	4,778.36
79	6,241	493,039	8.8882	4.2908	.012658228	248.19	4,901.67
80	6,400	512,000	8.9443	4.3089	.012500000	251.33	5,026.55
81	6,561	531,441	9.0000	4.3268	.012345679	254.47	5,153.00
82	6,724	551,368	9.0554	4.3445	.012195122	257.61	5,281.02
83	6,889	571,787	9.1104	4.3621	.012048193	260.75	5,410.61
84	7,056	592,704	9.1652	4.3795	.011904762	263.89	5,541.77
85	7,225	614,125	9.2195	4.3968	.011764706	267.04	5,674.50
86	7,396	636,056	9.2736	4.4140	.011627907	270.18	5,808.80
87	7,569	658,503	9.3274	4.4310	.011494253	273.32	5,944.68
88	7,744	681,472	9.3808	4.4480	.011363636	276.46	6,082.12
89	7,921	704,969	9.4340	4.4647	.011235955	279.60	6,221.14
90	8,100	729,000	9.4868	4.4814	.011111111	282.74	6,361.73
91	8,281	753,571	9.5394	4.4979	.010989011	285.88	6,503.88
92	8,464	778,688	9.5917	4.5144	.010869565	289.03	6,647.61
93	8,649	804,357	9.6437	4.5307	.010752688	292.17	6,792.91
94	8,836	830,584	9.6954	4.5468	.010638298	295.31	6,939.78
95	9,025	857,375	9.7468	4.5629	.010526316	298.45	7,088.22
96	9,216	884,736	9.7980	4.5789	.010416667	301.59	7,238.23
97	9,409	912,673	9.8489	4.5947	.010309278	304.73	7,389.81
98	9,604	941,192	9.8995	4.6104	.010204082	307.88	7,542.96
99	9,801	970,299	9.9499	4.6261	.010101010	311.02	7,697.69
100	10,000	1,000,000	10.0000	4.6416	.010000000	314.16	7,853.98

SECTION X—ELECTRICAL DATA

CONTENTS

X

SECTION X—ELECTRICAL DATA

ELECTRIC MOTORS—SERVICE CONDITIONS

Electric motors are manufactured in several types of frame enclosures. This makes it possible to install motors in a variety of atmospheric environments some of which are normally unfriendly to the efficient operation of electrical apparatus. The table following gives the normal temperature rating and overload rating or service factor for each type.

NORMAL TEMPERATURE RISE BY THERMOMETER, AND SERVICE FACTOR, 40 C AMBIENT

Enclosure	Class A Insulation		Class B Insulation		Class H Insulation	
Dripproof Dripproof, guarded Dripproof with moisture-sealed features Forced-ventilated (pipe- or base-)	40 C	1.15	60 C	1.15	90 C	1.15
Self-ventilated (base- and pipe-, where ducts are attached) Splashproof	50 C	1.00	70 C	1.00	110 C	1.00
Totally enclosed fan-cooled (std and exp-proof) TEFC with air-to-water heat exchanger Waterproof, totally enclosed fan-cooled	55 C	1.00	75 C	1.00	115 C	1.00
Weather-protected, NEMA Type I Weather-protected, NEMA Type II	40 C	1.15	60 C	1.15	90 C	1.15

These ratings apply where:

1. Temperature of the surrounding air does not exceed 40 deg. C. (104 deg. F.).

2. Voltage does not vary more than 10% above or below the nameplate rating.

3. Frequency does not vary more than 5% above or below the nameplate rating

4. Both voltage and frequency do not vary the maximum amount given in (2) and (3) simultaneously. Keeping the limit of 5% on frequency the combined variation is limited to 10%.

5. Altitude does not exceed 1000 meters (3300 ft.)

TABLE 59. MOTOR CHARACTERISTICS

Type of Driven Machinery	Motor Type Designation	Speed R.P.M.	Approx. Starting Torque in % of Full Load Torque	Approx. Max. Torque in % of Full Load Torque	Approx. Starting Current in % of Full Load Current	Approx. Speed Regulation % Slip	Load Conditions
Pumps, Centrifugals, Westco Peripheral, Rotary, Propeller	NEMA Design A & B	1800 / 1200 / 900	125 To 275 / 125 To 180 / 115 To 150	200 To 300 / 200 To 275 / 200 To 250	450 To 550 / 450 To 550 / 450 To 550	2 To 4 / 2 To 4 / 2 To 4	Require normal starting torque for continuous duty. Infrequent load fluctuations. Motor provides service factor for overload conditions. Constant speed. No special conditions.
Pumps, Positive Displacement	Ratings 3 H.P. & Larger NEMA Design C	1800 / 1200 / 900	225 To 275 / 200 To 250 / 190 To 225	200 To 300 / 200 To 275 / 190 To 250	450 To 550 / 450 To 550 / 450 To 550	3 To 5 / 3 To 5 / 3 To 5	Compressors and pumps requiring less than 7½Hp. under certain conditions may be successfully handled by type KZK Motors. Heavy starting, continuous or intermittent duty; service factor for overload conditions.
Pump, Centrifugal Propeller	30 H.P. & Larger NEMA Design F	1800 / 1200 / 900	75-100 / 75-100 / 75-100	150-160 / 150-160 / 150-160	350-400 / 350-400 / 350-400	3-5 / 3-5 / 3-5	Low starting and maximum torque. Low starting current. Continuous duty, service factor 1.0 and no overload capacity.
Pumps, Positive Displacement	Multi-Speed Constant Torque	1800/900 / 1800/1200/ 900/600	125-180 / 125-180	200-250 / 200-250	450-550 / 450-550	2-4 / 2-4	Require normal starting torque for continuous duty. Infrequent load fluctuations. Motor provides service factor for overload conditions. Constant speed. No special conditions.
Pumps, Centrifugal	Multi Speed Variable Torque	1800/900 / 1800/1200/ 900/600	125-180 / 125-180	200-250 / 200-250	450-550 / 450-550	2-4 / 2-4	Require normal starting torque for continuous duty. Infrequent load fluctuations. Motor provides service factor for overload conditions. Constant speed. No special conditions.

TABLE 60. SYNCHRONOUS AND APPROXIMATE FULL LOAD SPEEDS OF STANDARD A. C. INDUCTION MOTORS

No. of Poles	60 Cycle R.P.M.		50 Cycle R.P.M.		40 Cycle R.P.M.		30 Cycle R.P.M.		25 Cycle R.P.M.	
	Sync.	F. L.	Sync.	F. L.	Sync.	F. L.	Sync.	F. L.	Sync.	F. L.
2	3600	3500	3000	2900	2400	2310	1800	1750	1500	1450
4	1800	1770	1500	1450	1200	1150	900	860	750	720
6	1200	1170	1000	960	800	770	600	575	500	480
8	900	870	750	720	600	575	450	375	375	360
10	720	690	600	575	480	460	360	340	300	285
12	600	575	500	480	400	385	300	285	250	240
14	514	490	428	410	343	330	257	247	215	205
16	450	430	375	360	300	288	225	215	187	180
18	400	380	333	319	266	256	....	....	....	....
20	360	340	300	285	240	230	....	....	....	....
22	326	310	273	260	218	208	....	....	....	....
24	300	285	240	230	200	192	....	....	....	....
30	240	230	200	192	160	153	....	....	....	....

THE SPEED OF THE A.C. SQUIRREL CAGE INDUCTION MOTOR IS DETERMINED BY THE FREQUENCY OF THE SUPPLY SYSTEM AND THE NUMBER OF POLES FOR WHICH THE MOTOR IS WOUND:

$$\text{SYNC. R.P.M.} = \frac{F \times 60}{P}$$

WHERE: R.P.M. = REVOLUTIONS PER MINUTE; F = FREQUENCY OF SUPPLY IN CYCLES PER SECOND; P = NUMBER OF PAIRS OF POLES

TABLE 61. ELECTRICAL CONVERSION FORMULAS

TO FIND	DIRECT CURRENT	ALTERNATING CURRENT	
		Single Phase	† Three Phase
Amperes When Horse Power (Input) is Known	$\dfrac{H.P. \times 746}{Volts \times Efficiency}$	$\dfrac{H.P. \times 746}{Volts \times Efficiency \times P.F.}$	$\dfrac{H.P. \times 746}{Volts \times 1.73 \times Efficiency \times P.F.}$
Amperes When Kilowatts is Known	$\dfrac{KW \times 1000}{Volts}$	$\dfrac{KW \times 1000}{Volts \times P.F.}$	$\dfrac{KW \times 1000}{Volts \times 1.73 \times P.F.}$
Amperes When kva is Known		$\dfrac{kva \times 1000}{Volts}$	$\dfrac{kva \times 1000}{Volts \times 1.73}$
Kilowatts	$\dfrac{Amperes \times Volts}{1000}$	$\dfrac{Amps. \times Volts \times P.F.}{1000}$	$\dfrac{Amps. \times Volts \times 1.73 \times P.F.}{1000}$
kva		$\dfrac{Amps. \times Volts}{1000}$	$\dfrac{Amps. \times Volts \times 1.73}{1000}$
Power Factor		$\dfrac{Kilowatts \times 1000}{Amps. \times Volts}$ or $\dfrac{KW}{kva}$	$\dfrac{KW \times 1000}{Amps. \times Volts \times 1.73}$ or $\dfrac{KW}{kva}$
Horse Power (Output)	$\dfrac{Amps \times Volts \times Efficiency}{746}$	$\dfrac{Amps. \times Volts \times Efficiency \times P.F.}{746}$	$\dfrac{Amps. \times Volts \times 1.73 \times Efficiency \times P.F.}{746}$

Power Factor and Efficiency when used in above formulas should be expressed as decimals.

† For 2-phase, 4-wire substitute 2 instead of 1.73.

† For 2-phase, 3-wire substitute 1.41 instead of 1.73.

TABLE 62. FULL-LOAD CURRENTS OF MOTORS

The following data are approximate full-load currents for motors of various types, frequencies, and speeds. They have been compiled from average values for representative motors of their respective classes. Variations of 10 per cent above or below the values given may be expected.

Amperes—Full-load Current

Hp. of Motor	Direct-current Motors			Single-phase Motors		Squirrel-cage Induction Motors — Two-phase				Three-phase					Slip-ring Induction Motors — Two-phase					Three-phase				
	115-volt	230-volt	550-volt	110-volt	220-volt	110-volt	220-volt	440-volt	550-2300-volt	110-volt	220-volt	440-volt	550-volt	2300-volt	110-volt	220-volt	440-volt	550-volt	2300-volt	110-volt	220-volt	440-volt	550-volt	2300-volt
¼				4.8	2.4																			
½	4.5	2.3		7	3.5	4.3	2.2	1.1	.9	5.0	2.5	1.3	1.0											
¾	6.5	3.3	1.4	9.4	4.7	4.7	2.4	1.2	1.0	5.4	2.8	1.4	1.1			3.1	1.6	1.3						
1	8.4	4.2	1.7	11	5.5	5.7	2.9	1.4	1.2	6.6	3.3	1.7	1.3		7.2	3.4	1.7	1.4			3.6	1.8	1.5	
1½	12.5	6.3	2.6	15.2	7.6	7.7	4.0	2	1.6	9.4	4.7	2.4	2.0		7.8	5.9	3.0	2.3			3.9	2.0	1.6	
2	16.1	8.3	3.4	20	10	10.4	5	3	2.0	12.0	6	3.0	2.4		12.5	6.3	3.1	2.5		14.4	7.2	3.6	2.9	
3	23	12.3	5.0	28	14		8	4	3.0		9	4.5	4.0			8.7	4.3	3.5		20.2		5.0	4	
5	40	19.8	8.2	46	23		13	7	6		15	7.5	6.0			13.0	6.5	5.2			15	7.5	6	
7½	58	28.7	12	68	34		19	9	7		22	11	9.0			20.0	10.0	7.6			25	13	10	
10	75	38	16	86	43		24	12	10		27	14	11			24.3	12.1	10.0			28	14	11	
15	112	56	23				33	16	13		38	19	15			39	19.5	15.6			45	23	18	
20	140	74	30				45	23	19		52	26	21	5.7		49	24.7	19.8			56	28	22	
25	185	92	38				55	28	22		64	32	26	7		60	30.0	24.0	6.4		67	34	27	7.5
30	220	110	45				67	34	27		77	39	31	8		72	36.0	28.8	7.8		82	41	33	9
40	294	146	61				88	44	35		101	51	40	10		93	46.5	37.3	9.5		106	53	42	11
50	364	180	75				108	54	43		125	63	50	13		113	57	45	12.1		128	64	51	14
60	436	215	90				129	65	52		149	75	60	15		135	68	54	14.0		150	75	60	16
75	540	268	111				156	78	62		180	90	72	19		164	82	65	17.3		188	94	75	19
100		357	146				212	106	85		246	123	98	25		214	108		21.7		246	123	99	25
125		443	184				268	134	108		310	155	124	32		267	134	108	27		310	155	124	31
150			220				311	155	124		360	180	144	36		315	158	127	32		364	182	145	37
175																								
200			295				415	208	166		480	240	195	49		430	216	173	44		490	245	196	52

POWER MEASUREMENT BY WATT-HOUR METERS.

If the watt-hour meter is in correct adjustment it can be used as a convenient means of measuring electrical power. By measuring with a stop watch the exact time for a definite number of revolutions of the disk, the average speed of the disk can be determined accurately. The speed of the disk is directly proportional to the power being used, as expressed in the formulas:

$$\text{Watts} = K \times M \times \text{Revolutions per Hour}$$

$$\text{Kilowatts} = \frac{60 \times 60}{1000} \; K \times M \times \text{Rev. per Sec.}$$

$$= 3.6 \, K \times M \times \frac{R}{t}$$

$$\text{H.P. Input to Motor} = 1.826 \, K \times M \times \frac{R}{t}$$

$K =$ disk constant, representing watt-hours per revolution, found on the meter nameplate or painted on the disk.

$M =$ product of current transformer ratio and potential transformer ratio. (When either transformer is not used the equivalent ratio is one.)

$R =$ total revolutions of watt-hour meter disk.

$t =$ time for total revolutions of disk in seconds.

For convenient reference the disk constants of a number of commonly used meters are listed below and on the following page.

TABLE 63. DISK CONSTANTS FOR SINGLE-PHASE METERS
(Watt-Hours per Revolution of Disk)

METER RATING		GENERAL ELECTRIC			WESTING-HOUSE	SANGAMO			DUNCAN	
		Types			Types B, C, OA, OB, OC, CA, CB, CS,	Types			Types	
Volts	Amp	I-14	I-16 I-20 I-30	I-60S I-18 V-2	DS-3	H	J35 HC HF	M2	MQS MD MF
100 to 120	5	0.3	0.6	1.2	1/3	5/24	1/3	0.25	1/3
	10	0.6	1.2	2.4	2/3	5/12	2/3	0.5	2/3
	15	0.9	†1.8	3.6	1	5/8	1	0.75	1
	25	1.5	3.	6.	1-2/3	1-1/24	1-2/3	1.25	1-2/3
	50	3.	6.	12.	3-1/3	2-1/12	3-1/3	2.5	3-1/3
	75	4.5			5	3-1/8	5	3.5	5
	100	6.	12.		6-2/3	4-1/6	6-2/3	5.0	6-2/3
	150	9.			10	6-1/4	10	7.5	10
200 to 240	5	0.6	1.2	2.4	2/3	5/12	2/3	0.5	2/3
	10	1.2	2.4	4.8	1-1/3	5/6	1-1/3	1.0	1-1/3
	15	1.8	Δ3.6	7.2	2	1-1/4	2	1.5	2
	25	3.	6.	12.	3-1/3	2-1/12	3-1/3	2.5	3-1/3
	50	6.	12.	24.	6-2/3	4-1/6	6-2/3	5.	6-2/3
	75	9.			10	6-1/4	10	7.5	10
	100	12.	24.		13-1/3	8-1/3	13-1/3	10.	13-1/3
	150	18.			20	12-1/2	20	15.	20

† I-30 Meters have K = 1.5 in the 15 amp. size.
Δ I-30 Meters have K = 3.0 in the 15 amp. size.

TABLE 63A. DISK CONSTANTS FOR POLYPHASE METERS

(Watt-Hours per Revolution of Disk)

METER READING		GENERAL ELECTRIC Types			WESTING-HOUSE Types		SANGAMO Types		DUNCAN Types 2 element		
Volts	Amp.	D-6, D-7	D-14, V-3	D-15, V-4	CS-2, CA-2, C, C-2, R-2, OA, OB, RA, RB, RO	R-3, C-3, CA-3, CS-3	H	HC, HF, L2-P	M2	MD, MF, MG	3 element MD, MF, MG
	5	†1.2	1.8		2/3	1	5/12	2/3	0.5	2/3	1
	10	2.4	3.6		1-1/3	2	5/6	1-1/3	1.0	1-1/3	2
	15	1.8	3.6	5.4	2	3	1-1/4	2	1.5	2	3
100 to 120	25	3.	6.	9.	3-1/3	5	2-1/12	3-1/3	2.5	3-1/3	5
	50	6.	12.	18.	6-2/3	10	4-1/6	6-2/3	5.	6-2/3	10
	75	9.			10	15	6-1/4	10	7.5	10	15
	100	12.			13-1/3	20	8-1/3	13-1/3	10.	13-1/3	20
	150	18.			20	30	12-1/2	20	15.2	20	30
	5	1.2	†2.4	3.6	1-1/3	2	5/6	1-1/3	1.	1-1/3	2
	10	2.4	4.8	7.2	2-2/3	4	1-2/3	2-2/3	2.	2-2/3	4
	15	3.6	7.2	10.8	4	6	2-1/2	4	3.	4	6
200 to 240	25	6.	12.	18.	6-2/3	10	4-1/6	6-2/3	5.	6-2/3	10
	50	12.	24.	36.	13-1/3	20	8-1/3	13-1/3	10.	13-1/3	20
	75	18.			20	30	12-1/2	20	15.	20	30
	100	24.			26-2/3	40	16-2/3	26-2/3	20.	26-2/3	40
	150	36.			40	60	25	40	30.	40	60
	5	2.4	†4.8	7.2	2-2/3	4	1-2/3	2-2/3	2.	2-2/3	4
	10	4.8	9.6	14.4	5-1/3	8	3-1/3	5-1/3	4.	5-1/3	8
	15	7.2	14.4	21.6	8	12	5	8	6.	8	12
400 to 480	25	12.	24.	36.	13-1/3	20	8-1/3	3-1/3	10.	13-1/3	20
	50	24.	48.	72.	26-2/3	40	16-2/3	26-2/3	20.	26-2/3	40
	75	36.			40	60	25	40	30.	40	60
	100	48.			53-1/3	80	33-1/3	53-1/3	40.	53-1/3	60
	150	72.			80	120	50	80	60.	80	120
	5	3.	†6.	9.	3-1/3	5	2-1/12	3-1/3	2.5	3-1/3	5
	10	6.	12.	18.	6-2/3	10	4-1/6	6-2/3	5.	6-2/3	10
	15	9.	18.	27.	10	15	6-1/4	10	7.5	10	15
500 to 600	25	15.	30.	45.	16-2/3	25	10-5/12	16-2/3	12.5	16-2/3	25
	50	30.	60.	90.	33-1/3	50	20-5/6	33-1/3	25.	33-1/3	50
	75	45.	90.	135.	50	75	31-1/4	50	37.5	50	75
	100	60.	120.	180.	66-2/3	100	41-2/3	66-2/3	50.	66-2/3	100
	150	90.	180.	270.	100	150	62-1/2	100	75.	100	150

†Most modern meters with current transformers have 2½ amp. current coils which would make the constant one half of that shown above. This constant is marked on edge of disc.

X

TABLE 64. TABLE FOR SELECTING WIRE AND FUSE SIZES FOR MOTOR BRANCH CIRCUITS
(Based on Room Temperature 30°C. 86°F.)

	Minimum Allowable Size of Copper Wire, A. W. G. or MCM National Electric Code			For Running Protection of Motors		Maximum Allowable Rating of Branch-Circuit Fuses with Code Letters			
Full-load Current Rating of Motor—Amps.	Rubber Types R, RW, RU (14-6)	Type RH Heat-Resistant Grade Rubber	Types TA V. AVB	Max. Rating of N.E.C. Fuses—Amps.	Max. Setting of Time-Limit Protective Device—Amps.	Single-phase and Squirrel-cage Full Voltage, Resistor or Reactor Starting Code Letters F to R, Incl.	Single-phase and Squirrel-cage Full Voltage, Resistor or Reactor Starting Code Letters B to E, Incl. Autotransformer Starting F to R	Squirrel-cage, Auto-transformer Starting. Code Letters B to E, Incl.	All Motors Code Letter A. D.C. and Wound-rotor Motors
1	14	14	14	2	1.25	15	15	15	15
2	14	14	14	3	2.50	15	15	15	15
3	14	14	14	4	3.75	15	15	15	15
4	14	14	14	6	5.0	15	15	15	15
5	14	14	14	8	6.25	15	15	15	15
6	14	14	14	8	7.50	20	15	15	15
8	14	14	14	10	10.0	25	20	20	15
10	14	14	14	15	12.50	30	25	20	15
12	14	14	14	15	15.00	40	30	25	20
14	14	12	14	20	17.50	45	35	30	25
16	12	12	14	20	20.00	50	40	35	25
18	12	12	14	25	22.50	60	45	40	30
20	12	12	14	25	25.0	60	50	40	30
24	10	10	14	30	30.0	80	60	50	40
28	10	10	12	35	35.0	90	70	60	45
32	8	8	10	40	40.0	100	80	70	50
36	8	8	10	45	45.0	100	90	80	60
40	8	8	10	50	50.0	125	100	80	60
44	6	8	8	60	55.0	125	110	90	70
48	6	6	8	60	60.0	150	125	100	80
52	6	6	6	70	65.0	175	150	110	80
56	4	6	6	70	70.0	175	150	120	90
60	4	6	6	80	75.0	200	150	120	90
64	4	6	6	80	80.0	200	175	150	100
68	4	4	6	90	85.0	225	175	150	110
72	3	4	4	90	90.0	225	200	150	110
76	3	4	4	100	95.0	250	200	175	125
80	3	3	4	100	100.0	250	200	175	125
84	2	4	4	110	105.0	250	225	175	150
88	2	3	4	110	110.0	300	225	200	150
92	2	3	3	125	115.0	300	250	200	150
96	1	3	3	125	120.0	300	250	200	150
100	1	3	3	125	125.0	300	250	200	150
110	1	2	2	150	137.5	350	300	225	175
120	0	1	2	150	150.0	400	300	250	200
130	00	1	1	175	162.5	400	350	300	200
140	00	0	1	175	175.0	450	350	300	225
150	000	0	0	200	187.5	450	400	300	225
160	000	00	00	200	200.0	500	400	350	250
170	0000	00	00	225	213.0	500	450	350	300
180	0000	000	00	225	225.0	600	450	400	300
190	0000	000	000	250	238.0	600	500	400	300
200	250	0000	000	250	250.0	600	500	400	300
220	300	0000	0000	300	275.0	...	600	500	400
240	300	250	250	300	300.0	...	600	500	400

Wire sizes shown in this table are for single motor, for short distances from **feeder** center to motor, therefore the wire sizes are tabulated as minimum. Where a group **of** motors is involved, special consideration must be given in selecting proper wire size. Wire sizes are based on not more than three conductors in raceway or cable.

FROM NATIONAL ELECTRIC CODE 1947

SECTION XI—PUMP TESTING

CONTENTS

XI

SECTION XI — PUMP TESTING

MEASUREMENT OF PRESSURE

Pressures are usually measured by means of Bourdon tube type gauges although for pressures less than approximately 10 psi water or mercury manometers are often used. Any type of instrument used should be so located that it can reflect the true pressure inside the pipe line. To do so the pressure (or vacuum) connection should be located in a pipe, straight and smooth on the inside, of unvarying cross-section and preferably. five to ten pipe diameters down stream from any elbow, valve or other similar turn or obstruction that might cause turbulence at the gauging section.

The pressure tap should be $\frac{1}{8}''$ to $\frac{1}{4}''$ diameter, drilled at right angles to the wall of the water passage, perfectly smooth and flush with the inside of the pipe and any burrs carefully removed. Two pressure taps approved by the Hydraulic Institute are shown in Fig. 58.

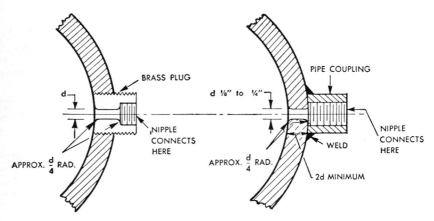

FIG. 58. Approved pressure taps.

The pressure gauge is constructed as shown in Fig. 59. Being a mechanical device and adjustable the gauge must always be calibrated before use. Very few gauges will be found to be accurate over their entire scale range. On important tests or where considerable heat is present the gauge should be calibrated both before and after the test. This may be done by means of a standard dead weight gauge tester. Whenever the pressure of hot water or steam is being measured, a syphon should always be used with the gauge. The water trapped in the syphon loses heat and the temperature of the water forced into the Bourdon tube is, therefore, relatively cool. The elastic qualities of the Bourdon tube will be destroyed if overheated.

FIG. 60.
Pressure gauge.†

FIG. 62.
Vacuum gauge.†

FIG. 59.
Gauge mechanism.†

FIG. 61.
Altitude gauge.†

FIG. 63.
Compound gauge.†

Gauges are available in most any dial graduation desired, but the units the gauge indicates is not always given on the face of the gauge. Custom in the industry has, however, made gauge users familiar with these units. The gauge illustrated in Fig. 60 reads from 0 to 100. When no indication is present on the face of the gauge to indicate the units, it is always understood in the industry to indicate the pressures in psi. When the word ALTITUDE appears on the face as in Fig. 61 the gauge reads head in feet of water. The word VACUUM on the face of the gauge as illustrated in Fig. 62 indicates negative pressures (vacuum) in in.hg. and the compound gauge illustrated in Fig. 63 reads vacuum in in. hg. and pressure in psi. Any gauge reading in inches of water, ounces/sq.ft. or in any other units, will be clearly marked on the face of the gauge.

In using gauges when the pressure is positive or above atmospheric pressure any air in the gauge line should be vented off by

XI

†Courtesy American Machine & Metals, Inc. See page 6.

loosening the gauge until liquid appears. When this is done it can be assumed that the gauge is reading the pressure at the elevation of the center line of the gauge. However, in measuring vacuum the gauge line will be empty of liquid and the gauge will be reading the vacuum at the elevation of the point of attachment of the gauge line to the pipe line.

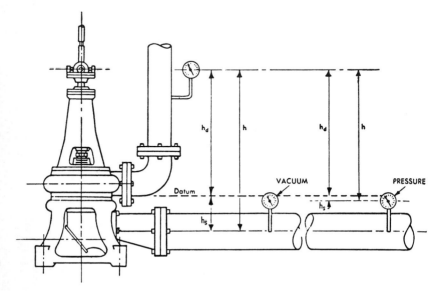

FIG. 64. Determination of total head from gauge readings.

In pump tests the total head can be determined by gauges as illustrated in Fig. 64. In this illustration the total Head would be determined as follows.

$H = $ Discharge gauge reading, corrected, Ft. liquid + Vacuum gauge reading, corrected, ft. liquid + distance between point of attachment of vacuum gauge to the center line of discharge gauge, h, ft. $+ \left(\dfrac{V_d^2}{2g} - \dfrac{V_s^2}{2g} \right)$

or $H = $ Discharge gauge reading, corrected, Ft. liquid − pressure gauge reading in suction line, corrected, ft. liquid + distance between center of discharge and center of suction gauges, h, Ft. $+ \left(\dfrac{V_d^2}{2g} - \dfrac{V_s^2}{2g} \right)$

The method of head determination above applies specifically to pumping units installed so that both suction and discharge flanges of the pump and adjacent piping are located so as to be accessible for installation of gauges for testing the pump. In such an installation it is possible to determine the head losses in both the suction and discharge piping and, therefore, the test will determine the true efficiency of the pump. In this case the pump is charged only with the head losses in the pump itself and all other head losses are right-fully charged against the piping system.

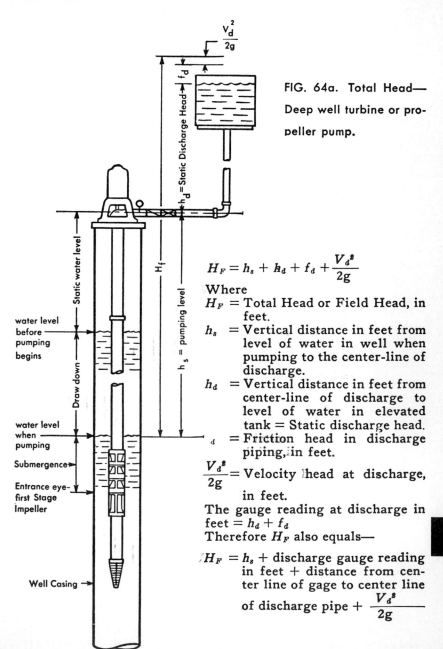

FIG. 64a. Total Head—Deep well turbine or propeller pump.

$$H_F = h_s + h_d + f_d + \frac{V_d^2}{2g}$$

Where

H_F = Total Head or Field Head, in feet.

h_s = Vertical distance in feet from level of water in well when pumping to the center-line of discharge.

h_d = Vertical distance in feet from center-line of discharge to level of water in elevated tank = Static discharge head.

$_d$ = Friction head in discharge piping, in feet.

$\dfrac{V_d^2}{2g}$ = Velocity head at discharge, in feet.

The gauge reading at discharge in feet = $h_d + f_d$

Therefore H_F also equals—

H_F = h_s + discharge gauge reading in feet + distance from center line of gage to center line of discharge pipe + $\dfrac{V_d^2}{2g}$

XI

The installation of vertical Propeller and Turbine Pumps is invariably such that it is not possible to obtain pressures at the suction and discharge of the submerged basic pumping unit. Therefore, the method of head determination and testing must necessarily vary from the practice used on horizontal pumps. The only fair method of head determination to the user of the pump is one that will permit checking of pump performance in the field. Such a method will be described here. The Total Head determined by this method will be called "Field Head", H_f, for it can be obtained by field measurements. Please refer to Figure 64a.

Notice in this method of figuring that all velocity, entrance and friction losses at the suction of the pump are charged against the pump. Also all exit losses from pump discharge as well as all column friction losses are charged against the pump. This makes the efficiency of the pump appear lower than it really is. These losses exist whether charged to the pump or not. When not charged to the pump it makes field checking of pump performance impractical.

In the illustrations and text relating to calculations of total head the simplest type of pumping has been used—i.e. from one open vessel to another. Often closed vessels under pressure or vacuum are involved. To avoid error convert all elements of total head i.e., pressure or vacuum, static, friction and velocity to head in feet of the liquid pumped and proceed algebraically as described and illustrated in the preceding text.

Pressures may also be measured by manometers. The liquid used in the manometer is generally water or mercury. However, any liquid of known specific gravity may be used. Manometers are most often used for low pressures for the instrument becomes too long when used on the higher pressures. About 10 psi is the practical limit, for this would be equivalent to a water column 23 ft. high or a mercury column about 24 in. high. The advantage of using the manometer is, of course, that they do not need to be calibrated and since the deflection is greater they can be read more accurately.

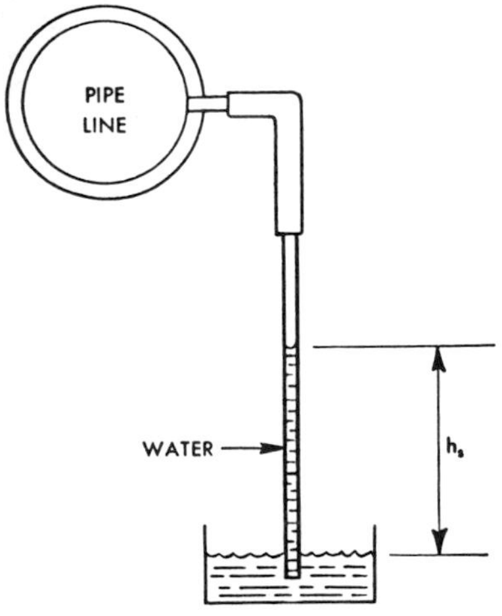

For field tests water manometers are quite convenient for they can often be fabricated out of readily obtainable materials. Fig. 65 shows a simple manometer installed on a suction pipe where h_s = the vacuum in the pipe line at the point of attachment of the manometer to the pipe. Mercury could also be used in this simple manometer but great

FIG. 65. Manometer indicating vacuum.

care should be used to see that the space between the pipe and the mercury meniscus is completely filled with air or completely filled with liquid.

To illustrate this point refer to Fig. 66 showing a mercury manometer measuring pressure in a water pipe line. If the space above the mercury in both legs of the manometer is filled with air the pressure in the pine line,

$$H, \text{ ft. water} = h_d, \text{ in. hg.} \times \frac{13.6}{12}$$
$$= h_d \times 1.133$$

where
13.6 = specific gravity of mercury.

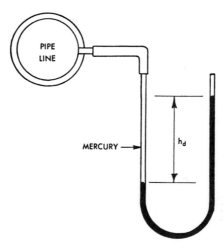

FIG. 66. Manometer indicating pressure.

However if the left hand leg above the mercury is filled with water the weight of the water, h_d, causes extra deflection of the mercury. In this case, therefore, it is necessary to subtract the specific gravity of water from the specific gravity of mercury in arriving at the head in the pipe, thus:

$$H, \text{ ft. water} = h_d, \text{ in. hg} \times$$
$$\frac{13.6 - 1}{12} = h_d \times 1.05$$

XI

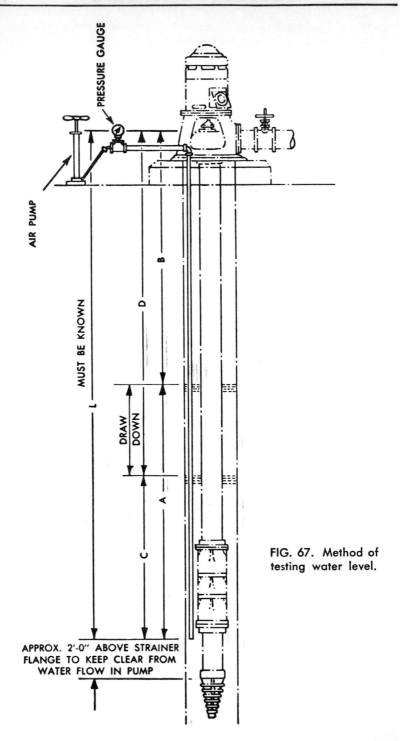

FIG. 67. Method of testing water level.

DETERMINING THE DEPTH TO WATER LEVEL IN A DEEP WELL

In testing a vertical submerged pump such as a Deep Well Turbine it is necessary to determine the water level in the well when pumping.

The most satisfactory method of determining the water level involves the use of a $\frac{1}{4}$ in. air line of known vertical length, a pressure gauge and an ordinary bicycle or automobile pump installed as shown in Fig. 67. If possible the air line pipe should reach at least twenty feet beyond the lowest anticipated water level in the well in order to assure more reliable gauge readings and preferably should not be attached to the column or bowls as this would hinder the removal of the pipe should any leaks develop. As noted in Fig. 67 an air pressure gauge is used to indicate the pressure in the air line.

The $\frac{1}{4}$ in. air line pipe is lowered into the well, a tee is placed in the line above the ground, and a pressure gauge is screwed into one connection and the other is fitted with an ordinary bicycle valve to which a bicycle pump is attached. All joints must be made carefully and must be air tight to obtain correct information. When air is forced into the line by means of the tire pump the gauge pressure increases until all the water has been expelled. When this point is reached the gauge reading becomes constant. The maximum maintained air pressure recorded by the gauge is equivalent to that necessary to support a column of water of the same height as that forced out of the air line. The length of this water column is equal to the amount of air line submerged.

Deducting this pressure converted to feet (pounds pressure × 2.31 equals feet) from the known length of the $\frac{1}{4}$ in. air line pipe, will give the amount of submergence. The following examples will serve to clarify the above explanation.

Assume a length L of 150 ft.

Pressure gauge reading before starting pump = P_1 = 25 lb. per sq. in. Then $A = 25 \times 2.31 = 57.7$ ft., therefore the water level in the well before starting the pump would be $B = L - A = 150 - 57.7 = 92.3$ feet.

Pressure gauge reading when pumping = P_2 = 18 lb. per sq. in. Then $C = 18 \times 2.31 = 41.6$ feet, therefore the water level in the well when pumping would be $D = L - C = 150 - 41.6$ ft. = 108.4 ft.

The drawdown is determined by the following equation:

$D - B = 108.4 - 92.3 = 16.1$ feet.

MEASUREMENT OF CAPACITY

The most accurate method of measuring the capacity of a pumping unit is by weighing the liquid pumped or measuring its volume in a calibrated vessel. For obvious reasons either method is practical only for small capacities. It has been necessary therefore, to devise other means, some of which are quite accurate, others only approximations. Some are suitable for measuring flow in a pipe line under pressure—others can be used only in open channels. Typical methods of measuring flow will be described here.

XI

VENTURI METER

The Venturi Meter is a common device for accurately measuring the discharge of pumps, particularly when a permanent meter installation is required. When the coefficient for the meter has been determined by actual calibration, and the meter is correctly installed and accurately read, the probable error in computing the discharge should be less than one per cent.

As usually constructed the meter consists of a converging portion, a throat having a diameter of approximately one third the main pipe diameter, and a diverging portion to reduce loss of energy from turbulence, see Fig. 68. The length of the converging portion is usually 2 to $2\frac{1}{2}$ times the diameter of the main pipe, while the best angle of divergence is about 10 degrees included angle.

For accurate results the distance from the nearest elbow or fitting to the entrance of the meter should be at least 10 times the diameter of the pipe. Otherwise straightening vanes should be used to prevent spiral flow at entrance.

From a consideration of Bernoulli's Theorem:

$$\text{Gallons per Minute} = 3.118 \text{ c a } \sqrt{\frac{2\,gh}{R^4 - 1}}$$

$c =$ coefficient of discharge from calibration data. While this coefficient may vary from about 0.94 to more than unity it is usually about 0.98.

$a =$ area of entrance section where the upstream manometer connection is made, in square inches.

$R =$ ratio of entrance to throat diameter $= \dfrac{d}{d_1}$

$g =$ acceleration of gravity (32.2 ft./sec.²).

$h = h_1 - h_2 =$ difference in pressure between the entrance section and throat, as indicated by a manometer, in feet.

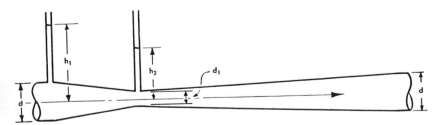

FIG. 68. Venturi meter.

In the illustration Fig. 68 the pressures h_1 and h_2 may be taken by manometer as illustrated when the pressures are low. When pressures are high a differential mercury manometer which indicates the difference in pressure $h_1 - h_2$ directly, is most often used. Gauges can also be used, but they can be read less accurately than a manometer and do require calibration. In commercial installations of venturi meters instruments are often installed that will continuously indicate, record and/or integrate the flow. They also require calibration so, when conducting a test, it is best to use a differential manometer connected directly to the meter to measure $h_1 - h_2$.

NOZZLES

A nozzle is, in effect, the converging portion of a venturi tube. The water issues from the nozzle throat into the atmosphere. The pressure h_2, therefore, is atmospheric pressure. To calculate the flow from a nozzle use the same formula as for the venturi meter. The head, h, in the formula will be the gauge reading h_1.

ORIFICES

Approximate discharge through orifice

$$Q = 19.636 \ Kd^2 \sqrt{h} \sqrt{\frac{1}{1 - \left(\frac{d}{D}\right)^4}} \qquad \text{where} \frac{d}{D} \text{is greater than } .3$$

$$Q = 19.636 \ Kd^2 \sqrt{h} \qquad \text{where} \frac{d}{D} \text{is less than } .3$$

$Q = $ flow, in Gpm

$d = $ dia. of orifice or nozzle opening, in.

$h = $ head at orifice, in feet of liquid.

$D = $ dia. of pipe in which orifice is placed.

$K = $ discharge coefficient

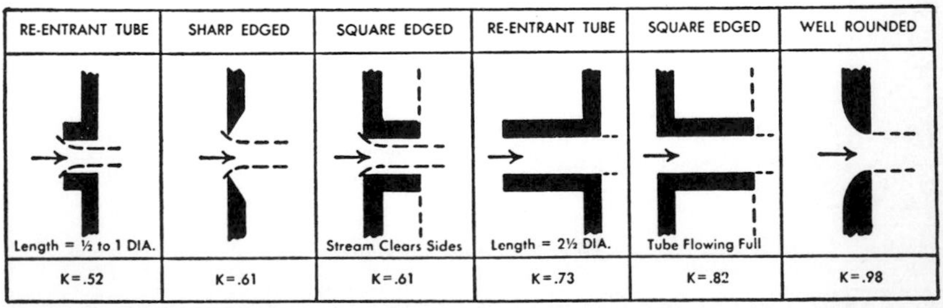

RE-ENTRANT TUBE	SHARP EDGED	SQUARE EDGED	RE-ENTRANT TUBE	SQUARE EDGED	WELL ROUNDED
Length = ½ to 1 DIA.		Stream Clears Sides	Length = 2½ DIA.	Tube Flowing Full	
K=.52	K=.61	K=.61	K=.73	K=.82	K=.98

FIG. 69. Typical orifice coefficients.†

†*Courtesy Ingersoll-Rand Co. See page 6.*

TABLE 65. THEORETICAL DISCHARGE OF ORIFICES, U.S. GPM.

Head		Velocity of Discharge Feet per Second	Diameter of Orifice in Inches												
Lbs.	Feet		1/16	1/8	3/16	1/4	3/8	1/2	5/8	3/4	7/8	1	1 1/8	1 1/4	1 3/8
10	23.1	38.6	0.37	1.48	3.32	5.91	13.3	23.6	36.9	53.1	72.4	94.5	120	148	179
15	34.6	47.25	0.45	1.81	4.06	7.24	16.3	28.9	45.2	65.0	88.5	116.	147	181	219
20	46.2	54.55	0.52	2.09	4.69	8.35	18.8	33.4	52.2	75.1	102.	134.	169	209	253
25	57.7	61.0	0.58	2.34	5.25	9.34	21.0	37.3	58.3	84.0	114.	149.	189	234	283
30	69.3	66.85	0.64	2.56	5.75	10.2	23.0	40.9	63.9	92.0	125.	164.	207	256	309
35	80.8	72.2	0.69	2.77	6.21	11.1	24.8	44.2	69.0	99.5	135.	177.	224	277	334
40	92.4	77.2	0.74	2.96	6.64	11.8	26.6	47.3	73.8	106.	145.	189.	239	296	357
45	103.9	81.8	0.78	3.13	7.03	12.5	28.2	50.1	78.2	113.	153.	200.	253	313	379
50	115.5	86.25	0.83	3.30	7.41	13.2	29.7	52.8	82.5	119.	162.	211.	267	330	399
55	127.0	90.4	0.87	3.46	7.77	13.8	31.1	55.3	86.4	125.	169.	221.	280	346	418
60	138.6	94.5	0.90	3.62	8.12	14.5	32.5	57.8	90.4	130.	177.	231.	293	362	438
65	150.1	98.3	0.94	3.77	8.45	15.1	33.8	60.2	94.0	136.	184.	241.	305	376	455
70	161.7	102.1	0.98	3.91	8.78	15.7	35.2	62.5	97.7	141.	191.	250.	317	391	473
75	173.2	105.7	1.01	4.05	9.08	16.2	36.4	64.7	101.	146.	198.	259.	327	404	489
80	184.8	109.1	1.05	4.18	9.39	16.7	37.6	66.8	104.	150.	205.	267.	338	418	505
85	196.3	112.5	1.08	4.31	9.67	17.3	38.8	68.9	108.	155.	211.	276.	349	431	521
90	207.9	115.8	1.11	4.43	9.95	17.7	39.9	70.8	111.	160.	217.	284.	359	443	536
95	219.4	119.0	1.14	4.56	10.2	18.2	41.0	72.8	114.	164.	223.	292.	369	456	551
100	230.9	122.0	1.17	4.67	10.5	18.7	42.1	74.7	117.	168.	229.	299.	378	467	565
105	242.4	125.0	1.20	4.79	10.8	19.2	43.1	76.5	120.	172.	234.	306.	388	479	579
110	254.0	128.0	1.23	4.90	11.0	19.6	44.1	78.4	122.	176.	240.	314.	397	490	593
115	265.5	130.9	1.25	5.01	11.1	20.0	45.1	80.1	125.	180.	245.	320.	406	501	606
120	277.1	133.7	1.28	5.12	11.5	20.5	46.0	81.8	128.	184.	251.	327.	414	512	619
125	288.6	136.4	1.31	5.22	11.7	20.9	47.0	83.5	130.	188.	256.	334.	423	522	632
130	300.2	139.1	1.33	5.33	12.0	21.3	48.0	85.2	133.	192.	261.	341.	432	533	645
135	311.7	141.8	1.36	5.43	12.2	21.7	48.9	86.7	136.	195.	266.	347.	439	543	656
140	323.3	144.3	1.38	5.53	12.4	22.1	49.8	88.4	138.	199.	271.	354.	448	553	668
145	334.8	146.9	1.41	5.62	12.6	22.5	50.6	89.9	140.	202.	275.	360.	455	562	680
150	346.4	149.5	1.43	5.72	12.9	22.9	51.5	91.5	143.	206.	280.	366.	463	572	692
175	404.1	161.4	1.55	6.18	13.9	24.7	55.6	98.8	154.	222.	302.	395.	500	618	747
200	461.9	172.6	1.65	6.61	14.8	26.4	59.5	106.	165.	238.	323.	423.	535	660	799
250	577.4	193.0	1.85	7.39	16.6	29.6	66.5	118.	185.	266.	362.	473.	598	739	894
300	692.8	211.2	2.02	8.08	18.2	32.4	72.8	129.	202.	291.	396.	517.	655	808	977

NOTE—To determine actual discharge multiply values from table by coefficient of discharge.

TABLE 65. (Cont.) THEORETICAL DISCHARGE OF ORIFICES, U. S. GPM.

| Head | | Velocity of Discharge Feet Per Second | Diameter of Orifice in Inches | | | | | | | | | | | | |
Lbs.	Feet		1½	1¾	2	2¼	2½	2¾	3	3½	4	4½	5	5½	6
10	23.1	38.6	213	289	378	479	591	714	851	1158	1510	1915	2365	2855	3405
15	34.6	47.25	260	354	463	585	723	874	1041	1418	1850	2345	2890	3490	4165
20	46.2	54.55	301	409	535	676	835	1009	1203	1638	2135	2710	3340	4040	4819
25	57.7	61.0	336	458	598	756	934	1128	1345	1830	2385	3025	3730	4510	5380
30	69.3	66.85	368	501	655	828	1023	1236	1473	2005	2615	3315	4090	4940	5895
35	80.8	72.2	398	541	708	895	1106	1335	1591	2168	2825	3580	4415	5340	6370
40	92.4	77.2	425	578	756	957	1182	1428	1701	2315	3020	3830	4725	5710	6810
45	103.9	81.8	451	613	801	1015	1252	1512	1802	2455	3200	4055	5000	6050	7210
50	115.5	86.25	475	647	845	1070	1320	1595	1900	2590	3375	4275	5280	6380	7600
55	127.0	90.4	498	678	886	1121	1385	1671	1991	2710	3540	4480	5530	6690	7970
60	138.6	94.5	521	708	926	1172	1447	1748	2085	2835	3700	4685	5790	6980	8330
65	150.1	98.3	542	737	964	1220	1506	1819	2165	2950	3850	4875	6020	7270	8670
70	161.7	102.1	563	765	1001	1267	1565	1888	2250	3065	4000	5060	6250	7560	9000
75	173.2	105.7	582	792	1037	1310	1619	1955	2330	3170	4135	5240	6475	7820	9320
80	184.8	109.1	602	818	1070	1354	1672	2020	2405	3280	4270	5410	6690	8080	9630
85	196.3	112.5	620	844	1103	1395	1723	2080	2480	3375	4400	5575	6890	8320	9920
90	207.9	115.8	638	868	1136	1436	1773	2140	2550	3475	4530	5740	7090	8560	10210
95	219.4	119.0	655	892	1168	1476	1824	2200	2625	3570	4655	5900	7290	8800	10500
100	230.9	122.0	672	915	1196	1512	1870	2255	2690	3660	4775	6050	7470	9030	10770
105	242.4	125.0	689	937	1226	1550	1916	2312	2755	3750	4890	6200	7650	9250	11020
110	254.0	128.0	705	960	1255	1588	1961	2366	2820	3840	5010	6350	7840	9470	11300
115	265.5	130.9	720	980	1282	1621	2005	2420	2885	3930	5120	6490	8010	9680	11550
120	277.1	133.7	736	1002	1310	1659	2050	2470	2945	4015	5225	6630	8180	9900	11800
125	288.6	136.4	751	1022	1338	1690	2090	2520	3005	4090	5340	6760	8350	10100	12030
130	300.2	139.1	767	1043	1365	1726	2132	2575	3070	4175	5450	6900	8530	10300	12290
135	311.7	141.8	780	1063	1390	1759	2173	2620	3125	4250	5550	7030	8680	10400	12510
140	323.3	144.3	795	1082	1415	1790	2212	2670	3180	4330	5650	7160	8850	10600	12730
145	334.8	146.9	809	1100	1440	1820	2250	2715	3235	4410	5740	7280	8990	10880	12960
150	346.4	149.5	824	1120	1466	1853	2290	2760	3295	4485	5850	7410	9150	11070	13200
175	404.1	161.4	890	1210	1582	2000	2473	2985	3560	4840	6310	8000	9890	11940	14250
200	461.9	172.6	950	1294	1691	2140	2645	3190	3800	5175	6750	8550	10580	12770	15220
250	577.4	193.0	1063	1447	1891	2392	2955	3570	4250	5795	7550	9570	11820	14290	17020
300	692.8	211.2	1163	1582	2070	2615	3235	3900	4650	6330	8260	10480	12940	15620	18610

NOTE—To determine actual discharge multiply values from table by coefficient of discharge.

XI

CONSTRUCTION AND USE OF PIPE CAP ORIFICE

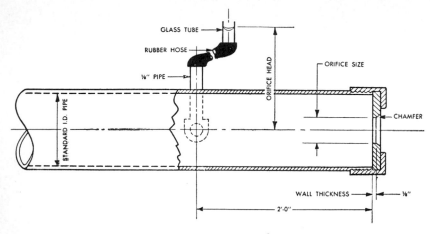

FIG. 70. Pipe cap orifice.

A pipe cap orifice is a form of sharp-edged orifice and is free flowing, since it is placed on the end of a pipe and allows the water to discharge into the atmosphere.

A number of precautions must be taken to insure accuracy of measurement.

1. Approach pipe must be smooth inside, straight and horizontal.

2. The distance between the orifice and any valves or fittings in the approach pipe must be greater than 8 pipe diameters.

3. The $\frac{1}{8}''$ pressure opening should be two feet back of, and in the centerline plane of, the orifice. It should be fitted with a standard nipple, at right angles to the approach pipe and flush on the inside. A rubber tube and a piece of glass pipe complete the arrangement for easy reading of the head on the orifice. The rubber tube may be used as shown, or may be connected directly to the horizontal nipple.

4. The orifice must be a true bore, smooth, diameter accurate to $\pm$ 0.001$''$, inside wall flush and smooth, edges square and sharp and $\frac{1}{8}''$ thick, excess material chamfered at an angle of 45 deg. on outside as illustrated in Fig. 70.

Capacities may be read directly in GPM from Fig. 71.

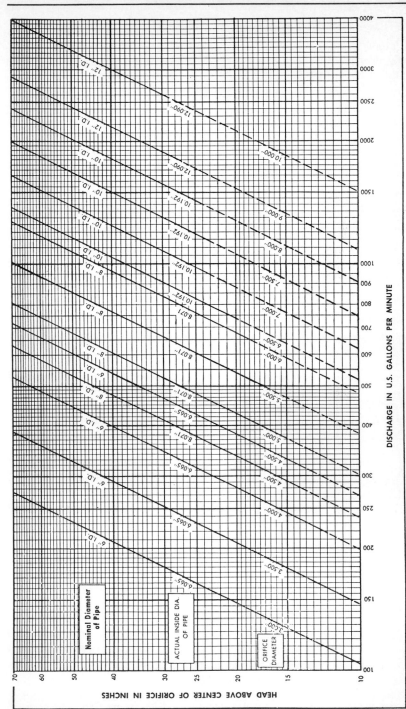

DISCHARGE IN U.S. GALLONS PER MINUTE

HEAD ABOVE CENTER OF ORIFICE IN INCHES

FIG. 71. Pipe cap orifice chart.

WEIRS

There are a number of forms of the weir in use as capacity measuring devices, but this discussion concerns itself primarily with the rectangular suppressed weir, the only form approved in the Standards of the Hydraulic Institute.

This is the rectangular sharp crested weir with smooth vertical crest wall, complete crest contraction, free overfall and with end contraction suppressed. It is often called, simply, a full width rectangular weir. This weir is of the specific proportions of weirs that have been calibrated by precision methods and proper coefficient determined and these data are applicable to this specific form only.

When a weir is constructed, certain dimensional relationships should be incorporated to insure accuracy of flow measurement. See Fig. 72.

When using an existing weir, a tolerance of plus or minus two percent may be expected when the Head, h, is accurately read and the following flow limitations obtain:

a. Head, h, not less than 0.2 feet.

b. Head, h, not greater than $\frac{1}{2}$ height of weir crest, ($\frac{1}{2}$ of Z).

c. Head, h, not greater than $\frac{1}{2}$ length of weir crest, ($\frac{1}{2}$ of B).

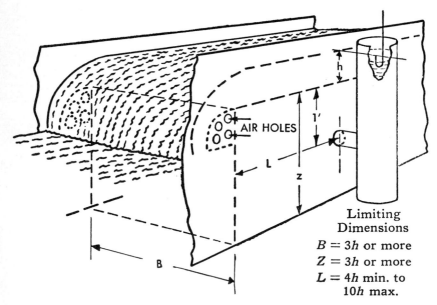

Limiting
Dimensions

$B = 3h$ or more
$Z = 3h$ or more
$L = 4h$ min. to
10h max.

FIG. 72. Rectangular suppressed weir.

The weir plate shall be constructed of non-corrosive metal about $\frac{1}{4}''$ thick, sharp right angle corner on upstream edge, actual crest width ⅛″, with plate beveled at 45° angle from crest on the downstream face. The crest shall be smooth and free from rust, grease, algae, etc., during testing. The plate must be mounted in a vertical plane at right angles to the line of flow, with the crest absolutely level. The channel walls shall be smooth and parallel and shall extend downstream beyond the overfall, and above the crest level. Complete aeration of the nappe is required, and observations before and during test are necessary to provide evidence of complete freedom from adhering nappe, disturbed or turbulent flow, or surging. The weir shall be located sufficiently downstream from the source to insure that smooth flow, free from eddies, surface disturbance, or excessive air in suspension, is maintained at all flow rates. Since slight deviation from proper conditions can cause appreciable variation in the indicated quantity, proper baffling is very important in order to give approximately uniform velocity across the approach channel. This channel must be of uniform cross section, straight and free from stilling racks or other obstructions for a length equal to at least fifteen times the maximum head on the weir. If out of doors, protection should be provided against surface disturbance from wind.

The head on the weir shall be measured by hook gages, securely placed in stilling boxes located at the side of the approach channel, upstream from the crest a distance, L, of between four and ten times the maximum head, h, on the weir. The stilling boxes shall communicate with the channel by a pipe about 1½″ in diameter, flush with the side of the channel and approximately one foot below the level of the crest. If located out of doors, protection against wind pressure and entrance of foreign material shall be provided.

Table 66 gives the flow over this type of weir, based on the Francis formula, $Q = 3.33Bh^{3/2}$, where Q = flow in cu. ft./second, B = crest length in feet, and h = head on the weir in feet. While this is an approximation, it is a close one, and is accurate enough for many field tests.

However, where accurate field testing is desired and precise instruments are available to measure the head, h, the Rehbock formula should be used as follows:

$$Q = \left(3.228 + 0.435\frac{h_e}{z}\right)Bh_e^{3/2}$$

where:

Q = quantity in Cu. ft./sec.

$h_e = h + 0.0036$

h = observed head on crest, in feet, without correction for velocity of approach.

z = height of weir crest above bottom of channel of approach, in feet.

B = length of weir crest, in feet.

TABLE 66. FLOW OVER RECTANGULAR SUPPRESSED WEIR IN CU. FT. PER SECOND. $Q = 3.33Bh^{3/2}$

Crest Length in Feet

Head Ft.	1.0	1.5	2.0	3.0	4.0	5.0	6.0	7.0	8.0
0.1	0.11	0.16	0.21	0.32	0.42	0.53	0.63	0.74	0.84
0.2	0.30	0.45	0.60	0.89	1.19	1.49	1.79	2.08	2.38
0.3	0.55	0.82	1.09	1.64	2.19	2.74	3.28	3.83	4.38
0.4	0.84	1.26	1.68	2.53	3.37	4.21	5.05	5.90	6.74
0.5	1.18	1.77	2.35	3.53	4.71	5.89	7.06	8.24	9.42
0.6	1.55	2.32	3.10	4.64	6.19	7.74	9.29	10.83	12.38
0.7	1.95	2.93	3.90	5.85	7.80	9.75	11.70	13.65	15.60
0.8	2.38	3.57	4.77	7.15	9.53	11.91	14.30	16.68	19.06
0.9	2.84	4.26	5.69	8.53	11.37	14.22	17.06	19.90	22.75
1.0	3.33	5.00	6.66	9.99	13.32	16.65	19.98	23.31	26.64
1.1	3.84	5.76	7.68	11.53	15.37	19.21	23.05	26.89	30.73
1.2	4.38	6.57	8.75	13.13	17.51	21.89	26.26	30.64	35.02
1.3	4.94	7.40	9.87	14.81	19.74	24.68	29.61	34.55	39.49
1.4	5.52	8.27	11.03	16.55	22.06	27.58	33.10	38.61	44.13
1.5	6.12	9.18	12.24	18.35	24.47	30.59	36.71	42.82	48.94
1.6	6.74	10.11	13.48	20.22	26.96	33.70	40.44	47.18	53.92
1.7	7.38	11.08	14.76	22.14	29.52	36.91	44.29	51.67	59.05
1.8	8.04	12.06	16.08	24.13	32.17	40.21	48.25	56.29	64.33
1.9	8.72	13.08	17.44	26.16	34.89	43.61	52.33	61.05	69.77
2.0	9.42	14.13	18.84	28.26	37.68	47.10	56.51	65.93	75.35
2.1	10.13	15.20	20.27	30.40	40.54	50.67	60.80	70.94	81.07
2.2	10.87	16.30	21.73	32.60	43.46	54.33	65.20	76.06	86.93
2.3	11.62	17.42	23.23	34.85	46.46	58.08	69.69	81.31	92.92
2.4	12.38	18.57	24.76	37.14	49.52	61.91	74.29	86.67	99.05
2.5	13.16	19.74	26.33	39.49	52.65	65.82	78.98	92.14	105.30
2.6	13.96	20.94	27.92	41.88	55.84	69.81	83.77	97.73	111.69
2.7	14.77	22.16	29.55	44.32	59.10	73.87	88.64	103.42	118.19
2.8	15.60	23.40	31.20	46.81	62.41	78.01	93.61	109.21	124.82
2.9	16.45	24.67	32.89	49.34	65.78	82.23	98.67	115.12	131.56
3.0	17.30	25.95	34.61	51.91	69.21	86.52	103.82	121.12	138.42

Following are sketches of various weir types, with formulas for calculation of flow over each:

Rectangular Suppressed

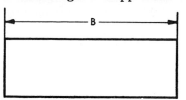

Francis Formula, $Q = 3.33Bh^{3/2}$ or the more accurate Rehbock Formula,

$$Q = \left(3.228 + 0.435\frac{h_e}{z}\right) Bh_e^{3/2}$$

Rectangular Contracted

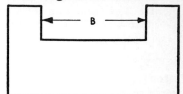

Francis Formula,

$$Q = 3.33h^{3/2} (B - 0.2h)$$

V-Notch

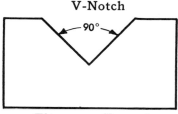

Thompson Formula,
$$Q = 2.54h^{5/2}$$

Cipolletti

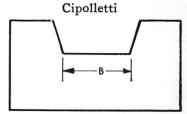

Sides Slope 1:4

Cipolletti Formula,
$$Q = 3.367Bh^{3/2}$$

FIG. 73. Various weir formula.

PITOT TUBE

The Pitot Tube is a device used for measuring the velocity of flowing fluids. Many forms of Pitot Tube are used but the principle of all are the same. Two pressure readings are taken on the pipe interior—one receiving the full impact of the flowing stream reads a pressure equal to the static head plus the velocity head—the other reads the static head only. The difference between the two readings, therefore, is the velocity head. The velocity can be calculated by the equation $V = C \sqrt{2gh}$ where C is a cofficient for the meter determined by calibration. The quantity of fluid flowing equals the pipe area $\times$ average velocity.

Since the velocity varies from a minimum at a point adjacent to the pipe wall to a maximum at the pipe center a traverse of the pipe must be made to determine the average velocity. This is not easily done. The use of a commercially manufactured Pitot Tube gives results accurate to approximately 97% when used by a carefully trained operator.

TESTING FIRE PUMPS

A specialized type of Pitot Tube is used when testing Fire Pumps.

It is an instrument used manually by holding the tip of the Pitot Tube in the stream of water issuing from the hose nozzle. A gauge indicates the velocity pressure in Psi. Fire stream formula and tables have been prepared for use with these Pitot Tube measurements. The following data and tables are published by permission of Associated Factory Mutual Fire Insurance Companies.

TABLE 67. NOZZLE DISCHARGE TABLES[†]

The following formulas may be used to determine the volume of discharge, hydrant pressure, or nozzle pressure for nozzles of varying size and with different lengths of 2½-inch cotton rubber-lined hose when one factor is unknown.

The use of these formulas will give the same result as Freeman's Fire Stream Tables, since the constants indicated have been derived from the tables. The detailed nozzle discharge tables are limited to the 1⅛- and 1¾-inch smooth nozzles as these are the most common sizes encountered in private fire protection. The discharge from nozzles of other sizes can be calculated from the following formulas and tables.

$$G = K \sqrt{p} \qquad P = p(AB+1) \qquad p = \frac{P}{AB+1}$$

G = Discharge, gal. per min.
p = Nozzle (pitot) pressure, lb. per sq. in.
P = Hydrant pressure, lb. per sq. in.
K = Constant for discharge
A = Constant for size of nozzle
B = Constant for length of hose

Nozzle Size (inches)	K	A	Length of 2½-in. C.R.L. Hose (feet)	B
1	29.1	.024	50	4.9
1-1/16	32.8	.031	100	8.8
1-1/8	36.8	.039	150	12.8
1-3/16	41.0	.048	200	16.7
1-1/4	45.4	.059	250	20.6
			300	24.5
1-5/16	50.1	.072	350	28.4
1-3/8	54.9	.087	400	32.4
1-7/16	60.0	.104	450	35.3
1-1/2	65.4	.123	500	40.2
			550	44.1
1-9/16	70.9	.145	600	48.1
1-5/8	76.8	.170	650	52.1
1-11/16	82.8	.197	700	55.9
1-3/4	89.0	.228	750	58.8
			800	63.8
1-13/16	95.5	.262	850	67.7
1-7/8	102.0	.300	900	71.6
1-15/16	109.0	.343	950	75.5
2	116.0	.389	1000	79.4

[†]*Courtesy of Associated Factory Mutual Fire Insurance Companies. See page 6.*

TABLE 67 (Continued) NOZZLE DISCHARGE TABLES

Showing Pressures Required at Hydrant or Fire Department
Pumper, while Stream is Flowing, to Maintain Nozzle Pressure
Indicated in First Column Through Various Lengths of Best
Quality Cotton Rubber-Lined Hose

1⅛-INCH SMOOTH NOZZLE

Nozzle Pressure psi.	Discharge (G.P.M.)	Hydrant Pressure, psi. Single 2½-Inch Lines (Feet)			
		50	100	150	200
2	52	2	3	3	3
4	74	5	6	6	7
6	90	7	8	9	10
8	104	9	11	12	13
10	116	12	13	14	16
12	127	14	16	17	19
14	137	17	18	20	23
16	146	19	21	23	26
18	155	21	24	26	29
20	164	24	27	29	33
22	172	26	29	32	36
24	180	29	32	35	39
26	187	31	35	38	43
28	194	33	38	41	46
30	201	36	40	44	50
32	208	38	43	47	53
34	213	40	45	50	56
36	220	42	48	53	59
38	226	45	51	56	63
40	232	47	54	59	66
42	238	50	56	62	69
44	243	52	59	65	73
46	248	54	61	68	76
48	254	57	64	71	80
50	259	59	66	74	83
52	264	62	69	77	86
54	269	64	72	80	89
56	274	66	75	83	92
58	279	68	78	86	95
60	283	71	80	89	98
62	288	73	83	92	101
64	293	76	86	95	104
66	298	78	89	98	107
68	302	81	91	101	110
70	307	83	94	104	113
72	311	85	97	107	116
74	315	88	99	110	120
76	319	90	102	113	123
78	323	92	105	116	126
80	328	95	108	119	130
82	332	97	111	122	133
84	336	100	113	125	136
86	340	103	116	128	140
88	343	105	118	131	143
90	347	107	121	133	146
92	351	110	124	136	150
94	355	113	127	139	153
96	359	115	129	142	156
98	363	117	132	145	160
100	367	119	135	148	164

XI

Nozzle Pressure = Pitot Tube Pressure. Discharge Coef. = .97

TABLE 67. (Cont.) NOZZLE DISCHARGE TABLES.

Showing Pressures Required at Hydrant or Fire Department Pumper, while Stream is Flowing, to Maintain Nozzle Pressure Indicated in First Column Through Various Lengths of Best Quality Cotton Rubber-Lined Hose

1¾-INCH SMOOTH NOZZLE

Nozzle Pressure psi.	Discharge (G.P.M.)	Hydrant Pressure, psi. Single 2½-Inch Lines (Feet)			
		50	100	150	200
2	125	4	6	8	9
4	178	8	12	16	19
6	217	13	18	23	29
8	251	17	24	31	39
10	280	21	30	38	48
12	307	25	36	46	58
14	332	29	42	54	68
16	355	34	48	62	77
18	376	38	54	69	87
20	397	42	60	77	96
22	416	46	66	85	106
24	435	50	72	93	116
26	452	54	78	101	126
28	469	58	84	112	135
30	486	63	90	120	145
32	502	67	96	128	155
34	517	72	102	135	165
36	532	76	108	143	175
38	547	80	114	150	······
40	561	85	120	158	······
42	574	89	126	165	······
44	588	93	132	173	······
46	601	97	138	181	······
48	614	101	144	······	······
50	627	106	149	······	······
52	639	110	154	······	······
54	651	115	160	······	······
56	663	119	166	······	······
58	675	123	172	······	······
60	687	127	······	······	······
62	698	131	······	······	······
64	709	135	······	······	······
66	720	140	······	······	······
68	731	145	······	······	······
70	742	149	······	······	······
72	753	154	······	······	······
74	763	158	······	······	······
76	773	163	······	······	······
78	783	167	······	······	······
80	793	172	······	······	······
82	803	177	······	······	······
84	813	······	······	······	······
86	823	······	······	······	······
88	832	······	······	······	······
90	841	······	······	······	······
92	850	······	······	······	······
94	859	······	······	······	······
96	868	······	······	······	······
98	877	······	······	······	······
100	887	······	······	······	······

Nozzle Pressure = Pilot Tube Pressure. Discharge Coef. = .97

THE PARSHALL MEASURING FLUME

The Parshall measuring flume, as shown in Fig. 74, is an excellent device for the measurement of irrigation water since it is relatively simple to build and operate. It will not easily get out of order, and is not likely to be affected by silt deposit because of the increased velocity of flow in the approach channel and the throat. As long as the depth of water at the lower gage, H_b, is less than 0.7 of the depth at the upper gage, H_a, for flumes with throat widths of one foot or more, or 0.6 for the smaller flumes, the flow can be determined from a single gage reading, H_a.

Discharge under these conditions is called free flow and the measurement is not affected by conditions in the channel downstream. This is the only condition for which information is given in the table in this Handbook.

When the depth at the lower gage, H_b, is more than 70% of the depth at the upper gage, the flow is considered to be submerged, and determination of flow requires readings at both gages plus application of necessary correction factors.

Information on submerged flow, plus complete formulae for both types of flow, may be found in Bulletin 423, Colorado State College, Fort Collins, Colorado.

Dimensions for building the Parshall flume, plus information on discharge capacities for the free flow condition, are included herewith.

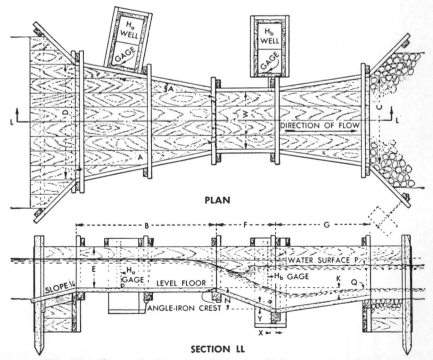

FIG. 74. Plan and elevation of the Parshall measuring flume.†
From U.S.D.A. Farmers' Bulletin No. 1683.

TABLE 68. DIMENSIONS AND CAPACITIES—PARSHALL FLUMES.
SEE FIGURE 74.

Throat Width	A	⅔ A	B	C	D	E	F	G	K	N	X	Y	Free Flow Cu.ft./Sec. Max.	Min.
0'3"	1'6⅜"	1'0¼"	1'6"	0'7"	0'10 3/16"	1'4"	½'	1'	1"	2¼"	1"	1½"	1.1	0.03
0'6"	2'0 7/16"	1'4 5/16"	2'0"	1'3⅝"	1'3⅝"	2'0"	1'	2'	3"	4½"	2"	3"	3.9	0.05
0'9"	2'10⅝"	1'11⅛"	2'10"	1'3"	1'10⅝"	2'6"	1'	1½'	3"	4½"	2"	3"	8.8	0.09
1'0"	4'6"	3'0"	4'4⅞"	2'0"	2'9¼"	3'0"	2'	3'	3"	9"	2"	3"	16.1	0.35
1'6"	4'9"	3'2"	4'7⅞"	2'6"	3'4⅜"	3'0"	2'	3'	3"	9"	2"	3"	24.6	0.51
2'0"	5'0"	3'4"	4'10⅞"	3'0"	3'11½"	3'0"	2'	3'	3"	9"	2"	3"	33.1	0.66
3'0"	5'6"	3'8"	5'4¾"	4'0"	5'1⅞"	3'0"	2'	3'	3"	9"	2"	3"	50.4	0.97
4'0"	6'0"	4'0"	5'10⅝"	5'0"	6'4¼"	3'0"	2'	3'	3"	9"	2"	3"	67.9	1.26
5'0"	6'6"	4'4"	6'4½"	6'0"	7'6⅝"	3'0"	2'	3'	3"	9"	2"	3"	85.6	2.22
6'0"	7'0"	4'8"	6'10⅜"	7'0"	8'9"	3'0"	2'	3'	3"	9"	2"	3"	103.5	2.63
7'0"	7'6"	5'0"	7'4¼"	8'0"	9'11⅜"	3'0"	2'	3'	3"	9"	2"	3"	121.4	4.08
8'0"	8'0"	5'4"	7'10⅛"	9'0"	11'1¾"	3'0"	2'	3'	3"	9"	2"	3"	139.5	4.62

TABLE 69. FREE FLOW DISCHARGE—PARSHALL FLUME—CU. FT./SEC.

$$Q = 4 W H_a^{1.522 W^{0.026}}$$

Size of Flume, W.

Head, H_a Feet	3"	6"	9"	1'0"	1'6"	2'0"	3'0"	4'0"	5'0"	6'0"	7'0"	8'0"
0.1	.028	.05	.09	.....	.....	.....	.....	.....	.....	.....	.....	.....
0.2	.082	.16	.26	.35	.51	.66	.97	1.26	.....	.....	.....	.....
0.3	.154	.31	.49	.64	.94	1.24	1.82	2.39	2.96	3.52	4.08	4.62
0.4	.241	.48	.76	.99	1.47	1.93	2.86	3.77	4.68	5.57	6.46	7.34
0.5	.339	.69	1.06	1.39	2.06	2.73	4.05	5.36	6.66	7.94	9.23	10.51
0.6	.450	.92	1.40	1.84	2.73	3.62	5.39	7.15	8.89	10.63	12.36	14.08
0.7	.571	1.17	1.78	2.33	3.46	4.60	6.86	9.11	11.36	13.59	15.82	18.04
0.8	.702	1.45	2.18	2.85	4.26	5.66	8.46	11.25	14.04	16.81	19.59	22.36
0.9	.843	1.74	2.61	3.41	5.10	6.80	10.17	13.55	16.92	20.29	23.66	27.02
1.0	.992	2.06	3.07	4.00	6.00	8.00	12.00	16.00	20.00	24.00	28.00	32.00
1.1	.....	2.40	3.55	4.62	6.95	9.27	13.93	18.60	23.26	27.94	32.62	37.30
1.2	.....	2.75	4.06	5.28	7.94	10.61	15.96	21.33	26.71	32.10	37.50	42.89
1.3	.....	.....	4.59	5.96	8.99	12.01	18.10	24.21	30.33	36.47	42.62	48.78
1.4	.....	.....	5.14	6.68	10.10	13.48	20.32	27.21	34.11	41.05	47.99	54.95
1.5	.....	.....	.....	7.41	11.20	15.00	22.64	30.34	38.06	45.82	53.59	61.40
1.6	.....	.....	.....	8.18	12.40	16.58	25.05	33.59	42.17	50.79	59.42	68.10
1.7	.....	.....	.....	8.97	13.60	18.21	27.55	36.96	46.43	55.95	65.48	75.08
1.8	.....	.....	.....	9.79	14.80	19.90	30.13	40.45	50.83	61.29	71.75	82.29
1.9	.....	.....	.....	10.62	16.10	21.63	32.79	44.05	55.39	66.81	78.24	89.76
2.0	.....	.....	.....	11.49	17.40	23.43	35.53	47.77	60.08	72.50	84.94	97.48
2.1	.....	.....	.....	12.37	18.80	25.27	38.35	51.59	64.92	78.37	91.84	105.40
2.2	.....	.....	.....	13.28	20.20	27.15	41.25	55.52	69.90	84.41	98.94	113.60
2.3	.....	.....	.....	14.21	21.60	29.09	44.22	59.56	75.01	90.61	106.20	122.00
2.4	.....	.....	.....	15.16	23.00	31.09	47.27	63.69	80.25	96.97	113.70	130.70
2.5	.....	.....	.....	16.13	24.60	33.11	50.39	67.93	85.62	103.50	121.40	139.50

NOTE: Approximate values of flow for heads other than those shown may be found by direct interpolation in the table.

OTHER METHODS OF APPROXIMATING WATER FLOW

Often an approximation of water flow is required when it is not practical to use weirs, orifices, nozzles or other means of determination. This can be done by taking the coordinates of a point in the stream flow as indicated in Fig. 75. The accuracy of this method will vary from 90-100%. The pipe must be flowing full.

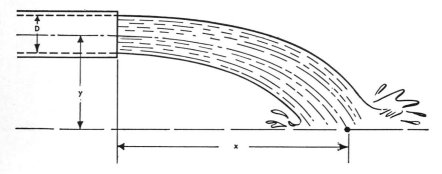

FIG. 75. Approximating flow from horizontal pipe.

$$\text{Capacity, Gpm} = \frac{2.45\, D^2\, x}{\sqrt{\dfrac{2\,y}{32.16}}}$$

Where D = Pipe diameter, in.

x = Horizontal distance, ft.

y = Vertical distance, ft.

This can be further simplified by measuring to the top of the flowing stream and always measuring so that y will equal 12 inches and measuring the horizontal distance "X" in inches as illustrated in Fig. 76.

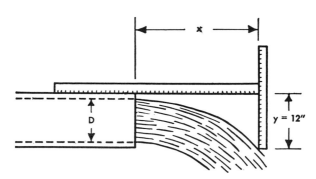

FIG. 76. Approximating flow from horizontal pipe.

Capacity, Gpm = $0.818\, D^2 X$

TABLE 70. APPROXIMATE CAPACITY, GPM, FOR FULL FLOWING HORIZONTAL PIPES ILLUSTRATED IN FIG. 76.

Std. Wt. Steel Pipe, Inside Dia., In.		Distance x, in., when y = 12"										
Nominal	Actual	12	14	16	18	20	22	24	26	28	30	32
2	2.067	42	49	56	63	70	77	84	91	98	105	112
2½	2.469	60	70	80	90	100	110	120	130	140	150	160
3	3.068	93	108	123	139	154	169	185	200	216	231	246
4	4.026	159	186	212	239	266	292	318	345	372	398	425
5	5.047	250	292	334	376	417	459	501	543	585	627	668
6	6.065	362	422	482	542	602	662	722	782	842	902	962
8	7.981	627	732	837	942	1047	1150	1255	1360	1465	1570	1675
10	10.020	980	1145	1310	1475	1635	1800	1965	2130	2290	2455	2620
12	12.000	1415	1650	1890	2125	2360	2595	2830	3065	3300	3540	3775

In like manner flow can be estimated from a vertical pipe as shown in Fig. 77 by measuring the vertical height H.

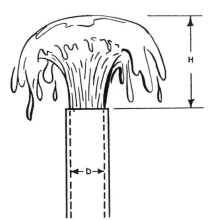

Capacity, Gpm. $= 5.68 \, KD^2 \, H^{1/2}$

$D =$ I.D. of Pipe, In.

$H =$ Vertical Height of water jets, in.

$K =$ a constant, varying from .87 to .97 for pipes 2 to 6 in. dia. and $H = 6$ to 24 in.

FIG. 77. Approximating flow from vertical pipe.

TABLE 71. FLOW FROM VERTICAL PIPES, GPM.

Nominal	Vertical Height, H, of Water Jet, in.										
I.D. Pipe, in.	3	3.5	4	4.5	5	5.5	6	7	8	10	12
2	38	41	44	47	50	53	56	61	65	74	82
3	81	89	96	103	109	114	120	132	141	160	177
4	137	151	163	174	185	195	205	222	240	269	299
6	318	349	378	405	430	455	480	520	560	635	700
8	567	623	684	730	776	821	868	945	1020	1150	1270
10	950	1055	1115	1200	1280	1350	1415	1530	1640	1840	2010

SECTION XII. FAIRBANKS MORSE PUMPS

CONTENTS

XII

TURBINE AND PROPELLER PUMPS

6920, 6970 & 7000 OIL AND WATER LUBRICATED DEEP WELL & SUMP TURBINE PUMPS

8211 & 8312 PROPELLER PUMPS

6930 POT PUMP

6900F & 7000F SKID MOUNTED UNIT FOR OFFSHORE FIRE PROTECTION

FIRE PUMPS

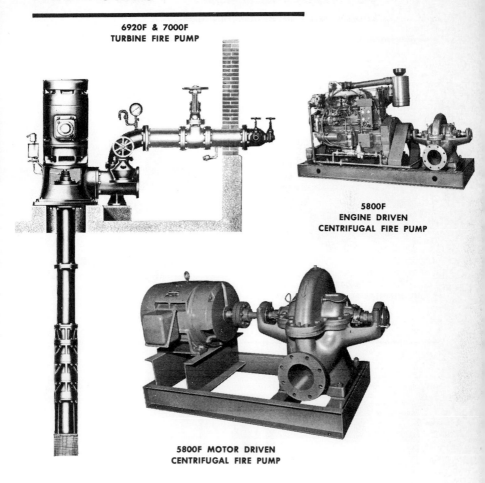

**6920F & 7000F
TURBINE FIRE PUMP**

**5800F
ENGINE DRIVEN
CENTRIFUGAL FIRE PUMP**

**5800F MOTOR DRIVEN
CENTRIFUGAL FIRE PUMP**

**5876F
HI-SPEED CENTRIFUGAL FIRE PUMP**

XII

NON-CLOG PUMPS

5400 with Bladed Impeller
5400 K with Bladeless Impeller

5420P
HORIZONTAL SELF PRIMER PUMP

5410 & 5410K
VERTICAL PUMP

5430
VERTICAL BILTOGETHER PUMP

5430M
PULL-UP
SUBMERSIBLE PUMP

5440
NON CLOG PUMP

END SUCTION AND SUBMERSIBLE PUMPS

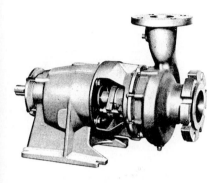

5520R
FRAME MOUNTED END SUCTION

5553ER
END SUCTION
HORIZONTAL BILTOGETHER

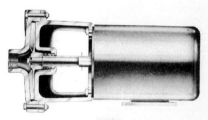

5553F
RADIAL VANE DIFFUSER

5430AW
SUBMERSIBLE-NONCLOG PUMP

5426
NON-CLOG
HI-HEAD
PUMP

ANGLEFLOW & SPLIT CASE

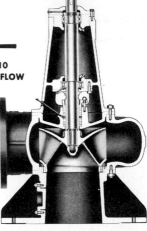

**5710
ANGLEFLOW**

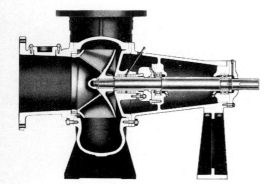

**5720
ANGLEFLOW**

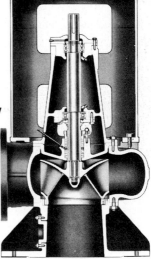

**5740
ANGLEFLOW**

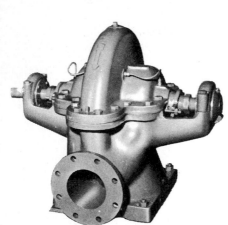

**5800
SPLIT CASE**

**5900
MULTISTAGE SPLIT CASE**

PERIPHERAL PUMPS

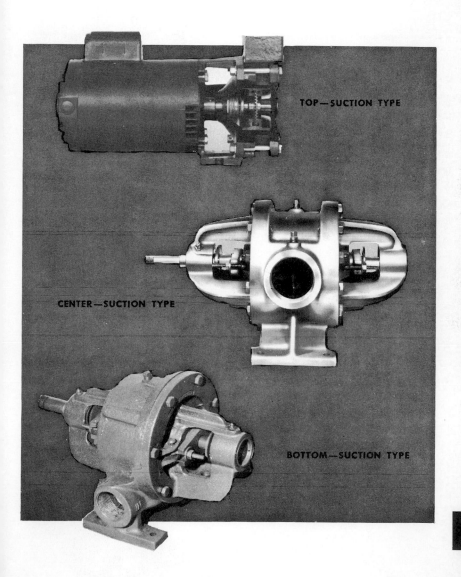

TOP—SUCTION TYPE

CENTER—SUCTION TYPE

BOTTOM—SUCTION TYPE

XII

WATER SYSTEMS

From nearly a century of service to the farm and the rural home, Fairbanks Morse continues to pioneer in the development of machinery which will bring prosperity, health and luxury to rural living.

MULTIPLE VERTICAL PUMP

**SD70
CELLAR DRAINER**

**SUBMERSIBLE
DEEP WELL PUMP**

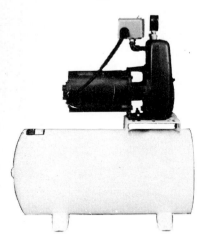

**CONVERTIBLE JET PUMP
WITH 12 GAL. PRESSURE TANK**

**SHALLOW WELL
JET PUMP**

UTILITY PUMPS

"Rain Maker"
CENTRIFUGAL PUMP

ESP 315-320 ENGINE DRIVEN
SELF-PRIMING CENTRIFUGAL PUMP

58 MAGNUM HIGH PRESSURE
UTILITY PUMP

1 ½ C1JE ENGINE DRIVEN
CENTRIFUGAL FERTILIZER PUMP

C1J CENTRIFUGAL PUMP

XII

VTSH Pump

The Vertical Turbine Solids Handling (VTSH) pump is a wet pit solids handling pump combining the advantages of the classic solids handling pump with the well-proven vertical pump. The design is patented by Fairbanks Morse.

GENERAL INDEX

Continued next page

INDEX

Continued next page

Continued next page

INDEX

Continued next page

Continued next page

INDEX

Continued next page

INDEX OF TABLES

INDEX

INDEX

INDEX OF FIGURE NUMBERS

INDEX

TABLE 72.

TABLE FRICTION LOSS OF WATER PER 100 FEET OF FLEXIBLE PIPE

FRICTION LOSS OF WATER PER 100 FEET OF FLEXIBLE PLASTIC PIPE

SIZE	1/2"		3/4"		1"		1¼"		1½"		2"		3"		4"	
GPM	Head in Feet	PSI	Head in Feet	PSI	Head in Feet	PSI	Head in Feet	PSI	Head in Feet	PSI	Head in Feet	PSI	Head in Feet	PSI	Head in Feet	PSI
1	1.50	.65	.32	.14	.09	.04										
2	5.08	2.20	1.13	.49	.30	.13	.09	.04								
3	10.51	4.55	2.40	1.04	.60	.26	.18	.08	.09	.04						
4	17.81	7.71	3.81	1.65	1.02	.44	.32	.14	.16	.07						
5	26.01	11.26	5.61	2.43	1.43	.62	.46	.20	.23	.10	.09	.04				
6	36.01	15.59	7.51	3.25	1.94	.84	.65	.28	.30	.13	.14	.06				
8	61.00	26.41	12.01	5.20	3.19	1.38	1.04	.45	.51	.22	.23	.10				
10	92.15	39.89	18.32	7.93	4.90	2.12	1.59	.69	.76	.33	.49	.21				
15			38.83	16.81	10.12	4.38	3.30	1.43	1.55	.67	.83	.36				
20					16.52	7.15	5.50	2.38	2.54	1.10	1.22	.53	.12	.05		
25							8.11	3.51	3.81	1.65	1.69	.73	.18	.08		
30							10.81	4.68	5.20	2.25	2.19	.95	.25	.11	.09	.04
35							14.02	6.07	6.61	2.86	2.80	1.21	.32	.14	.12	.05
40									8.92	3.86	3.40	1.47	.42	.18	.14	.06
45									10.12	4.38	4.09	1.77	.53	.23	.16	.07
50									11.92	5.16	5.71	2.47	.85	.37	.23	.10
60											7.30	3.16	1.11	.48	.30	.13
70											9.22	3.99	1.41	.61	.37	.16
80											11.20	4.85	1.80	.78	.46	.20
90											13.91	6.02	2.19	.95	.55	.24
100													3.30	1.43	.88	.38

FIG. 78

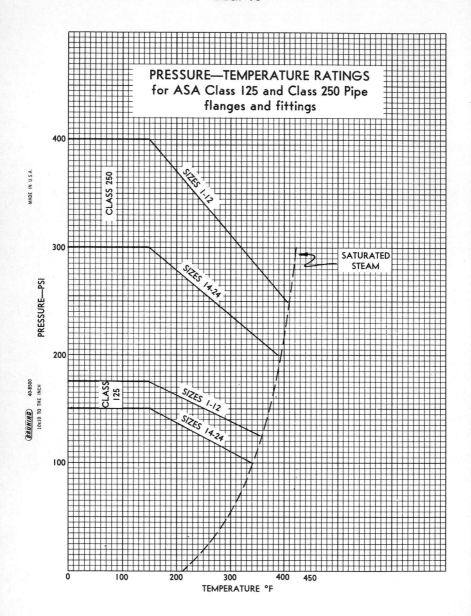

PRESSURE—TEMPERATURE RATINGS
for ASA Class 125 and Class 250 Pipe
flanges and fittings

MEMORANDA

Fairbanks Morse
Pump Corporation

Fire Protection Market Sales Offices

P.O. Box 1007
218 Glenview Court
Marlton, NJ 08053
609-596-9676
Telex: 62915524

800 Roosevelt Road
Building B, Suite 400
Glen Ellyn, IL 60137
312-790-8106

1687 Tullie Circle
Suite 118
Atlanta, GA 30329
404-328-6908
Telecopier: 404-320-6909

Pump Services Group Sales Office

3601 Fairbanks Avenue
Kansas City, KS 66110
913-371-5000
Telex: 249461
Telecopier: 913-371-2272

Industrial Market Sales Offices

1687 Tullie Circle
Suite 118
Atlanta, GA 30329
404-320-6908
Telecopier: 404-320-6909

1499 Bayshore Highway
Burlingame, CA 94010
415-692-3336
Telecopier: 415-692-0259

372 Broad Street
Office #5
Bloomfield, NJ 07003
201-680-1009
NYC Tie-in: 594-4378
Telex: 62016522
Telecopier: 201-680-1008

2767 Ridge Road
Library, PA 15129
412-655-1895

1138A North Gilbert Street
Anaheim, CA 92801
714-635-9220
Telex: 685681
Telecopier: 714-635-1896

P.O. Box 1265
Sugar Land, TX 77487-1265
713-242-5803
Telex: 62884873

3601 Fairbanks Avenue
Kansas City, KS 66110
913-371-6387
Telex: 249461
Telecopier: 913-371-2272

Directory of Operations

Fairbanks Morse
Pump Corporation

Public Works Market Sales Offices

800 Roosevelt Road
Building B, Suite 400
Glen Ellyn, IL 60137
312-790-8106

1600 South Main Plaza
Suite 170
Walnut Creek, CA 94596
415-935-9601
Telecopier: 415-934-9460

372 Broad Street
Office #5
Bloomfield, NJ 07003
201-680-1009
NYC Tie-in: 594-4378
Telex: 62016522
Telecopier: 201-680-1008

1687 Tullie Circle
Suite 118
Atlanta, GA 30329
404-320-6908
Telecopier: 404-320-6909

International Sales Office

83 East Shaw Avenue
Suite 250
Fresno, CA 93710
209-224-5030
Telex: 172406
Telecopier: 209-222-2630

Water Well Market Offices & Assembly Plants

Main Office & Assembly Plant
P.O. Box 3028
108 Fairbanks Avenue
Thomasville, GA 31799
912-228-4400
Telex: 249264
Telecopier: 912-228-9116

Sales Office & Assembly Plant
4637 North Blythe
Fresno, CA 93722
209-276-2552
Telecopier: 209-276-2570

Sales Office
23107 East Williams Road
Escalon, CA 95320
209-838-1151

Sales Office
2195 Ealing
Apt. 4
Germantown, TN 38138
901-757-5629